IMPACT STRENGTH OF MATERIALS

IMPACT STRENGTH OF MATERIALS

W. JOHNSON

Professor of Mechanical Engineering
University of Manchester Institute of Science and Technology

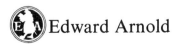Edward Arnold

© W. Johnson 1972

First Published 1972
by Edward Arnold (Publishers) Limited
41 Maddox Street
London W1R OAN

ISBN 0 7131 3266 3

Filmset and printed by J. W. Arrowsmith Ltd., Bristol, England.

Preface

My principal aim in this book is to bring within the scope of advanced first degree students and those studying background courses for the Master's degree in mechanical or civil engineering, a simple compilation of information and analytical methods in the subject of Impact Strength of Materials not otherwise easily available in a single textbook.†

Today there is a great need for engineers to be thoroughly familiar with elementary ideas surrounding stress waves in solids and high speed metal deformation, because more situations than hitherto now involve considerations of impact loading. In the design of structures and in the study of high speed metal processing, the necessity to be able to think quantitatively to some extent in discussing these areas of work has been quite evident for some time. To judge from available textbooks on Strength of Materials or Continuum Mechanics it is a curious fact however that undergraduate teaching in the U.K. and the U.S.A. includes little or no exposure to knowledge of the phenomena and the stress calculations of impact situations; few students graduate thoroughly familiar with the equations '$\sigma = \rho c v$' and '$c_0 = \sqrt{E/\rho}$'. Another reason for writing a book of this kind is that I believe present day Materials has become a dull subject for students, often because it is one that has changed little, or too little, in the course of the last half century; there is a need to inject more interest into the subject, to enlarge its scope beyond conventional preoccupations with static situations and to introduce students to a wider awareness of some of the other interesting facets of the mechanics of solids under stress. Also, it will be clear, my concern has been *not* to emphasise analytical treatments. I have done this in order not to put off the mass of students or practising engineers who have little facility in mathematics and in order that simple useful ideas should not be obscured by having to attend to mathematical derivations. The engineers' world is full of difficult boundary value problems of one sort or another and it is therefore important for the student that he should learn to understand certain elementary ideas very well indeed so that they can easily be adapted or manipulated in dealing with new, complex situations. The simple model, and relatively simple mathematics, can long be remembered after formal teaching has ceased and can rapidly be called up to furnish terms in which a new situation can be discussed and for which 'numbers' can be obtained often with sufficient precision. Thus, because I have adopted a distinctly technological approach, the

---

† The book by Goldsmith (ref. 1.2) is intended for use by research engineers and that by Kolsky (ref. 1.1) for physicists.

book is in the tradition of 'strength of materials' rather than 'the mechanics of a continuous medium' and hence the choice of title.

On two especial counts can the material in this book be criticised. First, that it is pedagogically wrong to separate impact from static strength of materials and second, that the contents are ill-chosen. To the first criticism I can only reply by saying that I shall welcome the all-embracing book on strength of materials when it is published. In respect of the second, the choice of material reflects my own experience and interests in this subject; I came to it mainly through the study of high velocity metal forming operations and large plastic deformation, not from the end of structural engineering. It has, however, become clear to me over the years that a common approach for both these facets of the subject is desirable and possible.

The classification of the material presented, together with the subjects I have *not* treated, e.g. many of the structural aspects of impact as in the book by Kornhauser (ref. 9.14), may also be a matter of dispute and objection by some; in this case I hope that subsequent writers on this topic will correct whatever shortcomings become clear.

I have tried to make this book largely self-contained, but it can only be introduced properly to students already reasonably well versed in elementary strength of materials; in the U.K. this applies to undergraduates towards the end of the second of their three year course, as far as Chapters 1 and 2 are concerned. Some of the other material can only be presented to students in their third and final year. The whole of the material in the book (together with laboratory demonstrations) has at one time or another comprised one of a group of options taken by students in partial fulfilment of the requirements for the Master's degree in mechanical engineering at U.M.I.S.T.

Chapters 1 and 2 are deliberately elementary in mathematical terms because my experience is that students find the ideas surrounding stress waves less than straightforward and easy to appreciate. I have found too that the average engineering student shows facility with the one-dimensional wave equation, i.e. $\partial^2 u/\partial t^2 = c^2 . \partial^2 u/\partial x^2$, but has little physical feel for what it represents. The intention in these two chapters is to present and to re-present primitive ideas and to develop a confident facility with them. There are also a number of features to the two chapters introduced in order to familiarise students with possibly new terms, e.g. the Hopkinson bar. As remarked earlier, these two chapters contain material especially suitable for undergraduates; where it appears in small type this indicates that it is of lesser importance than other material or is intended by way of exemplification.

The third chapter has two aims; these are to present more general ideas concerning elastic stress waves and at the same time to emphasise the complexity of the subject so that the student will gain an appreciation of the limitations of elementary theory.

Chapter 4 reviews elementary plasticity theory and endeavours to employ it in solving a number of slow speed impact problems. Some of the material it contains is included as being indispensable for the reading of latter chapters.

Chapter 5 introduces elementary concepts concerning one-dimensional elastic-plastic stress waves—a complex subject at any time and one containing topics about which there is still disagreement. My aim here has simply been to familiarise the reader with some new ideas and to encourage him to go to more advanced texts for further study, e.g. ref. 4.40.

For each of the remaining chapters I have taken specific elements and brought together a collection of straightforward pieces of work which are generally mutually supporting. It is my hope that in these chapters readers new to this field of study will find descriptions of phenomena which will stimulate them to further and deeper study.

I have tried to acknowledge all the sources I have used, but unfortunately I have been unable to identify them all; to authors not acknowledged I apologise. I have also given references to help readers interested in a particular topic pursue their interest in more detail.

Dr. S. T. S. Al-Hassani, Dr. N. R. Chitkara, Dr. S. R. Reid, Dr. J. B. Hawkyard, Mr. E. Appleton and Mr. Md. Hashmi have read parts of this book in typescript and helped to clarify it at numerous points, and for this I am grateful.

I would like to thank Mrs. S. Moss for her careful typing of my manuscript, a task which has not always been easy.

My thanks are also due to Mr. C. J. Johnson and Miss S. Johnson for preparing the Index.

W. Johnson
December 1970

Contents

4 Plasticity Theory and Some Quasi-Static Analyses

5   One-Dimensional Elastic-Plastic Stress Waves in Bars

6   Impulsive Loading of Beams

7 Dynamic Loading of Rings and Frames

8 Dynamic Plastic Deformation of Plates

9 Plastic Deformation in a Semi-Infinite Medium Due to Impact

10 Plastic Deformation in Plates Due to Impact

Appendices

Plates appear between pages 148 and 149

1: Elementary one-dimensional elastic stress waves in long uniform bars due to impact

The study of the theory and phenomena of elementary one-dimensional elastic waves or pulses is of value to engineers,

(i) because there are many occasions in engineering design when it is useful to be able to estimate the magnitude of the elastic stress created by the impact or collision of two bodies, and

(ii) because a sound knowledge of elementary elastic wave theory is indispensable for an understanding of the phenomena of impact behaviour, e.g. spalling or scabbing, and because explanations in terms of static stress analysis may be misleading.

Definitions

A stress *wave* or *pulse* is transmitted through a body when the different parts of it are not in equilibrium, as is the case when one solid impinges on another; and because of the material properties of the body, a finite time is required for this disequilibrium to be felt by other parts of the body. The lack of local equilibrium manifests itself by specific particles moving and adjusting themselves to the instantaneous stress distribution and this ability to adjust is propagated and takes place at certain definite speeds—characteristic speeds of *wave* propagation. Note throughout this work that the *particle displacement*, or *particle speed*, is one thing and that the *wave speed* is another.

Waves which travel through the mass of a body are called *body waves*, and those which travel over its surface are referred to as *surface waves*. Bodies may convey both body waves and surface waves at the same time, see Chapter 3. There are, however, at an elementary level (see p. 101), two basic kinds of elastic stress waves, or pulses, which are propagated through long uniform bars. These are

(i) *longitudinal waves*, and

(ii) *torsional waves*.

For the time being we do not consider bending waves.

In the term *bar* we understand that the length is at least one magnitude greater than any cross-sectional dimension.

In thinking of these waves when they are transmitted in relation to a long stationary bar, it will be recognised that in category (i) there will be *longitudinal compression waves* and *longitudinal tensile waves*. If we consider a stationary bar, then, for *longitudinal compression* waves (neglecting the Poisson's ratio effect), the individual particles of the bar are displaced, or *move, in the same direction as that in which the wave travels*; and in the case of *longitudinal tensile waves the particles move in the opposite direction to that in which the wave travels*. In the case of *torsional waves* in category (ii), the individual particles of the solid are displaced, or move, or *oscillate entirely in a plane which is transverse or at right angles to the direction of wave travel*.

Propagation of a compressive pulse

Figure 1.1. shows a stationary uniform isotropic rod which is to transmit a longitudinal compressive pulse. Let u denote the displacement undergone by a plane AB in the rod which is originally distance x from O. The origin of coordinates O, is fixed in space; the end of the bar is also at O at time $t = 0$, i.e. when the bar is unstressed. O may be referred to as the origin of a system of fixed coordinates. Then $[u + (\partial u/\partial x) \cdot \delta x]$ denotes the displacement of plane $A'B'$ which is parallel to AB but initially distant $(x + \delta x)$ from O in the unstrained state. A modest force applied rapidly from time $t = 0$, over the end plane at $x = 0$, will cause a disturbance to be propagated elastically along the bar so that over typical plane AB at, say, time t there will be a compressive *nominal* stress, $-\sigma_0$.

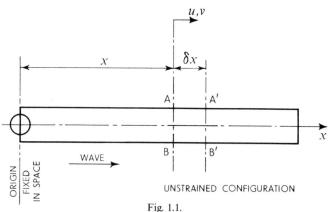

Fig. 1.1.

The effects of transverse strain and inertia will be neglected in the following analysis (but see p. 101), as are also gravitational and all dissipative forces, e.g. damping. For the elementary theory now being developed to apply with the prospect of reasonable success, it may be shown that the pulse length should be several, say at least six, times that of a typical cross-sectional dimension of the bar, see p. 101.

The net force on element $ABB'A'$, shown in Fig. 1.2 in its unstrained state, causes it to accelerate so that the equation of motion for an element of the rod of initial cross-sectional area A_0 is,

$$-\frac{\partial \sigma_0}{\partial x} \cdot \delta x \cdot A_0 = A_0 \rho_0 \, \delta x \cdot \frac{\partial^2 u}{\partial t^2}$$

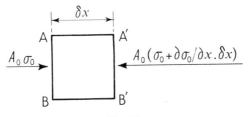

Fig. 1.2.

and thus,

$$\frac{\partial \sigma_0}{\partial x} = -\rho_0 \frac{\partial^2 u}{\partial t^2},$$ (1.1i)

where ρ_0 is the density of the material in its unstrained state. The negative sign applies because the acceleration of the element for the compressive stress system shown, is in the direction of x decreasing.

The strain in an element of length ∂x is $\partial u / \partial x$. Thus,

$$-\frac{\sigma_0}{\partial u / \partial x} = E,$$

where E is Young's Modulus.

Differentiating,

$$\frac{\partial \sigma_0}{\partial x} = -E \frac{\partial^2 u}{\partial x^2}$$ (1.1ii)

and using this in (1.1i),

$$\rho_0 \frac{\partial^2 u}{\partial t^2} = E \frac{\partial^2 u}{\partial x^2}$$

or

$$\frac{\partial^2 u}{\partial t^2} = \frac{E}{\rho_0} \cdot \frac{\partial^2 u}{\partial x^2} = c_L^2 \frac{\partial^2 u}{\partial x^2},$$ (1.2i)

where

$$c_L = \sqrt{\frac{E}{\rho_0}}$$ (1.2ii)

Solution to the wave equation

In the *one-dimensional* wave equation

$$\frac{\partial^2 u}{\partial t^2} = c^2 \frac{\partial^2 u}{\partial x^2},$$ (1.3)

put

$$u = f(x - ct) + F(x + ct),$$ (1.4i)

where f and F are independent arbitrary functions, so that

$$\frac{\partial u}{\partial t} = -cf'(x - ct) + cF'(x + ct) \tag{1.5i}$$

and

$$\frac{\partial^2 u}{\partial t^2} = c^2 f''(x - ct) + c^2 F''(x + ct) \tag{1.5ii}$$

Also,

$$\frac{\partial u}{\partial x} = f'(x - ct) + F'(x + ct) \tag{1.6i}$$

and thus

$$\frac{\partial^2 u}{\partial x^2} = f''(x - ct) + F''(x + ct) \tag{1.6ii}$$

Hence from (1.5ii) and (1.6ii) we have,

$$\frac{\partial^2 u}{\partial t^2} = c^2 \frac{\partial^2 u}{\partial x^2};$$

equation (1.4i) is the *general solution* to equation (1.3). For $f(x - ct)$ or $F(x + ct)$ we could have functions such as $\sin w$, $\exp w$, w^n, etc., where w is $(x - ct)$ or $(x + ct)$.

Suppose in the solution (1.4i) that one of the functions is zero, and we have simply,

$$u = f(x - ct) \tag{1.4ii}$$

Then if $u = s$ when $t = t_1$ and $x = x_1$, and also $u = s$ when $t = t_2$ and $x = x_2$, see Fig. 1.3, the rate of propagation of the disturbance with respect to the axis of coordinates Ox which are presumed to be fixed in space, is then $c = (x_2 - x_1)/(t_2 - t_1)$; or using $u = f(x - ct)$ we have

$$s = f(x_1 - ct_1) = f(x_2 - ct_2)$$

and thus,

$$x_1 - ct_1 = x_2 - ct_2$$

Hence,

$$c = \frac{x_2 - x_1}{t_2 - t_1}$$

Thus in equation (1.2i) c_L denotes the speed of propagation of the elastic disturbance through the space occupied by the bar in its initial or unstressed state; or c_L is the speed of elastic wave propagation along the fixed axis of the bar Ox.

Note too that equation (1.4ii) implies that the wave travels in the direction of *increasing x*.

Similarly after considering $u = F(x + ct)$ we should have $x_1 + ct_1 = x_2 + ct_2$ or $c = (x_2 - x_1)/(t_1 - t_2)$; since c is a positive quantity and $x_2 > x_1$, and $t_2 > t_1$, this implies that *this wave is one which moves in the direction of x decreasing*.

Thus the wave $f(x - ct)$ is a *forward* travelling wave whilst $F(x + ct)$ is a *backward* moving wave of different shape and size, in as far as f and F are different.

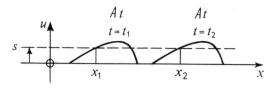

Fig. 1.3.

Both of the waves $f(x - ct)$ and $F(x + ct)$ in relation to (1.3) advance without changing their shape or amplitude and with constant speed c, i.e. they are *non-dispersive*.

That $u = f(x - ct)$ and $u = F(x + ct)$ are *separately* solutions to (1.1) and also that combined as in (1.4i), they still constitute a solution, i.e. the two separate solutions may be taken together to give another solution, means that (1.3) is a simple partial *linear* differential equation. The implication of this is that at a given section of a bar at a given instant, the separate effects of the two solutions, i.e. as regards displacement or stress, may simply be added together to give the total displacement or total stress at that section.

Observe that the equations relate to *plane waves* since the displacement u has the same value at all points in the plane $x = $ constant, at the same instant.

Elastic longitudinal wave speed

Following the solution for the simple wave equation given above, it is evident that in equation (1.2i), c_L is the speed of a longitudinal elastic pulse of tension or compression in the unstrained bar and that $c_L = \sqrt{E/\rho_0}$.

Note incidentally that the speed of propagation c_L is independent of $\partial u/\partial t$, or the local velocity, or speed of shift, of the elements transmitting the wave; c_L depends only on the elastic properties of the transmitting medium and its density and $\partial u/\partial t$ on the form of the disturbing force, i.e. the function f and F.

In Table 1.1 some typical values for common materials at $0\,°C$ are given. Note also that c_L varies with temperature because E especially is a function of temperature. Further, c_L in grained materials varies with direction (i.e. in aelotropic or non-isotropic materials); in substances such as concrete, unexpected effects may arise because E has different values in tension and compression.

TABLE 1.1   ELASTIC LONGITUDINAL AND TORSIONAL WAVE SPEEDS

$$c_L = \sqrt{\frac{E}{\rho_0}} \quad \text{and} \quad c_T = \sqrt{\frac{G}{\rho_0}}$$

	Cast Iron	Carbon Steel	Brass	Copper	Lead	Aluminium	Glass
E lbf/in^2	$16{\cdot}5 . 10^6$	$29{\cdot}5 . 10^6$	$13{\cdot}5 . 10^6$	$16{\cdot}5 . 10^6$	$2{\cdot}5 . 10^6$	$10 . 10^6$	$8 . 10^6$
$\rho_0 = $ lb/in^3	$0{\cdot}26$	$0{\cdot}28$	$0{\cdot}30$	$0{\cdot}32$	$0{\cdot}41$	$0{\cdot}096$	$0{\cdot}070$
$c_L = \sqrt{E/\rho_0}$ ft/sec $(g \simeq 384$ in/sec/sec$)$	13 025	16 900	11 000	12 100	3 900	16 700	17 500
$c_T = \sqrt{G/\rho_0}$ ft/sec	8 100	10 600	6 700	7 500	2 300	10 200	10 700

Expression for the intensity of stress propagated

The strain in an element of the bar is $\partial u/\partial x$ and therefore $\sigma_0 = -E\partial u/\partial x = (E/c_L) . \partial u/\partial t$ using (1.5i) and (1.6i) but neglecting the second term on the right hand side. The speed of movement of a particle at location x, is $\partial u/\partial t$, and denoting this by v_0.

$$\sigma_0 = E v_0/c_L \qquad (1.7i)$$

or substituting for c_L,

$$\sigma_0 = \rho_0 c_L v_0 \qquad (1.7ii)$$

(Note that unless specifically stated, buckling or instability is not a consideration here).

The expression (1.7ii) also applies for the propagation of a tensile wave.

Since $v_0 = \sigma_0/\sqrt{E\rho_0}$, then for steel if the stress is 16 tonf/in^2, the particle speed would be

$$v_0 = \frac{16 \times 2240 \text{ in/sec}}{\sqrt{30 \cdot 10^6 \cdot 0 \cdot 28/384}} \simeq 20 \text{ ft/sec}$$

For pure lead, at its yield stress of about 1 tonf/in^2, v_0 is only about 4 ft/sec.

The quantity $\rho_0 c_L$ is often referred to as the *mechanical impedance* of the bar.

Propagation of a torsional pulse along a circular prismatic bar

Let a torque T, which varies with time, be suddenly applied at the left hand end of a long bar at time $t = 0$ and take the origin for an axis along the shaft to be in this end section which, of course, does not move. At distance x from the origin, see Fig. 1.4, assume that a transverse plane section has rotated through angle θ relative to the original position at time $t = 0$, of the section containing the origin; suppose also that ω is the angular velocity at this section. Then an element of the bar of length δx, sustains a relative rotation of one end with respect to the other of $\delta x \cdot \partial\theta/\partial x$. Let $\partial T/\partial x$ denote the rate of change in torque along the rod with distance x. The net torque on the element is $\delta x \cdot \partial T/\partial x$ and this produces an angular acceleration of $\partial^2\theta/\partial t^2$, so that

$$\frac{\partial T}{\partial x} \cdot \delta x = (I \cdot \delta x) \cdot \frac{\partial^2\theta}{\partial t^2}. \qquad (1.8)$$

$I \cdot \delta x$ is the moment of inertia of the element of length δx about the axis of the bar. Now, using elementary torsion theory,

$$T = JG\frac{\partial\theta/\partial x \cdot \delta x}{\delta x} = JG\frac{\partial\theta}{\partial x} \qquad (1.9)$$

J is a constant depending on the shape and size of the section of the bar, and in the case of a circular section bar is the second moment of area about the bar axis; G is the torsion modulus. From (1.9) we have,

$$\frac{\partial T}{\partial x} = JG\frac{\partial^2\theta}{\partial x^2} = I\frac{\partial^2\theta}{\partial t^2},$$

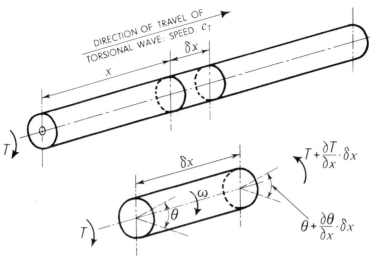

Fig. 1.4.

using (1.8). Thus

$$\frac{\partial^2 \theta}{\partial x^2} = \frac{I}{JG} \cdot \frac{\partial^2 \theta}{\partial t^2}$$

or

$$\frac{\partial^2 \theta}{\partial t^2} = \frac{JG}{I} \cdot \frac{\partial^2 \theta}{\partial x^2} \tag{1.10i}$$

Equation (1.10i) is identical in form with the simple one-dimensional equation (1.3) and for comparison is written as,

$$\frac{\partial^2 \theta}{\partial t^2} = c_T^2 \frac{\partial^2 \theta}{\partial x^2}, \tag{1.10ii}$$

where

$$c_T^2 = JG/I \tag{1.11}$$

Obviously c_T is the speed of propagation of an elastic torsional pulse along the bar.

Now, $I = \pi a^4 \rho_0/2$ per unit length of the bar and $J = \pi a^4/2$ for a solid cylinder of circular section, so that,

$$c_T^2 = \frac{G \cdot \pi a^4/2}{\rho_0 \pi a^4/2} = \frac{G}{\rho_0}$$

Some typical values for c_T are given in Table 1.1. Observe that a torsional pulse is transmitted through a circular bar without dispersion especially because the various expressions and derivations employed are *exact* and have involved no approximations such as the neglect of radial inertia effects, etc., as was the case for longitudinal waves.

Note, $c_L/c_T = \sqrt{E/G} = \sqrt{2(1+v)}$ and since $0 \le v \le 0{\cdot}5$ then $\sqrt{2} \le c_L/c_T \le \sqrt{3}$.

If we allow the use of (1.11) for a bar of square cross-section of side $2a$ the value of c_T would be $0{\cdot}919(G/\rho_0)^{1/2}$, because $J \equiv 2{\cdot}25a^4$.

To calculate the torsional stress at a point, the torque at the section must be evaluated. Following the same procedures as before, put $\theta = g(x - c_T t)$, i.e. the angle of rotation of a section of the bar is some function g of $(x - c_T t)$. Then,

$$\frac{\partial \theta}{\partial x} = g'(x - c_T t)$$

and,

$$\frac{\partial \theta}{\partial t} = -g'c_T(x - c_T t)$$

and hence

$$\frac{\partial \theta}{\partial x} = -\frac{1}{c_T}\frac{\partial \theta}{\partial t}$$

But,

$$T = JG\frac{\partial \theta}{\partial x}$$

and thus

$$T = -\frac{JG}{c_T}\cdot\frac{\partial \theta}{\partial t} = J\sqrt{G\rho_0}\cdot\omega\,. \tag{1.12i}$$

$\omega = -\partial\theta/\partial t$ is the angular velocity of a section which may be supposed to be given.

For a uniform thin-walled tube, $J \simeq 2\pi a_0^3 t_0$, where a_0 is the mean tube radius and t_0 the tube wall thickness. And if τ is the mean shear stress,

$$\tau\,.\,2\pi a t_0\,.\,a_0 = 2\pi a_0^3 t_0\,.\,\sqrt{G\rho_0}\omega$$

or

$$\tau = \rho_0 c_T(a\omega) \tag{1.12ii}$$

Equation for the propagation of flexural pulses in beams of arbitrary but uniform cross-section

The speed of bending or flexural waves is found to depend on their wavelength and therefore simple results as for compressive longitudinal waves are not available. Assume that the motion of each element of the bar in pure bending is purely translatory and perpendicular to the bar axis. A_0 is the cross-sectional area of the beam and ρ_0 is the density, see Fig. 1.5a. The equation of motion in

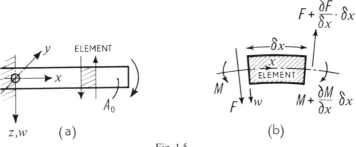

Fig. 1.5.

the Oz-direction where w is the vertical deflection, is

$$-(\rho_0 A_0 \, dx)\frac{\partial^2 w}{\partial t^2} = \frac{\partial F}{\partial x} \cdot dx \tag{1.13}$$

where F is the shear force across a section at location x. But

$$EI\frac{\partial^3 w}{\partial x^3} = F \tag{1.14}$$

and hence putting (1.14) into (1.13)

$$\rho_0 A_0 \frac{\partial^2 w}{\partial t^2} = -EI\frac{\partial^4 w}{\partial x^4}$$

or

$$\frac{\partial^2 w}{\partial t^2} = -c^2 k^2 \frac{\partial^4 w}{\partial x^4} \tag{1.15}$$

k denotes the radius of gyration of the cross-section about an axis in the neutral surface, perpendicular to the bar axis, or $I = A_0 k^2$. If we try a solution of the form $w = f(x - ct)$ or $w = f(x + ct)$ the equation is found *not* to be satisfied. Thus flexural disturbances of arbitrary form are not propagated without dispersion. For further discussion, see the books of Kolsky[1.1] and Goldsmith[1.2] and p. 103 below.

Alternative approaches for finding the expressions concerning longitudinal and torsional wave propagation

Many of the above equations may be obtained more simply and directly by momentum considerations and it is instructive to do this.

(i) *Longitudinal waves*

In Fig. 1.6, after time t, where c_L denotes the compressive wave front speed through the space occupied by the bar at time $t = 0$, the compressed zone length is $c_L t$. If the bar is originally stationary and the end face is caused to move

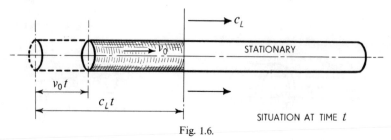

Fig. 1.6.

with and maintains uniform speed v_0, then the whole length will be moving with uniform speed v_0 at time t. Equating the change in momentum of this length $c_L t$ to the impulse, we have

$$(A_0 c_L t \rho_0) v_0 = (\sigma_0 A_0) \cdot t$$

Thus,

$$\sigma_0 = \rho_0 c_L v_0 \qquad (1.7\text{ii})$$

Because the end at which impact occurs will have moved through distance $v_0 t$, the strain in the compressed zone is $v_0 t / c_L t$ and thus $\sigma_0 = E v_0 / c_L$. Substituting in (1.7ii) for σ_0 gives

$$E \frac{v_0}{c_L} = \rho_0 c_L v_0 \quad \text{and hence} \quad c_L = \sqrt{E/\rho_0} \qquad (1.2\text{ii})$$

The total energy acquired by the rod at time t is made up of
(a) kinetic energy $= \frac{1}{2} A_0 (c_L t) \rho_0 v_0^2$ and
(b) stored strain energy $= A_0 (c_L t) \cdot \sigma_0^2 / 2E$
Now the latter,

$$A_0 c_L t \cdot \frac{\sigma_0^2}{2E} = A_0 (c_L t) \cdot \frac{\rho_0^2 c_L^2 v_0^2}{2E} = \frac{1}{2} \cdot A_0 (c_L t) \rho_0 v_0^2$$

and thus the total energy acquired by the bar at time t is composed equally of strain energy and kinetic energy.

(ii) Torsional wave

A uniform thin hollow tube of radius a and cross-sectional area A_0 is rotating at angular speed ω_0 when at time $t = 0$ the end DD is suddenly brought to rest, see Fig. 1.7. A wave of torsional stress is then propagated parallel to the axis of the bar with speed c_T so that at time t, a length $c_T t$ will have been brought to rest and the remainder of the tube will still be rotating at speed ω_0. The mean shear stress τ which prevails in length $c_T t$ is arrived at by equating the impulsive torque, $t \cdot (A_0 \tau \cdot a)$, to the loss in angular momentum of the tube in time t, i.e. $[(t c_T \cdot A_0) \rho_0 \cdot a^2] \cdot \omega_0$. Thus,

$$t A_0 \tau a = t \cdot c_T \cdot A_0 a^2 \rho_0 \omega_0$$

or

$$\tau = \rho_0 c_T (a \omega_0) \qquad (1.12\text{ii})$$

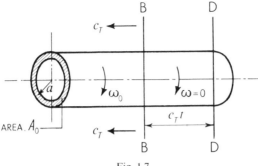

Fig. 1.7.

This is identical with (1.12ii) on p. 8. However, the torsional strain ϕ acquired by $c_T t$ is $\omega_0 t a / c_T t$, i.e. the angular rotation of section BB at time t, with respect to the end DD, divided by length $c_T t$. Hence,

$$\tau = G\phi = G\frac{\omega_0 a}{c_T} \qquad (1.12\text{iii})$$

Substituting for τ in (1.12ii) using (1.12iii)

$$G . \frac{\omega_0 a}{c_T} = \rho_0 c_T a \omega_0$$

or

$$c_T = \sqrt{G/\rho_0} \qquad (1.11)$$

A thick-walled tube can be considered as composed of a number of thin tubes for each of which $c_T = \sqrt{G/\rho_0}$.

Wave transmission along a bar constrained to deform under conditions of plane strain

Figure 1.8(a) shows a bar whose width perpendicular to the plane of the paper is w and whose length parallel to axis Ox is much greater than its thickness, T.

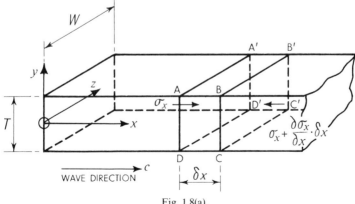

Fig. 1.8(a).

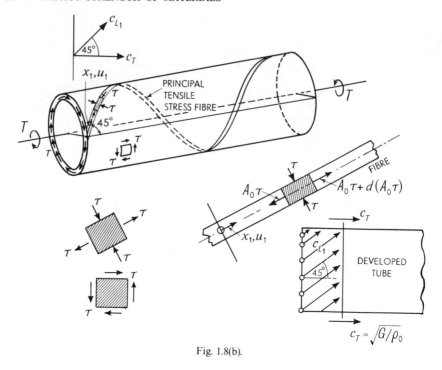

Fig. 1.8(b).

As before origin O and axis Ox are fixed in space and the compressive pulse length which is applied at $x = 0$ and $t = 0$ is also much greater than T. As before, the equation of motion for an element of the bar $ABCD$, $A'B'C'D'$, at time t is

$$-A_0 \frac{\partial \sigma_x}{\partial x} \cdot \delta x = A_0 \rho_0 \cdot \delta x \cdot \frac{\partial^2 u}{\partial t^2}$$

where A_0 is its original cross-sectional area and σ_x is the normal stress on a section.

Thus,

$$\frac{\partial \sigma_x}{\partial x} = -\rho_0 \frac{\partial^2 u}{\partial t^2} \tag{1.1ii}$$

where u is the displacement of a particle originally distance x from the fixed origin O. σ_x, σ_y and σ_z refer to the stresses on an element whose dimensions are those possessed in the unstrained state, i.e. they are nominal stresses. Now this element is, by definition, elastically stressed under conditions of plane strain, i.e. there is no expansion or contraction in the Oz-direction, and thus we have strain $e_z = (-\sigma_z - v\sigma_x)/E = 0$, where v is Poisson's ratio.

Thus $\sigma_z = -v\sigma_x$. Also,

$$e_x = \frac{-\sigma_x - v\sigma_y - v\sigma_z}{E} = \frac{-\sigma_x - v.0 + v.v\sigma_x}{E} \tag{1.16}$$

Hence, writing $\partial u/\partial x$ for e_x in (1.16),

$$\frac{\partial u}{\partial x} = e_x = -\frac{(1 - v^2)}{E} \cdot \sigma_x \tag{1.17}$$

and thus,

$$\frac{\partial^2 u}{\partial x^2} = -\frac{(1 - v^2)}{E} \cdot \frac{\partial \sigma_x}{\partial x} \tag{1.18}$$

Hence using (1.18) in (1.1ii) above,

$$\frac{\partial^2 u}{\partial t^2} = \frac{E}{\rho_0(1 - v^2)} \cdot \frac{\partial^2 u}{\partial x^2} \tag{1.19}$$

The longitudinal wave speed c'_L is,

$$c'_L = \sqrt{\frac{E}{\rho_0(1 - v^2)}}, \quad \text{or} \quad \frac{c'_L}{c_L} = \frac{1}{\sqrt{1 - v^2}} \tag{1.20}$$

Wave transmission along a uniform bar constrained to have zero transverse deformation

The analysis below follows that of the preceding section and arrives at an equation similar to (1.19), for the propagation of a plane compressive wave.

If e_y and e_z denote the transverse strains, and σ_y and σ_z the corresponding nominal stresses, then from symmetry $e_y = e_z$ and $\sigma_y = \sigma_z$, so that

$$E e_y = \sigma_y - v(\sigma_y - \sigma_x)$$
$$= \sigma_y(1 - v) + v \cdot \sigma_x$$

Also for zero transverse strain, $e_y = 0$ and thus

$$\sigma_y = -v\sigma_x/(1 - v) \tag{1.21}$$

Further,

$$\frac{\partial u}{\partial x} = e_x = \frac{-\sigma_x - 2v\sigma_y}{E}$$

and using (1.21)

$$\frac{\partial u}{\partial x} = -\sigma_x \frac{(1 - v - 2v^2)}{E(1 - v)}$$

Hence,

$$\frac{\partial \sigma_x}{\partial x} = -E \frac{(1 - v)}{(1 + v)(1 - 2v)} \cdot \frac{\partial^2 u}{\partial x^2} \tag{1.22}$$

Substituting (1.22) in (1.1ii),

$$\frac{\partial^2 u}{\partial t^2} = \frac{E}{\rho_0} \cdot \frac{(1-v)}{(1+v)(1-2v)} \cdot \frac{\partial^2 u}{\partial x^2} \tag{1.23}$$

and thus the speed of elastic longitudinal wave propagation c_L'' is,

$$c_L'' = \sqrt{\frac{E}{\rho_0} \cdot \frac{(1-v)}{(1+v)(1-2v)}}$$

or

$$\frac{c_L''}{c_L} = \sqrt{\frac{(1-v)}{(1+v)(1-2v)}} \tag{1.24}$$

We may also write

$$c_L'' = \sqrt{(\lambda + 2G)/\rho_0}$$

where

$$\lambda = vE/(1+v)(1-2v).$$

λ is known as Lamé's constant.

TABLE 1.2   LATERAL RESTRAINT AND WAVE
PROPAGATION SPEED

v	$\frac{1}{4}$	$\frac{1}{3}$	$\frac{1}{2}$
c_L'/c_L	$\dfrac{4}{\sqrt{15}}$	$3\sqrt{2}/4$	$2\sqrt{3}/3$
(from (1.20))	$\simeq 1{\cdot}03$	$\simeq 1{\cdot}06$	$\simeq 1.15$
c_L''/c_L (from (1.24))	$\sqrt{1{\cdot}2}$ $\simeq 1.1$	$\sqrt{1{\cdot}5}$ $\simeq 1{\cdot}22$	∞

Torsional wave transmission approached via longitudinal wave transmission

Another interesting calculation concerning wave speed in a long bar subject to certain lateral stress restraints is that of the case already dealt with on p. 11; this deals with the torsional wave speed in a long thin-walled tube which may be approached as follows.

Note first that if the transverse shear stress in the tube wall is τ, the principal stresses in a long uniform helical fibre at 45° to the tube axis are $+\tau$ and $-\tau$, see Fig. 1.8(b). Now this fibre lying along a principal axis may be considered simply as a bar, so that the initiation of a torsional wave at the end of the tube can be identified with the propagation of a longitudinal wave along the fibre. The equation of motion of an element of the fibre, along the principal *tensile* stress axis, is, using an obvious notation,

$$\rho_0 A_0 dx_1 \cdot \frac{\partial^2 u_1}{\partial t^2} = A_0 \cdot d\tau$$

but

$$e_1 = \frac{\partial u_1}{\partial x_1} = \frac{\tau(1 + v)}{E}$$

and substituting this in the equation above,

$$\frac{\partial^2 u_1}{\partial t^2} = \frac{E}{\rho_0(1 + v)} \cdot \frac{\partial^2 u_1}{\partial x_1^2}$$

Thus the speed of longitudinal wave propagation is

$$c_{L_1} = \sqrt{\frac{E}{\rho_0(1 + v)}} \; ;$$

the speed of the compressive wave along the other principal axis at right angles to the latter one, in the tube wall, is of course identical.

The speed of the wave parallel to the axis of the tube which is just the torsional wave speed c_T is $c_{L_1} \cos 45°$.

Thus,

$$c_T = \frac{c_{L_1}}{\sqrt{2}} = \sqrt{\frac{E}{2(1 + v)\rho_0}} = \sqrt{\frac{G}{\rho_0}}$$

Coaxial collision of two bars of identical cross-sectional area but unequal impedance: the change in particle speed

Before impact let the two square-ended bars which have different mechanical impedances ($\rho_0 c$) possess speeds v_1 and v_2, where $v_1 < v_2$, see Fig. 1.9(a). After impact, see Fig. 1.9(b) (in which c_1 and c_2 refer to wave speed in the bars), compressive longitudinal waves will propagate from the impact interface into each bar; the impact interface and the material engulfed by each wave will all have the same speed v'. Since the action and reaction across the interface are equal and because the cross-sectional area of each bar is the same, therefore the stress created in each bar is the same.

Earlier, we derived the expression (1.7ii) as $\sigma_0 = \rho_0 c_L v_0$, relating stress intensity, mechanical impedance and particle speed, in respect of a stationary

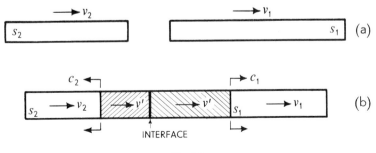

Fig. 1.9.

bar. The expression to be applied in respect of a bar which has an initial speed of translation v_1 is $\rho_0 c_L \cdot (v' - v_1)$ where v' is the new particle speed after the wave has travelled through it. Thus, v_0 of equation (1.7ii) is properly to be understood as a *change* in particle speed due to the passage of a wave or the *magnitude of the velocity discontinuity* across a wave front. The quantity $(v' - v_1)$ in respect of the initially translating bar and v_0 for the stationary bar are therefore identical quantities for the purpose of calculation. Henceforth, when we use the expression $\sigma = \rho_0 c_0 v_0$ it must be remembered that v_0 refers to a *change* in particle speed.

Thus, bearing in mind the precise meanings to be given to ρ_0 and c_L or c

$$\sigma = \rho_2 c_2 (v_2 - v') = \rho_1 c_1 (v' - v_1)$$

Thus,

$$v' = \frac{\rho_1 c_1 v_1 + \rho_2 c_2 v_2}{\rho_1 c_1 + \rho_2 c_2} \tag{1.25}$$

and

$$\sigma = \frac{v_2 - v_1}{\dfrac{1}{\rho_1 c_1} + \dfrac{1}{\rho_2 c_2}} \tag{1.26}$$

(As found later on p. 20, if $\rho_1 c_1 = \rho_2 c_2$ and $v_1 = -v_2$ then $v' = 0$ and $\sigma = \rho_1 c_1 v_1$.)

Impact of a square-ended solid cylinder with a sheet of water

This section is an example of the use of (1.7ii) or (1.26) and really repeats the last section. Consider a square-ended cylindrical metallic projectile of initial density ρ_0 impinging normally upon a plane sheet of water. Let the elastic compressive stress generated in the cylinder, which is initially moving with speed v_0, be σ_0. Then the particle speed in that part of the cylinder traversed by the stress wave is reduced to $v = v_0 - \sigma_0/(\rho_0 c_L)$ Now, at the instant of impact, v is also the particle speed of the contiguous water surface (neglecting effects about the perimeter of the rod) and if we assume that the compressive stress immediately created in the water σ_w, can in this complicated situation be related to particle speed through (1.7ii),

$$\sigma_w = \rho_w c_w v = \rho_w c_w \left(v_0 - \frac{\sigma_0}{\rho_0 c_0} \right)$$

Suffix 0 refers to the cylinder and w to the water. Now, $\sigma_w = \sigma_0$ as in the previous section and hence,

$$\sigma_0 = \frac{\rho_w c_w v_0}{1 + \dfrac{\rho_w c_w}{\rho_0 c_0}} = \frac{v_0}{\dfrac{1}{\rho_w c_w} + \dfrac{1}{\rho_0 c_0}} \tag{1.27}$$

According to (1.27) a square-ended steel bullet moving at 2500 ft/sec. would give rise to an elastic stress σ_0 of 283 000 lbf/in² $\simeq$ 126 tonf/in², on hitting the water.

The wave speed through stressed material and the wave speed through the space occupied by the material in the unstressed state

Refer to Fig. 1.10 and let the *right hand* end of the stationary rod be given a speed of v which is maintained until the whole of the bar has the same speed; this

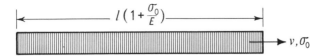

Fig. 1.10.

movement of the whole bar is brought about by a *leftwards* moving wave, initiated on first moving the end of the bar. The length of the bar will have then become $l(1 + \sigma_0/E)$ if σ_0 denotes the tensile stress throughout the length of the bar. Denote the wave speed through the space occupied by the bar in its final stressed state by C_E, then

$$\frac{l\left(1 + \dfrac{\sigma_0}{E}\right)}{C_E} = \frac{l\dfrac{\sigma_0}{E}}{v}$$

because the right hand end of the bar will have moved a distance $l\sigma_0/E$ in the same time. Hence,

$$c_E = \frac{v(1 + \sigma_0/E)}{\sigma_0/E} = c_L + v$$

using (1.7i) or,

$$c_E = c_0 + v \tag{1.28}$$

using the more conventional symbol c_0 for c_L; c_0 is the speed of the wave through the space originally occupied by the unstressed bar, or against a background of fixed laboratory coordinates. If the bar had been put into compression instead of tension, as above, then instead of (1.28) we should have,

$$c'_E = c_0 - v \tag{1.29}$$

Again, since an element initially of unit length when stressed by a tension wave becomes $(1 + e)$, then

$$\frac{1}{c_0} = \frac{1 + e}{c_E}$$

i.e.

$$c_E = c_0(1 + e) = c_0 + v$$

or

$$c_E/c_0 = 1 + v/c_0 \tag{1.30}$$

Since speed, v, for elastic behaviour is of the order of 10 ft/sec (see page 6) and c_0 is of the order of 10 000 ft/sec (see Table 1.1), then v/c_0, or indeed v/c_E are $\simeq 1/1000$. Thus *for cases of elastic impact*, for all practical purposes, we need not distinguish between c_0 and c_E.

Reflection and superposition of waves

Recall that in a tensile pulse, the direction of wave propagation and the direction of particle movement are opposite, whilst in a compressive pulse the direction of wave propagation and the direction of particle movement are the same. Also, remember that the basic wave equation $\partial^2 u/\partial t^2 = c^2 \partial^2 u/\partial x^2$ is linear and therefore that solutions may be superimposed; further, that c, c_L or c_0 are henceforth considered identical.

(a) (i) Let the end A of an unstrained stationary bar S, see Fig. 1.11(a), be moved with constant speed v_0 to the right for a time t, so that A moves to A' and $AA' = v_0 t$. At the same time a *compressive* wave $\sigma = \rho_0 c_0 v_0$ is caused to travel along the bar from A to the right as far as B, as shown in the Figure, with speed c_0, so that $AB = c_0 t$.

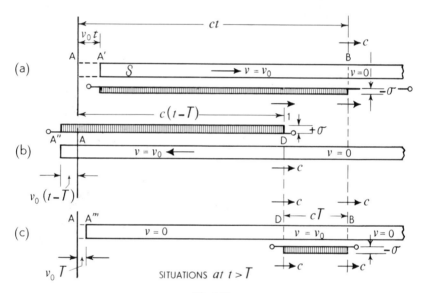

Fig. 1.11.

(ii) Consider a bar identical with S the end A of which is caused to move to the left to A'' with speed v_0 but only commencing at a time $t = T$, see Fig. 1.11(b); the magnitude of the induced tensile stress is $\sigma = \rho_0 c_0 v_0$ and the wave travels to the right so that at time $t > T$, $AD = c(t - T)$; also $AA'' = v_0(t - T)$.

(iii) Suppose now that the left hand end of unstrained stationary bar S, at $t = 0$ is moved to the right as in (i) above and that this is maintained for all t; also, suppose that time $t = T$, there is imposed on this the situation as in (ii) and to the end of the bar is added a speed to the left of v_0. *The net effect of these two superimposed situations* i.e. (i) and (ii), at time $t > T$, is as shown in Fig. 1.11(c). Length $A'''D$ is stationary and unstressed having undergone a rigid body movement to the right of AA''' or $v_0 T$; DB which has an unstrained length $c_0 T$ is subject to compressive stress σ, is actually compressed amount $v_0 T$, (so that the strain in it is $v_0 T/cT = v/c$, and as a whole has a speed to the right of v_0. The portion of bar to the right of B is of course stationary and unstressed.

A rectangular pulse of length cT can thus be considered in itself, and the properties associated with it are as just described and as shown in Fig. 1.11(c).

(b) Assume an elastic, rectangular pulse of *tension* to be moving along a uniform rod in the positive x-direction and that we wish to know what happens when it is reflected at its free end AB. Introduce a hypothetical rectangular compressive wave of the same pulse length and stress magnitude moving in the opposite direction, see Fig. 1.12(a). At AB the two wave fronts first meet and after some time have moved through one another completely, see Fig. 1.12(d).

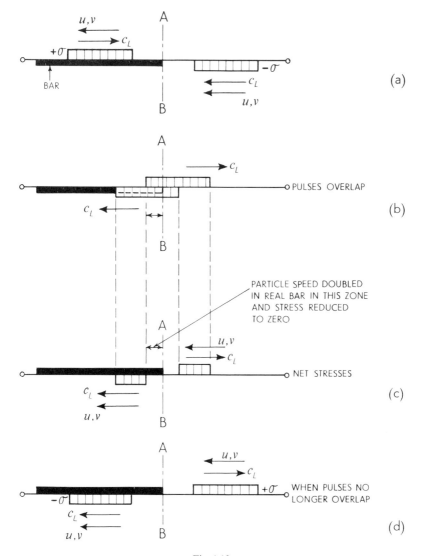

Fig. 1.12.

At AB, when the pulses overlap, the stresses in these waves annul one another so that across AB especially the stress is zero; at all times whilst the two waves overlap, see Figs. 1.12(b) and (c), AB carries zero stress and is, in effect, a *free end*. As far as the bar is concerned, the pulse moving *from* the right after it has crossed AB may be viewed simply as the front part of the original rightward moving pulse reflected from the end; the total pulse length in the real bar remains constant. Hence, for a *free-ended* bar, i.e. one on the end of which there is no stress, a *tensile wave is reflected as a compressive wave*; similarly, a wave of compression is reflected as a tensile wave at the free end of a rod. Observe in this instance that *in the portion of the bar where the two pulses overlap the total stress is zero and the particle speed is twice what it was when covered by the incident tensile wave alone.*

(c) In a similar way, if we consider two identical tensile waves moving towards one another, see Fig. 1.13(a), at CD, *where the heads of the two pulses first meet, the stress is doubled and the particle speed is zero*; this is so over any common length shared by both pulses and thus CD may be regarded as the *fixed end* of a bar, see Fig. 1.13(c). Hence, an elastic wave reflected from a fixed-ended bar is entirely unchanged in shape or intensity.

Of course, when the two waves can no longer be superimposed at any section, they continue to be propagated without alteration.

(d) It should now be evident that the net stress on, or the speed of particles in, a given plane are easily obtained by adding together the separate effects of the operative waves at that plane, e.g. the incident and reflected waves, provided, of course, that the waves are elastic.

It is often difficult to obtain a fixed end which does not move; an artifice that might be used to do this is to arrange for the normal impact of identical bars travelling in opposite directions. However, even this situation demands that the end of each bar is perfectly square.

The normal collinear impact of identical bars

When two identical bars travelling in opposite directions with the same speed, v_0, undergo normal impact, see Fig. 1.14(a), with the help of (b) and (c) above we can describe the sequence of events. Immediately after impact a compressive wave of intensity, $\rho_0 v_0 c_L$, moves into each bar from the common plane of impact; for $0 < t < l/c_L$ the situation is as shown in Fig. 1.14(b). The particles encompassed by the wave are brought to rest and at the end of time $t = l/c_L$, each bar will be completely stationary but stressed in compression; the whole of the kinetic energy, K, of a bar will have been changed to strain energy, E. We shall have,

$$K = \tfrac{1}{2}(\text{mass of bar}) \cdot v_0^2 = \tfrac{1}{2} \cdot A_0 l \cdot \rho_0 \cdot v_0^2$$

and

$$E = \text{volume} \cdot \frac{\sigma^2}{2E} = \frac{A_0 l \cdot (\rho_0 v_0 c_L)^2}{2E} = \frac{A_0 l \rho_0 v_0^2}{2}$$

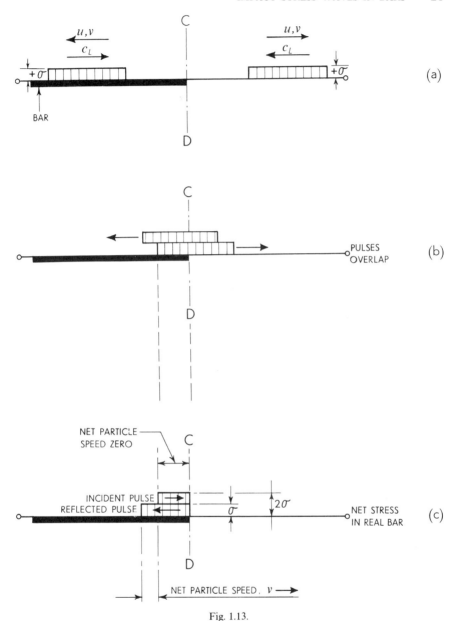

Fig. 1.13.

Immediately after $t = l/c_L$, the compressive wave will be reflected from the free end of the bar as a tensile wave which is, in effect, an unloading wave, see Fig. 1.14(c), and the reflected tensile wave gradually cancels the incident compressive wave. At the end of time $t = 2l/c_L$, the bars will be completely stress-free. The reflected tensile wave will confer a speed v_0 on the particles, whose direction is opposite to that of the bars at incidence, see Fig. 1.14(d).

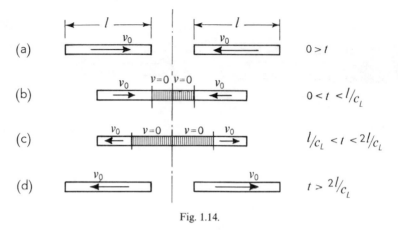

Fig. 1.14.

Thus at $t = 2l/c_L$ the particles in the common plane of impact will move away from one another with equal but opposite speeds. The bars will thus rebound as unstressed bodies at a time $t = 2l/c_L$ after impact first took place. The coefficient of restitution $e = 1$ in this case.

Exact solutions for the case of the collinear impact of two identical semi-infinite circular-section bars, which take into account the effects of radial inertia, are discussed by Goldsmith[1.2] but at length especially by Redwood[1.3] who also describes experimental and theoretical results for non-circular bars. See also p. 102.

Normal impact of two bars of identical material and of unequal length moving at equal speeds

The situation envisaged is that shown in Fig. 1.15; the length of two originally stress free bars S_1 and S_2 is l_1 and l_2, $l_2 < l_1$, both moving with speed v_0 but in opposite directions. Soon after impact, see Fig. 1.16, equal lengths of each bar will have been brought to rest because the elastic wave speed in both is the same. A compressive stress $\sigma = \rho_0 c_0 v_0$ will have been propagated away from the common plane of impact. The compressive pulse is reflected as a wave of tension from the free end of each bar, so that for the period of time $l_2/c_0 < t < 2l_2/c_0$, S_2

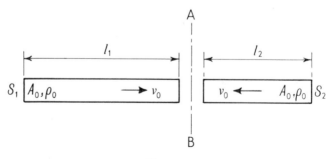

Fig. 1.15.

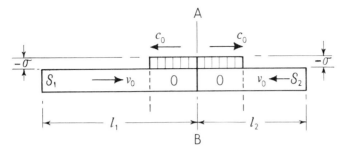

Fig. 1.16.

will be being unloaded. When $t = 2l_2/c_0$ S_2 is just completely stress free and the particle speed in it will everywhere have been exactly reversed; note that contact between the bars does not then cease; at this instant an unloading wave travels into S_1 from S_2 so that the particles at the right hand end of S_1 move to the right with speed v_0. *Contact ceases at* $t = 2l_1/c_0$ when the wave reflected from the left hand end of S_1 reaches the right hand end of S_2 and so cancels the speed there of v_0. If S_1 was infinitely long contact would be maintained for all time.

At this instant, i.e. $t = 2l_2/c_0$, let us ascertain how the energy is distributed in S_1 and S_2 if $2l_2 > l_1$, see Fig. 1.17. We note that unless $l_1 = l_2$ only part of S_1 will be stress free.

We have:

(a) the kinetic energy of S_2 which is unstressed is equal to

$$\tfrac{1}{2}A_0\rho_0 l_2 v_0^2 \tag{1.31}$$

and that of S_1

$$\tfrac{1}{2}A_0\rho_0(2l_2 - l_1)v_0^2 \tag{1.32}$$

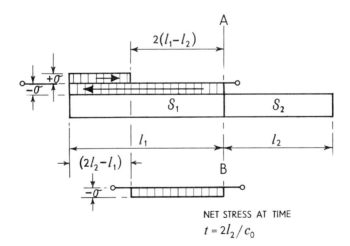

NET STRESS AT TIME
$t = 2l_2/c_0$

Fig. 1.17.

(b) the elastic strain energy in S_2 is zero and that in S_1

$$= \tfrac{1}{2}A_0[2(l_1 - l_2)]\frac{\sigma^2}{E}$$

$$= \tfrac{1}{2}A_0[2(l_1 - l_2)]v_0^2\frac{E\rho_0}{E},$$

because $\sigma = v_0\sqrt{E\rho_0}$,

$$= \tfrac{1}{2}\rho_0 A_0 v_0^2(2l_1 - 2l_2) \tag{1.33}$$

Adding together (1.31), (1.32) and (1.33) the total energy of the bars is found to be

$$\tfrac{1}{2}A_0\rho_0 l_2 v_0^2 + \tfrac{1}{2}A_0\rho_0 v_0^2(2l_2 - l_1) + \tfrac{1}{2}A_0\rho_0 v_0^2(2l_1 - 2l_2)$$

$$= \tfrac{1}{2}A_0\rho_0 v_0^2[l_2 + 2l_2 - l_1 + 2l_1 - 2l_2]$$

$$= \tfrac{1}{2}A_0\rho_0 v_0^2[l_1 + l_2] \tag{1.34}$$

which is just the kinetic energy of l_1 and l_2 before impact took place.

Note that in the elastic impact situation discussed there will appear to be a loss of translational kinetic energy; the 'loss' is, of course, conserved as elastic strain energy in the longer bar.

If we consider the case of $l_1 = 2l_2$, then at $t = l_1/c_0$, the whole of S_1 will be compressed and stationary. At $t = 1.5l_1/c_0$, S_1 will be completely unstrained because a tensile stress wave will have moved into the bar from both ends of S_1. The left hand half of S_1 will be moving to the left with speed v_0 and the right hand half to the right with speed v_0. The centre of gravity of S_1 at $l_1/2(1 - \rho_0 c_0 v_0/E)$ from the plane of impact is always stationary. At time $t = 2l_1/c_0$, each half of the bar will be in tension; at $t = 2 \cdot 5l_1/c_0$ the halves will be unloaded; and at $t = 3l_1/c_0$ they will again be entirely in compression. Thus the centre plane of S_1, after the unloading of S_2, is always at rest and the two halves of S_1 behave symmetrically about it, going alternately into compression and tension.

The coefficient of restitution e at the impact of S_1 and S_2, when $l_1 = 2l_2$, *calculated by reference to the centre of gravity of each*, is

velocity of separation of bar $= -e$ (velocity of approach of bars)

$$v_0 - (-v_0) = -e(0 - v_0) \quad \text{or} \quad e = \tfrac{1}{2}.$$

If the two bars had been treated as *rigid bodies* (or as if there was no elastic strain energy absorption), the equation of linear momentum would have applied and if the impact was non-dissipative and therefore $e = 1$, it would be predicted that after impact S_1 would move to the left with speed $\tfrac{1}{3}v_0$ and S_2 to the right with speed $\tfrac{5}{3}v_0$.

The treatment of situations in which impact between two elastic bodies occurs, as if the bodies were rigid, using the simple laws of linear momentum is justified as long as only a small fraction of the total kinetic energy available at impact, is converted into vibrational energy. This usually requires the time of contact to be greatly in excess of the period of lowest natural frequency of either body, so that several wave reflections in the bodies will have occurred during the time of contact (compare the situation of a relatively heavy rigid striker impinging on a long bar, see p. 51) and a state of nearly uniform stress is reached.

In the case just discussed the assumption that the two impinging bars are rigid leads to unacceptable results, but in the case of two spheres impinging at moderate speed v_0, it may be shown that the ratio of vibrational to total energy is $\frac{1}{50}(v_0/c_0)$—certainly small enough for all vibrational effects to be neglected. This latter important case is therefore analyzed statically as follows.

Central elastic impact of spheres

When two dissimilar solid spheres undergo simple central elastic impact, (i.e. without rotation and such that the velocity of each is along the straight line joining their centres), the time of contact of the spheres may be shown to be so great by comparison with the period of the lowest mode of vibration of the spheres that wave effects can be neglected, and because this is practically important and in sharp contrast with the case of two long thin elastic rods undergoing 'end impact' as just discussed, this situation and its consequences are now outlined following Timoshenko and Goodier.[1.4] The details of the motion of the spheres and the stress distribution over their common surface of contact, may be satisfactorily accounted for by using the static stress analysis for curved, contacting solid bodies or spheres as originally presented by Hertz in 1881. (See also refs. mentioned on p. 306.)

At time t after impact commences, see Fig. 18(a), the equation of motion for each sphere is given by,

$$m_1 \frac{dv_1}{dt} = -P \quad \text{and} \quad m_2 \frac{dv_2}{dt} = -P \tag{1.35}$$

where m denotes mass, and v current velocity and P is the reactive compressive force between the spheres. Denote by x the distance through which the two spheres approach by virtue of local compression, see Fig. 18(b), so that

$$\frac{dx}{dt} = v_1 + v_2 \quad \text{and} \quad \frac{d^2x}{dt^2} = \frac{dv_1}{dt} + \frac{dv_2}{dt} \tag{1.36}$$

Thus from (1.35),

$$\frac{d^2x}{dt^2} = -P \cdot \frac{m_1 + m_2}{m_1 m_2} = -P\mu, \tag{1.37}$$

denoting $(m_1 + m_2)/m_1 m_2$ by μ.

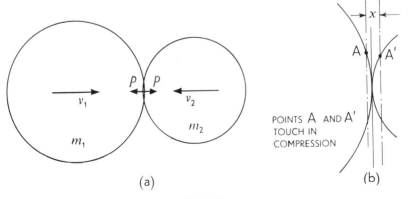

Fig. 1.18.

The force-displacement relation for static conditions is given by ref. 1.4 as

$$P = kx^{3/2} \qquad (1.38)$$

where

$$k = \frac{4}{3\pi \left[\dfrac{1 - v_1^2}{\pi E_1} + \dfrac{1 - v_2^2}{\pi E_2} \right]} \cdot \left(\frac{R_1 R_2}{R_1 + R_2} \right)^{1/2}. \qquad (1.39)$$

v and E have their usual meanings and R denotes the radius of a sphere. Substituting (1.38) in (1.37),

$$\ddot{x} = \frac{d^2 x}{dt^2} = -k\mu x^{3/2} \qquad (1.40)$$

Integrating (1.40),

$$\tfrac{1}{2}(\dot{x}^2 - v_0^2) = -\tfrac{2}{5} k\mu x^{5/2} \qquad (1.41)$$

where v_0 denotes the value of $(v_1 + v_2)$ when $t = 0$. Putting $\dot{x} = 0$ in (1.41), the maximum compression x_0 is found to be

$$x_0 = \left(\frac{5}{4} \frac{v_0^2}{k\mu} \right)^{2/5} \qquad (1.42)$$

From (1.41), we have,

$$\dot{x} = \frac{dx}{dt} = v_0 \left[1 - \frac{4}{5} \frac{k\mu x^{5/2}}{v_0^2} \right]^{1/2} = v_0 \left[1 - \left(\frac{x}{x_0} \right)^{5/2} \right]^{1/2}$$

and hence the time to maximum compression, T, is

$$T = \frac{x_0}{v_0} \int_0^1 \frac{dv}{[1 - v^{5/2}]^{1/2}} \doteqdot 1 \cdot 47 \frac{x_0}{v_0} \qquad (1.43)$$

The radius of the circle of contact, d, is given by

$$d = \left[3P \left(\frac{1 - v_1^2}{E_1} + \frac{1 - v_2^2}{E_2} \right) \frac{R_1 R_2}{4(R_1 + R_2)} \right]^{1/3}$$

The normal stress distribution is hemispherical over the contact circle and is greatest at the centre, where it is q_{max}; this is obviously greatest when the compressive force, P_{max}, is greatest. For a spherical body, or a spherical-nosed projectile, radius R_2, impinging against a plane surface, i.e. for a sphere of infinite radius,

$$P_{max} = kx_0^{3/2} = \frac{4 \cdot R_2^{1/5} (\tfrac{15}{16} \pi m_2 v_0^2)^{3/5}}{3\pi \cdot \left(\dfrac{1 - v_1^2}{\pi E_1} + \dfrac{1 - v_2^2}{\pi E_2} \right)^{2/5}}, \qquad (1.44)$$

and

$$d_{max} = R_2^{2/5} \left[\frac{15\pi \left(\dfrac{1 - v_1^2}{E_1} + \dfrac{1 - v_2^2}{E_2} \right) m_2 v_0^2}{16} \right]^{1/5} \qquad (1.45)$$

Also,

$$q_{max} = \frac{3 \cdot P_{max}}{2\pi \cdot d_{max}^2}$$

$$= \frac{E}{\pi(1 - v^2)} \cdot \left(\frac{x_0}{R_2} \right)^{1/2}, \qquad (1.46)$$

for identical materials. The maximum approach distance for identical spheres is given by,

$$\frac{x_0}{R} = \left[\frac{5\sqrt{2\pi\rho}}{4} \cdot \frac{1-v^2}{E} \cdot v_0^2 \right]^{2/5} \tag{1.47}$$

when ρ denotes the density of a sphere.

Energy and momentum transmission through three identical bars

Two identical bars, A and B, of mass m, length l and cross-sectional area A_0, are placed end-to-end touching one another, and one of them is hit on one end by a third identical bar, C, moving with speed v_0. The axes of all the bars are collinear. Let us describe the stress state and the particle speed in each bar at times $t = 0, l/c_0, 2l/c_0$ and $3l/c_0$ and show how at these instants momentum and energy are wholly conserved.

(i) The initial momentum is mv_0 and the initial kinetic energy is $\frac{1}{2}mv_0^2$, see Fig. 1.19(a).

(ii) Refer to Fig. 1.19(b); the momentum of B and C are each equal to $mv_0/2$ and therefore the total is mv_0. The kinetic energy of each of B and C is $\frac{1}{2}m(v_0/2)^2$. The strain energy in each is equal to

$$\text{volume of a bar} \cdot \sigma^2/2E = A_0 l \cdot [\rho_0 c_0(v_0/2)]^2/2E, \text{ or } A_0 l \cdot \frac{\rho_0^2 c_0^2 v_0^2/4}{2E} = mv_0^2/8$$

Thus, the kinetic energy plus the strain energy of both B and C

$$= 2 \times \frac{1}{2}m\frac{v_0^2}{4} + 2 \times m\frac{v_0^2}{8} = \frac{1}{2}mv_0^2 = \text{original kinetic energy}$$

(iii) See Fig. 1.19(c). Bars A and B have identical kinetic energy and the same amount of strain energy; bar C will have come to rest. Momentum and energy remain equal to that originally supplied.

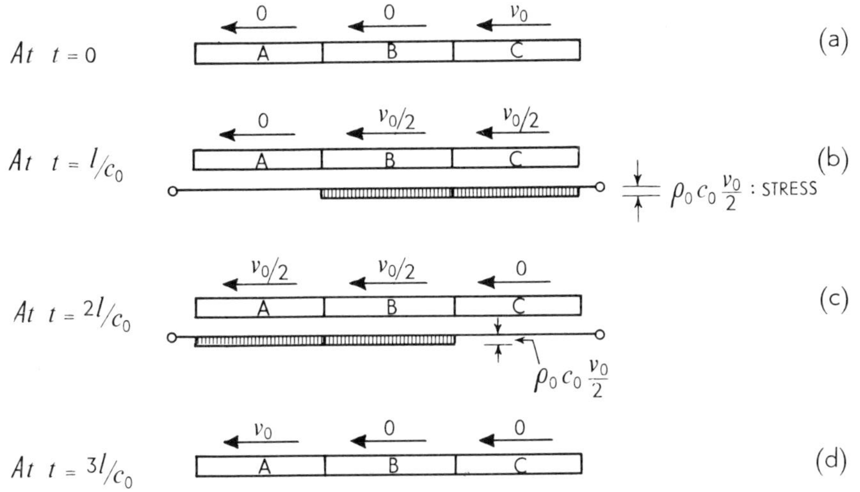

Fig. 1.19.

(iv) After stress relief as between B and C at $t = 2l/c_0$ an unloading wave moves into B from its right hand end and an equally intense unloading wave moves into A from its left hand end. At time $t = 3l_0/c$, B will have come to rest since the unloading tensile wave nullifies the compression in B and at the same time cancels the velocity, $v_0/2$, of particles in B. Likewise the compressive stress in A is removed, A becomes stress free but each particle of it will continue moving to the left with speed v_0.

Thus, at $t = 3l/c_0$, B and C are stress free and stationary whilst A is stress free but moving to the left, every particle having the same speed v_0; thus the initial momentum and kinetic energy of C is wholly transferred to A.

Impact between three bars of unequal impedance: an example of energy and momentum transmission

Let us review this latter situation when the mechanical impedance $(\rho_0 c_0)$ of each of the three bars is different, but subject to the condition that $l_1/c_1 = l_2/c_2 = l_3/c_3 = T$, where l denotes the length of a bar and c the speed of a longitudinal stress wave in it; suffices 1, 2 and 3 refer to the individual bars; all bars have the same cross-sectional area, A_0. On the assumption that the second and third bars are initially stationary and in contact, and that the first bar impinges collinearly on the second with an initial speed of v_0, we proceed to find the intensity of the stress and the particle speed, or change in speed, in each of the bars at times after impact first occurs of T, $2T$ and $3T$. We shall also show how the initial kinetic energy and momentum originally possessed by the first bar is distributed at time $3T$. (This given condition is identical to saying that the ratios of the bar masses are as the ratios of the mechanical impedances.)

Figs. 1.20(a) and (b) show the stress and speed situation at time $t = 0$ and $t = T$. The compressive force and hence stress at the interface between the first and second bar during the period $0 < t < T$ is the same in both bars; thus,

$$\sigma_1 = \rho_1 c_1 (v_0 - v_2)$$

$$\sigma_2 = \rho_2 c_2 . v_2$$

and

$$\sigma_1 = \sigma_2.$$

v_2 is the particle speed in the second bar when supporting the stress σ_2. Hence,

$$v_2 = \frac{\rho_1 c_1}{\rho_1 c_1 + \rho_2 c_2} . v_0 \tag{1.48}$$

and

$$\sigma_2 = \sigma_1 = \frac{\rho_1 c_1 . \rho_2 c_2}{\rho_1 c_1 + \rho_2 c_2} . v_0 \tag{1.49}$$

The head of the stress wave in each of the first and second bars reaches the end of the bar opposite to that at which impact took place, at the same instant and after time T.

For the period $T < t < 2T$ we have:

(i) The compressive wave in the first bar reflected from its free end after $t = T$, as an unloading wave of tension; the first bar is completely stress free at $t = 2T$. But each particle of the bar will have a speed to the left, see Fig. 1.20(c), of

$$v_2 - (v_0 - v_2) = 2v_2 - v_0 = (\rho_1 c_1 - \rho_2 c_2) v_0 / (\rho_1 c_1 + \rho_2 c_2),$$

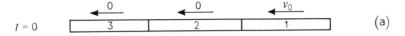

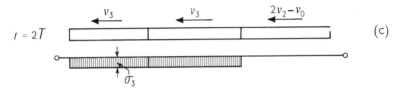

Fig. 1.20.

(ii) Because the stress at the interface between the second and third bars is the same and if v_3 denotes the particle speed in the third bar when stressed to the level σ_3,

$$\sigma_3 = \rho_3 c_3 v_3$$

and

$$\sigma_2' = \rho_2 c_2 (v_2 - v_3)$$

But,

$$\sigma_3 = \sigma_2 + \sigma_2'$$

and thus

$$v_3 = \frac{2\rho_2 c_2}{\rho_2 c_2 + \rho_3 c_3} \cdot v_2$$

And using (1.48),

$$v_3 = \frac{2\rho_1 c_1 \cdot \rho_2 c_2}{(\rho_1 c_1 + \rho_2 c_2)(\rho_2 c_2 + \rho_3 c_3)} \cdot v_0,$$

$$\sigma_3 = \frac{2\rho_1 c_1 \cdot \rho_2 c_2 \cdot \rho_3 c_3}{(\rho_1 c_1 + \rho_2 c_2)(\rho_2 c_2 + \rho_3 c_3)} \cdot v_0$$

and

$$2v_2 - v_3 = \frac{2\rho_1 c_1 \cdot \rho_3 c_3}{(\rho_1 c_1 + \rho_2 c_2)(\rho_2 c_2 + \rho_3 c_3)} \cdot v_0$$

At time $t = 2T$, the speed of the whole of the second and third bars is v_3. If there is no force between the first and second bars after $t > 2T$, then

$$2v_3 - 2v_2 > 2v_2 - v_0$$

i.e.

$$v_0 > 2(2v_2 - v_3)$$

or

$$\left(1 + \frac{\rho_1 c_1}{\rho_2 c_2}\right)\left(1 + \frac{\rho_3 c_3}{\rho_2 c_2}\right) > 4\frac{\rho_1 c_1}{\rho_2 c_2} \cdot \frac{\rho_3 c_3}{\rho_2 c_2} \tag{1.50}$$

(iii) At time $t = 3T$, assuming the first bar to be completely unloaded, its kinetic energy E_1 will be,

$$E_1 = \frac{1}{2} A_0 l_1 \rho_1 \left[\frac{i_1 - i_2}{i_1 + i_2} \cdot v_0\right]^2$$

where $i_1 = \rho_1 c_1$ and $i_2 = \rho_2 c_2$ and its momentum M_1 is

$$M_1 = A_0 l_1 \rho_1 v_0 (i_1 - i_2)/(i_1 + i_2)$$

The second bar will also be completely unloaded at $t = 3T$; its speed as a whole is then

$$v_3 - (2v_2 - v_3) = 2(v_3 - v_2) = 2i_1(i_2 - i_3)v_0/(i_1 + i_2)(i_2 + i_3);$$

its kinetic energy, E_2, is

$$E_2 = \tfrac{1}{2} A_0 l_2 \rho_2 \left[\frac{2i_1(i_2 - i_3)}{(i_1 + i_2)(i_2 + i_3)} \cdot v_0\right]^2$$

and its momentum, M_2, is

$$M_2 = A l_2 \rho_2 \left[\frac{2i_1(i_2 - i_3)v_0}{(i_1 + i_2)(i_2 + i_3)}\right]$$

The third bar is stress-free but the linear speed of the whole bar is $2v_3$; thus its kinetic energy, E_3, is

$$E_3 = \tfrac{1}{2} A_0 l_3 \rho_3 \left[\frac{4 \cdot i_1 i_2 v_0}{(i_1 + i_2)(i_2 + i_3)}\right]^2$$

and its linear momentum, M_3, is

$$M_3 = A l_3 \rho_3 \left[\frac{4i_1 i_2 \cdot v_0}{(i_1 + i_2)(i_2 + i_3)}\right]$$

The kinetic energy total, $E_1 + E_2 + E_3$,

$$= \tfrac{1}{2} A l_1 \rho_1 v_0^2 \left[\left(\frac{i_1 - i_2}{i_1 + i_2}\right)^2 + \left(\frac{l_2}{l_1} \cdot \frac{\rho_2}{\rho_1}\right) \cdot 4\left(\frac{i_1 \cdot (i_2 - i_3)}{(i_1 + i_2)(i_2 + i_3)}\right)^2 \right.$$

$$\left. + \left(\frac{l_3}{l_1} \cdot \frac{\rho_3}{\rho_1}\right) \cdot 16 \cdot \left(\frac{i_1 i_2}{(i_1 + i_2)(i_2 + i_3)}\right)^2\right]$$

$$= \tfrac{1}{2} m v_0^2 \left[(i_1 - i_2)^2 \cdot (i_2 + i_3)^2 + 4 \cdot \frac{i_2}{i_1} \cdot i_1^2 (i_2 - i_3)^2 \right.$$

$$\left. + 16 \cdot \frac{i_3}{i_1} \cdot i_1^2 \cdot i_2^2\right]/(i_1 + i_2)^2 \cdot (i_2 + i_3)^2$$

$$= \tfrac{1}{2} m v_0^2 \frac{[(i_1 - i_2)^2 \cdot (i_2 + i_3)^2 + 4i_1 i_2 (i_2 + i_3)^2 - 16 \cdot i_1 i_2^2 i_3 + 16 i_1 \cdot i_2^2 i_3]}{(i_1 + i_2)^2 \cdot (i_2 + i_3)^2}$$

$$= \tfrac{1}{2} m v_0^2 = \text{the original kinetic energy of the first bar whose mass } m = A_0 l_1 \rho_1.$$

The momentum total is $(M_1 + M_2 + M_3)$,

$$= A_0 l_1 \rho_1 v_0 \left[\frac{i_1 - i_2}{i_1 + i_2} + \frac{l_2 \rho_2}{l_1 \rho_1} \cdot \frac{2i_1(i_2 - i_3)}{(i_1 + i_2)(i_2 + i_3)} + \frac{l_3 \rho_3}{l_1 \rho_1} \cdot \frac{4i_1 i_2}{(i_1 + i_2)(i_2 + i_3)}\right]$$

$$= mv_0 \left[\frac{(i_1 - i_2)(i_2 + i_3) + 2i_2(i_2 - i_3) + 4i_2 i_3}{(i_1 + i_2)(i_2 + i_3)} \right]$$

$$= mv_0 \left[\frac{(i_2 + i_3)(i_1 + i_2) - 2i_2(i_2 + i_3) + 2i_2(i_2 + i_3)}{(i_1 + i_2)(i_2 + i_3)} \right]$$

$= mv_0 =$ the original momentum of the first bar.

Space-time diagram for the collinear impact of bars

The impact of collinear rods may be simply treated by using a space-time diagram—or as it is alternatively called a Lagrange diagram—or the characteristic plane. The latter term arises from the name of the formal solution to the one-dimensional wave equation; the characteristics $x \pm ct =$ constant, are the solutions to this equation. The characteristic defines a line across which there is a possibility of a jump in some quantity or other. In our simple problems above, at a given time, the wave front will usually have reached a particular location and on either side of it there will be a finite difference in the particle speed.

The space-time representation of longitudinal wave propagation is especially useful for examining problems where there is collinear impact of several bars, and we now illustrate its application to some very simple examples.

(i) Two identical bars

If two bars, I and II, have the same speed at impact, i.e. at $t = 0$, the progress of the waves in the bars may be represented as in the x, distance $-t$, time plot as in Fig. 1.21(a).

OA_1 shows the progression of the compression wave in bar I, with time, and OA_2 that in bar II. At time $t_1 = l/c_0$, the waves will have reached points A_1 and A_2 and at $t_2 = 2l/c_0$ the reflected unloading, tensile waves will meet at B, when the two bars will separate with their initial speed.

Note that in this x-t diagram the slope of the line represents the wave speed in a bar, c_0.

(ii) Three identical bars

Two identical bars, I and II, placed end-to-end touch one another and one of them is hit on one end by a third identical bar, III. The x-t diagram for this case, previously treated as in Fig. 1.19, is shown in Fig. 1.21(b). OA_1 and OA_2 represent the compressive waves after impact for $0 \le t \le l/c_0$; for $l/c_0 < t < 2l/c_0$ loading wave OA_2 continues through the third bar to give $A_2 A_3$ whilst $A_1 B$ is an unloading tensile wave. For $2l/c_0 < t < 3l/c_0$, the unloading wave continues from B to C whilst another unloading wave is initiated from A_3 to give rise to $A_3 C$. At time $t_3 = 3l/c_0$, bar III is stationary. Bar II is also stationary having been compressed as a whole for a time l/c_0, whilst bar I separates from bar II with the same speed as that initially possessed by III.

(iii) *Four bars*

Three identical bars are subject to the impact of a bar twice the length of either, but otherwise of identical properties, and moving with unit speed. It is easy to draw the space-time diagram shown in Fig. 1.21(c); the magnitudes entered in

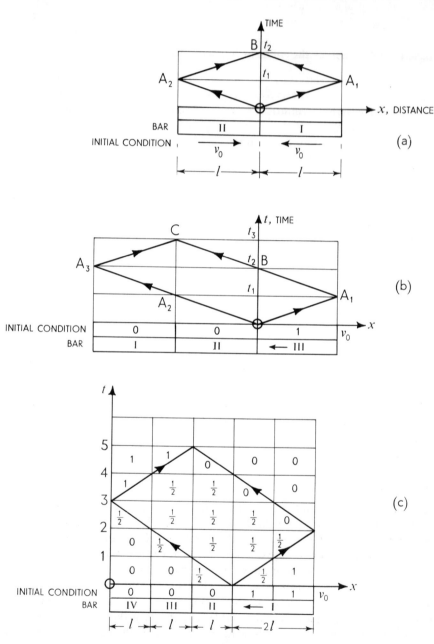

Fig. 1.21.

each square show the speed of a rod, or for each half of the long rod, at the end of integer intervals of time l/c_0. Bar I is stationary as a whole after time $4l/c_0$, bar II after a time of $5l/c_0$—but fully compressed as a whole for a time of $3l/c_0$—bar III is fully compressed as a whole for a time of $2l/c_0$, but together with bar IV it moves as a rigid body with unit speed, bar III following bar IV after a time of l/c.

Impact stress and uniform stress in a bar loaded by a falling weight

It is common in courses in Strength of Materials to estimate the greatest stress in a long uniform vertical rod due to the impact of a falling *rigid* mass M_1, see Fig. 1.22, by assuming that all the kinetic energy of M_1 is absorbed as uniformly distributed strain energy in the rod. Then the stress attained, σ, is given by

$$A_2 l_2 \cdot \frac{\sigma^2}{2E_2} = \frac{1}{2} M_1 v_0^2$$

or

$$\sigma^2 = \frac{M_1 v_0^2}{M_2/\rho_2} \cdot E_2 = \frac{M_1}{M_2} \cdot v_0^2 \cdot E_2 \rho_2 \tag{1.51}$$

A_2, l_2, ρ_2, E_2 and v_0 denote the cross-sectional area of the bar, its length, its density, its Young's Modulus and v_0 is the speed of impact of M_1 on the weightless collar at the bottom of the rod. M_2 is the mass of the rod.

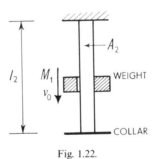

Fig. 1.22.

Now, the dynamic stress *initiated* at impact, σ_0, is really given by

$$\sigma_0 = \rho_2 v_0 \sqrt{\frac{E_2}{\rho_2}} \quad \text{or} \quad \sigma_0^2 = \rho_2 v_0^2 E_2; \tag{1.52}$$

σ_0 is independent of M_1.

Using (1.51) and (1.52), we have

$$\frac{\sigma}{\sigma_0} = \sqrt{\frac{M_1}{M_2}} = \sqrt{\frac{\text{Striker mass}}{\text{Struck rod mass}}}$$

When M_1/M_2 is very small, $\sigma^2 \ll \sigma_0$; it would then be quite inaccurate to use (1.51), or the resilience type of analysis common in elementary Strength of Materials.

No matter how small M_1, for a given v_0 the stress σ_0 would be generated at impact. The situation is, however, more complex than appears at first sight since at the first reflection of the wave at, say, the perfectly fixed end at the top of the rod, the stress would instantly become $2\sigma_0$. The subject of further stress intensification due to reflection is discussed on p. 51, from which it becomes apparent that the resilience approach is valid when $M_1 \gg M_2$.

It is sometimes asserted that the stress wave approach 'breaks down', or fails to give a result, if the mass is initially in contact with the collar. That this is not so will be evident from the cases discussed on p. 57.

Stress generated in two uniform bars of unequal cross-sectional area and dissimilar material when undergoing coaxial impact

Figure 1.23 shows bar S_1 moving with speed v_1 impinging on bar S_2 which moves in the same direction at speed v_2, where $v_1 > v_2$. Clearly this situation has much in common with that on p. 15. Let u_0 be the speed common to both bars after impact at time $0 < t < l_1/c_1, l_2/c_2$. The force acting on both bars at the common interface is the same and if σ_1 and σ_2 denote the stresses generated, then

$$A_1\sigma_1 = A_2\sigma_2$$

and

$$A_1\rho_1c_1(v_1 - u_0) = A_2\rho_2c_2(u_0 - v_2),$$

so that,

$$u_0 = \frac{v_2 + \dfrac{A_1\rho_1c_1}{A_2\rho_2c_2} \cdot v_1}{1 + \dfrac{A_1\rho_1c_1}{A_2\rho_2c_2}} \tag{1.53}$$

It is now straightforward to calculate σ_1 and σ_2 and find

$$\sigma_1 = \frac{\rho_1c_1v_1}{\left(1 + \dfrac{A_1\rho_1c_1}{A_2\rho_2c_2}\right)} \cdot \left[1 - \frac{v_2}{v_1}\right]$$

and

$$\tag{1.54}$$

$$\sigma_2 = \frac{\rho_2c_2v_2}{\left(1 + \dfrac{A_1\rho_1c_1}{A_2\rho_2c_2}\right)} \cdot \left(\frac{v_1}{v_2} - 1\right) \cdot \frac{A_1\rho_1c_1}{A_2\rho_2c_2}$$

If $\rho_1c_1 = \rho_2c_2$ and writing $A_1/A_2 = \mu$, then

$$u_0 = \frac{v_2 + \mu v_1}{1 + \mu} \tag{1.55}$$

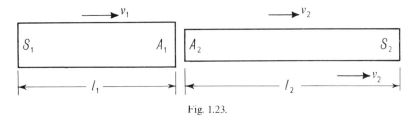

Fig. 1.23.

Suppose that $u_0 = 0$, then $v_2 = -\mu v_1$. Let $l_1 = 2l_2$ and $\rho_1 = \rho_2$, so that when S_2 is completely unloaded at time $t = 2l_2/c_2$, S_1 is wholly stationary and compressed. Thence for $t > 2l_2/c_2$, S_2 will be moving as a wholly unstressed bar having a translational speed of $(2u_0 - v_2)$ whilst the centroid of S_1 will henceforth always remain stationary. If the coefficient of restitution in this circumstance, defined with respect to the centroids of the two bars, is e then

$$2u_0 - v_2 = -e(v_2 - v_1)$$

i.e.

$$e = \frac{-2\dfrac{(v_2 + \mu v_1)}{(1 + \mu)} + v_2}{v_2 - v_1} = \frac{\mu}{1 + \mu}$$

When $\mu = 1$, $e = \frac{1}{2}$, as already seen and discussed on p. 24.

Stress transmission in shafts having a discontinuity in cross-sectional area and for bars composed of different materials

Consider an incident elastic wave of compressive stress of intensity σ_I moving to the right, see Fig. 1.24, through a stationary bar of material S_1 of cross-sectional area A_1. This is partly reflected and partly transmitted at the surface of

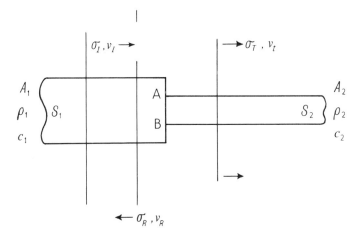

Fig. 1.24.

discontinuity AB where another bar of material, S_2, of cross-sectional area A_2 is perfectly attached to S_1. Note that if A_2 was zero the wave would be wholly reflected whilst if S_1 and S_2 were identical the wave would be wholly transmitted. Since S_1 and S_2 are of different areas and materials, then, at AB, the incident wave must be both reflected and transmitted.

The stress wave transmitted through S_2 of intensity σ_T, and that reflected back through S_1, σ_R, may be found with the aid of equations (1.7ii) after appreciating that the conditions to be satisfied at AB are:

(i) the forces on plane AB acting from S_1 and S_2 are at all times equal, and
(ii) the particle velocity in plane AB, in the material, for S_1 and S_2 are equal.

Now, if both σ_R and σ_T are taken to be compressive then

$$A_1(\sigma_I + \sigma_R) = A_2\sigma_T \tag{1.56}$$

and, noting that σ_I and σ_R are associated with waves travelling in opposite directions, therefore, (ii) gives

$$v_I - v_R = v_T \quad \text{or} \quad \sigma_I - \sigma_R = \sigma_T. \tag{1.57}$$

v denotes particle speed and subscripts I, R and T refer to incidence, reflection and transmission.

Hence,

$$\sigma_T = \frac{2A_1\rho_2c_2}{A_2\rho_2c_2 + A_1\rho_1c_1} \cdot \sigma_I \tag{1.58}$$

and

$$\sigma_R = \frac{A_2\rho_2c_2 - A_1\rho_1c_1}{A_2\rho_2c_2 + A_1\rho_1c_1} \cdot \sigma_I \tag{1.59}$$

From (1.59) note that for a simple change in cross-sectional area, i.e. when S_1 and S_2 are of the same material and $\rho_1 = \rho_2$ and $c_1 = c_2$, the incident and reflected waves have the same or opposite signs according to the increase or decrease in size of the cross-sectional area; and at the same time the intensity of the transmitted stress falls below or exceeds the intensity of the incident stress.

Equations (1.58) and (1.59) are, of course, approximate since the derivations included all the reservations made on p. 2; and at the discontinuity AB, condition (ii) is true only inside the material, not at the end surfaces. Complicated local stress wave interactions occur in the vicinity of AB and for a length equal to about the first diameter.

Inherent in equations (1.58) and (1.59) are the results of p. 20, because with $\rho_1 = \rho_2$ and $E_1 = E_2$, i.e. $c_1 = c_2$,

(a) if $A_2/A_1 \to 0$, the end of the rod is effectively free and (1.59) gives $\sigma_R \to -\sigma_I$ and $\sigma_T \to 2\sigma_I$, and
(b) if $A_2/A_1 \to \infty$, the end of the rod is effectively fixed, $\sigma_R \to \sigma_I$ and $\sigma_T \to 0$.

These results, i.e. (1.58) and (1.59) show that a small shaft on the end of one larger in cross-sectional area can act as a *wave trap* to a pulse or blow on the far end of the large shaft.

The stress magnification, for a single solid stepped shaft, can, as (a) above shows, amount to a factor of 2.

For the same amount of total reduction of area, however, this intensification factor is *not* reduced by using a solid two-step shaft but, on the contrary, is increased. This may be proved generally, but an example will suffice. In Fig. 1.25

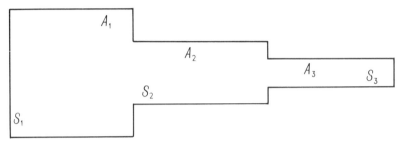

Fig. 1.25.

let $A_1/A_3 = 4$ and $A_1/A_2 = A_2/A_3 = 2$; then for an incident compressive stress wave σ_I, the transmitted stress σ_{T_2} in the section of area A_2 is given by

$$\frac{\sigma_{T_2}}{\sigma_I} = \frac{2A_1}{A_1 + A_2} = \frac{2 \times 2}{2 + 1} = \frac{4}{3}$$

And the transmitted stress in S_3, i.e. σ_{T_3}, is

$$\sigma_{T_3} = \frac{2A_2}{A_2 + A_3} \cdot \sigma_{T_2} = \frac{2 \times 2}{2 + 1} \cdot \frac{4}{3}\sigma_I = 1.78\sigma_I$$

If the step A_2 was omitted, so that the change in area from A_1 to A_3 occurred at once, then

$$\sigma_{T_3} = \frac{2A_1}{A_1 + A_3} \cdot \sigma_I = \frac{2 \times 4}{4 + 1} \cdot \sigma_I = 1.60\sigma_I$$

Thus the transmitted stress is increased by about 10% because of the inclusion of the extra step.[1.5] It is evident then that an abrupt change of section is better than a gradual one where shock loads have to be transmitted.

A result worth noting is that for no wave to be reflected from the discontinuity in the bar we require $\sigma_R = 0$ and then $A_2\rho_2 c_2 = A_1\rho_1 c_1$ so that

$$\sigma_T = \sigma_I\sqrt{E_2\rho_2/E_1\rho_1};$$

ensuring that $A_1\rho_1 c_1 = A_2\rho_2 c_2$ is known as *impedance matching*.

An example of the history of longitudinal stress wave changes due to a discontinuity in shaft cross-sectional area

As an example of the complexity of wave transmission and reflection due to an abrupt area change in a shaft, consider an infinitely long longitudinal compressive stress wave of unit intensity transmitted along a uniform shaft whose cross-sectional area is two units. Let it encounter an abrupt change in cross-sectional area at the end of the shaft to one unit, for a length l. We now endeavour to describe the early part of the subsequent history of the wave, in brief, using Fig. 1.26, which is largely self-explanatory. Two diagrams are given for each time range; the one on the left for the passage of the wave through each portion of the bar and the one on the right giving the net stress in each portion.

(i) $t < 0$: Fig. 1.26(a)

The initial situation is shown at time $t < 0$ where t is measured from the instant the wave reaches SS.

(ii) $0 < t < l/c_0$: Fig. 1.26(b)

After encountering SS, the discontinuity, the wave divides; part is transmitted at intensity σ'_T and proceeds down the end portion of the shaft whilst part is reflected, σ'_R. Thus, using equations (1.58) and (1.59),

$$\sigma'_T = \frac{2.2}{1+2} = \frac{4}{3}$$

and

$$\sigma'_R = \frac{1-2}{1+2}.1 = \frac{-1}{3}$$

(The −ve sign means that the wave is one of tension).

(iii) $l/c_0 < t < 2l/c_0$: Fig. 1.26(c)

σ'_T is reflected with a sign change at $t = l/c_0$ and at $t = 2l/c_0$, the end portion is completely unloaded and stress free.

(iv) $2l/c_0 < t < 3l/c_0$: Fig. 1.26(d)

When $t > 2l/c_0$, the tension wave is partly reflected back into the reduced section at the right hand end of the shaft and has an intensity

$$\sigma''_R = \frac{2-1}{2+1}.\left(\frac{-4}{3}\right) = \frac{-4}{9}$$

whilst the transmitted wave has an intensity

$$\sigma''_T = \frac{2.1}{2+1}.\left(\frac{-4}{3}\right) = \frac{-8}{9}$$

(v) $3l/c_0 < t < 4l/c_0$: Fig. 1.26(e)

The wave of intensity σ''_R is reflected with a sign change at $t = 3l/c_0$.

(vi) $4l/c_0 < t < 5l/c_0$

The compressive wave of intensity $\frac{4}{9}$ encounters SS and again divides to give rise to a reflected portion of intensity

$$\sigma'''_R = \frac{2-1}{2+1}.\left(\frac{4}{9}\right) = \frac{4}{27}$$

and a transmitted portion of intensity

$$\sigma'''_T = \frac{2.1}{2+1}.\left(\frac{4}{9}\right) = \frac{8}{27}$$

This process may be continued *ad infinitum*.

The end of the rod of reduced section was in tension, the stress magnitude being $\frac{4}{9}$, during the period $2l/c_0 < t < 4l/c_0$ and when σ'''_R is reflected is of magnitude of $\frac{4}{27}$ (compressive) during $4l/c_0 < t < 6l/c_0$.

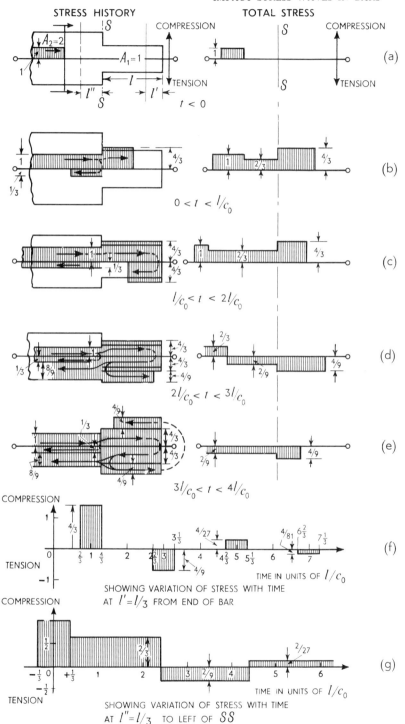

STRESS HISTORY   TOTAL STRESS

Fig. 1.26.

Any section in this end distant l' from the far right hand side, Fig. 1.26(a), is under a compressive stress of $\frac{4}{3}$ for time $2l'/c_0$ and then zero stress for the next period of time $2(l - l')/c_0$; next, a tension of $\frac{4}{9}$ ensues for the further time $2l'/c_0$, followed by zero stress for $2(l - l')/c_0$; and later by a compression of $\frac{4}{27}$ for $2l'/c_0$ and then zero stress for a period of time $2(l - l')/c_0$. A graph of stress intensity against time for this section may be obtained, assuming $l' = l/3$.

Obviously the 'steps' in Fig. 1.26(f) decrease in magnitude to $\frac{1}{3}$ of their value at each successive 'step'. Correspondingly, in the section of cross-sectional area equal to two units, at a distance l'' to the left of SS, we have, for the stresses reflected, the following:

For, $t > -l''/c_0,$ $\sigma = 1,$

$0 < t < l''/c_0,$ $\sigma = 1,$

$l'/c_0 < t < (l'' + 2l)/c_0,$ $\sigma = 1 - \frac{1}{3} = \frac{2}{3}$

$(l'' + 2l)/c_0 < t < (l'' + 4l)/c_0,$ $\sigma = \frac{2}{3} - \frac{8}{9} = -\frac{2}{9}$

and

$(l'' + 4l)/c_0 < (l'' + 6l)/c_0,$ $\sigma = -\frac{2}{9} + \frac{8}{27} = \frac{2}{27},$

etc. Assuming $l'' = l/3$, the above information may be represented as in Fig. 1.26(g).

Longitudinal waves in an approximated conical bar

In this Section we look for indications as to how a unit compressive pulse incident on the end of a conical bar is transmitted. The purpose of the approach adopted here is to make it easier for the reader to appreciate the mathematical results from an analysis of the conical bar which follows afterwards. The method now used is elementary and approximate.

Figure 1.27(a) shows a conical-ended bar which has been approximated as a stepped shaft; the axial length of all the segments is equal and the cross-sectional area of each is proportional to the square of the distance of the end section of the segment from the end of the bar; each segment is to be supposed long by comparison with a diameter.

Let a stress pulse of unit intensity and of length equal to that of a segment, impinge on section 5; T denotes the length of time taken by the pulse to traverse a segment of the shaft.

We make continual use of equations (1.58) and (1.59).

(i) At $t = 0$, immediately the pulse impinges on section 5, two waves are generated, one a reflected wave whose intensity is designated σ_{R_5} and the other a transmitted wave, σ_{T_5}. Thus,

$$\sigma_{T_5} = \frac{2 \cdot 36}{25 + 36} \cdot 1 = 1 \cdot 18$$

and

$$\sigma_{R_5} = \frac{25 - 36}{25 + 36} \cdot 1 = -0 \cdot 18.$$

(More directly, using (1.57), $\sigma_R = \sigma_I - \sigma_T = 1 - 1 \cdot 18 = -0 \cdot 18$.)

(ii) At time $t = T$, when the transmitted pulse σ_{T_5} has just reached section 4, it generates a transmitted pulse of intensity σ_{T_4} and a reflected pulse of intensity

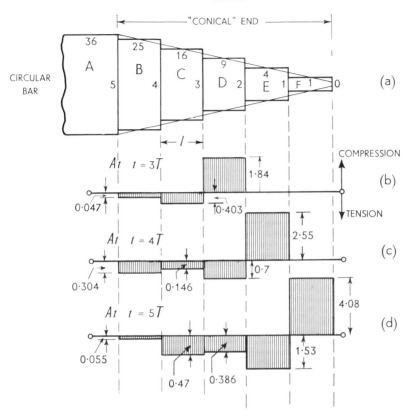

Fig. 1.27.

σ_{R_4}. We have

$$\sigma_{T_4} = \frac{2 \cdot 25}{16 + 25} \cdot 1 \cdot 18 = 1 \cdot 44$$

and

$$\sigma_{R_4} = \frac{16 - 25}{16 + 25} \cdot 1 \cdot 18 = -0 \cdot 26$$

(iii) At time $t = 2T$, when the transmitted pulse σ_{T_4} has just reached section 3, as before, we have

$$\sigma_{T_3} = \frac{2 \cdot 16}{9 + 16} \cdot 1 \cdot 44 = 1 \cdot 84$$

and

$$\sigma_{R_3} = \frac{9 - 16}{9 + 16} \cdot 1 \cdot 44 = -0 \cdot 403$$

Also at $t = 2T$, the pulse reflected from section 4 at $t = T$, i.e. σ_{R_4}, will have reached section 5 where it will be transmitted and reflected; we are primarily interested in the reflected pulse moving towards the apex of the bar, $\sigma_{R_{4,5}}$, so that,

$$\sigma_{R_{4,5}} = \frac{36 - 25}{36 + 25} \cdot (-0.26) = 0.047$$

(iv) At $t = 3T$, following the same notation as before, when section 2 is reached by σ_{T_3},

$$\sigma_{T_2} = \frac{2.9}{4 + 9} \cdot 1.84 = 2.55;$$

$\sigma_{R_{4,5}}$ will at this instant have reached section 4, and the transmitted pulse intensity is $\sigma_{R_{4,5,4}}$,

$$\sigma_{R_{4,5,4}} = \frac{2.25}{25 + 16} \cdot (-0.047) = -0.0574$$

To this latter stress must be added the effect of the pulse reflected from section 4, i.e. $\sigma_{R_{3,4}}$, which arose from reflection at section 3 as σ_{R_3}. Thus,

$$\sigma_{R_{3,4}} = \frac{25 - 16}{25 + 16} \cdot (-0.403) = -0.0885$$

and the total intensity of stress proceeding across section 4 towards the apex of the bar is $(-0.0574) + (-0.0885) = -0.146$. Also,

$$\sigma_{R_2} = \frac{4 - 9}{4 + 9} \cdot 1.84 = -0.71$$

(v) At $t = 4T$, at section 1,

$$\sigma_{T_1} = \frac{2.4}{1 + 4} \cdot 2.55 = 4.08$$

and

$$\sigma_{R_1} = \frac{1 - 4}{1 + 4} \cdot 2.55 = -1.53$$

At section 3,

$$R_{2,3} = \frac{16 - 9}{16 + 9} \cdot (-0.71) = -0.199$$

and

$$R_{3,4,3} = \frac{2.16}{9 + 16} \cdot (-0.1461) = -0.187$$

Thus the total intensity of stress two segment lengths behind the head of the successively transmitted initial unit pulse is $(-0.199) + (-0.187) = -0.386$.

The composite pictures of the wave shape with corresponding intensities at different successive times may now be arrived at. For $t = 3T$, see Fig. 1.27(b), for $t = 4T$, see Fig. 1.27(c) and for $t = 5T$, when the pulse has just reached the end of the bar, see Fig. 1.27(d). (Information contained in Fig. 1.28(a) concerning the pulse tail has been added to the last two Figures.)

It should be noted particularly that as the pulse travels towards the end of the bar, the stress intensity at the head increases, whilst a tail to the pulse is developed which has a smaller intensity but one of opposite sign. Intuitively, we might expect that the intensity at the head of a pulse which reached the apex of a conical bar would become infinite. However, in a bar which possesses an end segment, F, of constant length, a high compressive stress will be attained and,

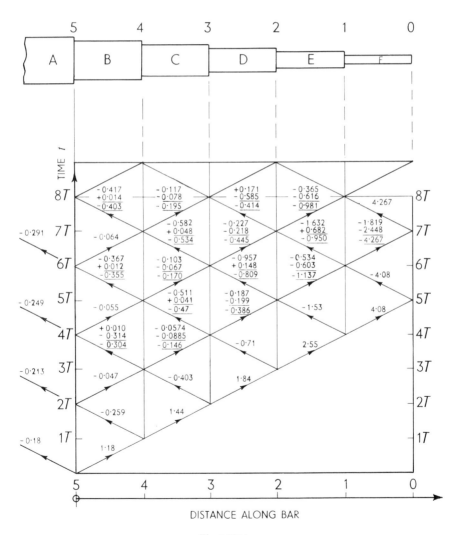

Fig. 1.28(a).

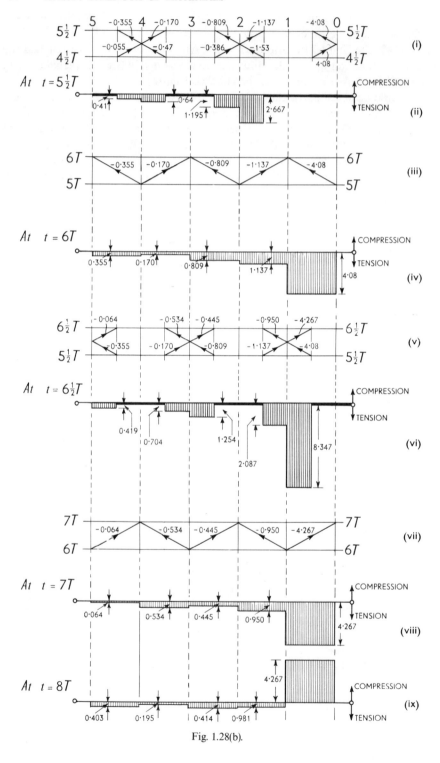

Fig. 1.28(b).

Section	A	B	C	D	E	F	Momentum Total
Time 0 t	1·36						36·00
T	0·18 . 36 6·48	1·18 . 25 29·50					35·98
$2T$	0·18 . 36 6·48	0·259 . 25 6·48	1·44 . 16 23·04				36·00
$3T$	0·18 . 36 +0·213 . 36 14·15	−0·047 . 25 −1·175	0·403 . 16 6·45	1·84 . 9 16·56			35·98
$4T$	0·18 . 36 +0·213 . 36 14·15	0·304 . 25 7·60	−0·146 . 16 −2·34	0·71 . 9 6·39	2·55 . 4 10·20		36·00
$5T$	0·18 . 36 +0·213 . 36 +0·249 . 36 23·12	−0·055 . 25 −1·375	0·47 . 16 7·52	−0·386 . 9 −3·47	1·53 . 4 6·12	4·08 . 1 4·08	36·01
$5\frac{1}{2}T$	23·12	−0·055 . 25 . $\frac{1}{2}$ +0·355 . 25 . $\frac{1}{2}$ 3·75	0·47 . 16 . $\frac{1}{2}$ −0·17 . 16 . $\frac{1}{2}$ 2·40	−0·386 . 9 . $\frac{1}{2}$ +0·809 . 9 . $\frac{1}{2}$ 1·853	1·53 . 4 . $\frac{1}{2}$ −1·137 . 4 . $\frac{1}{2}$ 0·786	4·08 . 1 . $\frac{1}{2}$ +4·08 . 1 . $\frac{1}{2}$ 4·08	36·09
$6T$	23·12	0·355 . 25 8·875	−0·170 . 16 −2·720	0·809 . 9 7·281	−1·137 . 4 −4·548	4·08 . 1 4·08	35·99
$6\frac{1}{2}T$	0·18 . 36 +0·213 . 36 +0·249 . 36 +0·291 . 36 . $\frac{1}{4}$ 28·36	0·355 . 25 . $\frac{1}{2}$ −0·064 . 25 . $\frac{1}{2}$ 3·637	0·534 . 16 . $\frac{1}{2}$ −0·170 . 16 . $\frac{1}{2}$ 2·912	−0·445 . 9 . $\frac{1}{2}$ +0·809 . 9 . $\frac{1}{2}$ 1·638	0·950 . 4 . $\frac{1}{2}$ −1·137 . 4 . $\frac{1}{2}$ −0·374	4·08 . 1 . $\frac{1}{2}$ −4·267 . 1 . $\frac{1}{2}$ −0·093	36·08
$7T$	33·59	−0·064 . 25 −1·60	0·534 . 16 8·54	−0·445 . 9 −4·00	0·95 . 4 3·80	−4·267 . 1 −4·267	36·00
$8T$	33·59	0·403 . 25 10·075	−0·195 . 16 −3·12	0·414 . 9 3·726	0·981 . 4 −3·924	−4·267 . 1 −4·267	36·07

after reaching the end of the bar, it will be reflected as a *tensile* stress pulse of equal intensity.

The stress wave intensity in other portions of the bar and at later times may be determined as above, but it becomes progressively more difficult to keep account of the wave interactions. The characteristic diagram becomes very helpful in this situation and Fig. 1.28(a) shows such a diagram for this problem for the period $t = 0$ to $t = 8T$. The reader should have little difficulty in corroborating the values of the stress intensities inserted in the diagram.

At $t = 5\frac{1}{2}T$, the state of stress in each section of the bar is found by considering the time band between $4\frac{1}{2}T$ and $5\frac{1}{2}T$ in the characteristic diagram of Fig. 1.28(a). At each cross-section in the bar the total stress on it is found by summing the operative stresses, e.g. in the smallest section F, the right-hand half is subject to zero stress because the equal intensity incident and reflected waves cancel, whilst in the left hand half there is also zero stress, but because no stress waves are passing through it at time $t = 5\frac{1}{2}T$. The stress wave intensity, whether it be compressive (counted positive) or tensile (counted negative), and the wave direction in each portion of the bar in the period $4\frac{1}{2}T$ to $5\frac{1}{2}T$ is shown in Fig. 1.28(b)i; the corresponding stress distribution at $t = 5\frac{1}{2}T$ is shown in Fig. 1.28(b)ii. Wave transmission and stress distribution diagrams pertaining to $t = 6T, 6\frac{1}{2}T, 7T$ and $8T$ are given also in Fig. 1.28(b). The momentum distribution at integer values of $T, 5\frac{1}{2}T$ and $6\frac{1}{2}T$ (assuming $T = 1$), are tabulated below so that the details may be checked; the main purpose of the calculations is to show how momentum is conserved at all times. (In verifying the entries in Table 1.3 note that with *rightward moving compressive waves* and *leftward moving tensile waves, positive* momentum is associated whilst *negative* momentum is associated with *leftward moving compression waves* and *rightward moving tensile waves.*)

Torsional stress transmission in bars composed of different materials and/or having a discontinuity in cross-sectional area

Consider two long circular shafts of different diameters and of different materials firmly fastened end-to-end so as to form a single shaft and let a torque T_I be suddenly applied and then maintained at the free end of one of them which is, say, of material 1. Designate quantities referring to the second part of the shaft by suffix 2 and let all local effects due to fastening of the two materials be neglected.

Then, when the impulsive torque reaches the area discontinuity, a torque T_R is reflected and a torque T_T is transmitted. We have

$$T_I + T_R = T_T \tag{1.60}$$

since the torque on either side of the area change must be the same for equilibrium. The angular velocity of each part of the shaft must be the same for there to be continuity through the section discontinuity, so that

$$\omega_I - \omega_R = \omega_T. \tag{1.61}$$

ω_R is negative because T_R acts in a direction opposite to that of T_I and T_T.

Using equation (1.12i) in (1.61),

$$\frac{T_I - T_R}{J_1\sqrt{G_1\rho_1}} = \frac{T_T}{J_2\sqrt{G_2\rho_2}} \tag{1.62}$$

Hence, from (1.60) and (1.62), we obtain

$$T_T = \frac{2T_I}{1 + \dfrac{J_1}{J_2} \cdot \dfrac{\sqrt{G_1\rho_1}}{\sqrt{G_2\rho_2}}} = \frac{2T_I}{1 + \dfrac{J_1\rho_1 c_{T_1}}{J_2\rho_2 c_{T_2}}} = \frac{2T_I}{1 + n} \qquad (1.63)$$

and

$$T_R = -T_I \frac{1 - \dfrac{J_1}{J_2} \cdot \dfrac{\sqrt{G_1\rho_1}}{\sqrt{G_2\rho_2}}}{1 + \dfrac{J_1}{J_2} \cdot \dfrac{\sqrt{G_1\rho_1}}{\sqrt{G_2\rho_2}}} = -T_I \cdot \frac{1 - n}{1 + n} \qquad (1.64)$$

where $n = J_1\rho_1 c_{T_1}/J_2\rho_2 c_{T_2}$.

If a circular shaft was composed of two portions but such that the diameter of one portion is twice the diameter of the other, then using (1.63), we have either

$$T_T = \frac{2T_I}{1 + \dfrac{J_1}{J_2}} = \frac{2T_I}{1 + \dfrac{2^4}{1^4}} = \frac{2}{17}T_I$$

or

$$T_T = \frac{2T_I}{1 + \dfrac{1}{2^4}} = \frac{32}{17}T_I$$

according as there is a decrease or an increase in diameter across the shaft discontinuity respectively.

Propagation of torsional waves through a bar having a length of reduced cross-sectional area. The pulse smoother

Consider a sinusoidal train of torsional waves of amplitude T_0 and wave length λ incident on a circular bar of material which consists of two identical portions A and A' separated by a circular bar, B, of different material, of length l_B; the middle bar is assumed to be perfectly joined to the other two portions, see Fig. 1.29(a), and constitutes the pulse smoother. We shall now deduce the effect of the length of the bar B on the transmitted wave train.

Concentrate on the progress of the greatest positive torque in the first wave of the train; this will be transmitted through the middle bar as a torque of intensity,

$$T = \frac{2}{1 + n}T_0 \qquad (1.65)$$

using the notation of the previous section. After passing into the portion of the bar A', through the second change in area YY, T will be transmitted and reflected as T_1 and T_1' respectively. We have

$$T_1 = \frac{2n}{n + 1} \cdot T = \frac{2n}{n + 1} \cdot \frac{2}{n + 1} \cdot T_0 \qquad (1.66)$$

and

$$T_1' = -\frac{n - 1}{n + 1} \cdot T = -\frac{n - 1}{n + 1} \cdot \frac{2}{n + 1} \cdot T_0 \qquad (1.67)$$

Measure time t from the instant at which T_1 first penetrates into A' and consider the effect of two different specific lengths of l_B as follows. Bear in mind throughout this work that because we are discussing torsional modes of wave propagation, there is no dispersion as there would be if longitudinal waves were propagated along similar bars.

(i) When $l_B = (\lambda/2)(c_B/c_A)$

The length l_B in the above equation is such that T'_1 will be able to travel from YY to XX and return to reach YY at the precise moment that the greatest positive torque in the second wave of the train also arrives at YY.

When $t = l_B/c_B$, T'_1 will have returned to XX there to be reflected as a torque,

$$T''_1 = -\frac{n-1}{n+1} \cdot T'_1 = \left(\frac{n-1}{n+1}\right)^2 \cdot T = \frac{2}{n+1} \cdot \left(\frac{n-1}{n+1}\right)^2 T_0$$

At time $t = 2l_B/c_B$, T''_1 reaches YY and is both transmitted, as torque,

$$T_2 = \frac{2n}{n+1} \cdot T''_1 = \frac{2n}{n+1} \cdot \frac{2}{n+1} \cdot \left(\frac{n-1}{n+1}\right)^2 \cdot T_0, \tag{1.68}$$

and reflected as torque,

$$T'_0 = -\frac{n-1}{n+1} \cdot T''_1 = -\left(\frac{n-1}{n+1}\right)^3 \cdot \frac{2}{n+1} \cdot T_0 \tag{1.69}$$

Thus, when $t = 2l_B/c_B$, the magnitude of the pulse just leaving YY and entering A' is the sum of T_1, due to the second wave and T_2 due to the reflection of T_0 in the first pulse at YY at $t = 0$.

It now follows easily, by extending the above consideration for a further period of time $2l_B/c_B$, that at $t = 4l_B/c_B$ the torque just entering A' from YY is $(T_1 + T_2 + T_3)$; T_1 is due to T_0 in the third wave arriving at YY, T_2 to the first passage up and down B due to the reflection at YY of T_0 from the second wave, and T_3 to the second passage up and down B of the reflected portion of T_0 from the first wave. Obviously, following (1.66) and (1.68),

$$T_3 = \frac{2n}{n+1} \cdot \frac{2}{n+1} \cdot \left(\frac{n-1}{n+1}\right)^4 \cdot T_0 \tag{1.70}$$

Thus at time $m(2l_B/c_B)$, where m is an integer, the maximum torque, T_T, will be being transmitted from YY and

$$T_T = \frac{2n}{n+1} \cdot \frac{2}{n+1} \cdot T_0 \left[1 + \left(\frac{n-1}{n+1}\right)^2 + \left(\frac{n-1}{n+1}\right)^4 + \cdots \right]$$

hence as $m \to \infty$

$$T_T \to \frac{4n}{(n+1)^2} \cdot T_0 \left[\frac{1}{1 - \left(\frac{n-1}{n+1}\right)^2} \right] = T_0$$

If then $l_B = (\lambda/2)(c_B/c_A)$ it will be seen that the argument above which applies to T_0 can be identically applied to the current torque at any location in the wave length, so that generally it is not difficult to see that the transmitted torsional wave train in A' will be almost identical with that transmitted through A initially. That the length $l_B = (\lambda/2)(c_B/c_A)$ is of course a condition for resonance in this system.

(ii) When $l_B = (\lambda/4)(c_B/c_A)$

The length l_B in the above equation is chosen such that the reflected portion of the maximum positive torque in the first wave at $t = 0$ will have been able to travel from YY to XX and return to YY at the precise moment that the following maximum negative torque in the first wave arrives at YY. The amplitude of the torque just being transmitted in A' at $t = 2l_B/c_B = (\lambda/2)(1/c_A)$ is thus $(-T_1 + T_2)$. After further time $2l_B/c_B$, the amplitude of the torque just entering into A' is $(T_1 - T_2 + T_3)$. Thus at the end of time $2m(2l_B/c_B)$, where m is an integer, the total torque T'_T being passed into A' is

$$T'_T = T_1 - T_2 + T_3 \ldots + T_{2m-1}$$

$$= \frac{2n}{n+1} \cdot \frac{2}{n+1} \cdot T_0 \left[1 - \left(\frac{n-1}{n+1}\right)^2 + \left(\frac{n-1}{n+1}\right)^4 \ldots + \left(\frac{n-1}{n+1}\right)^{2m} \right]$$

As $m \rightarrow \infty$,

$$T'_T \rightarrow \frac{4n}{(n+1)^2} \cdot T_0 \left[\frac{1}{1 + \left(\dfrac{n-1}{n+1}\right)^2} \right] = \frac{2n}{n^2+1} \cdot T_0$$

As $n > 1$, therefore T'_T/T_0 is always < 1. The degree to which T_0 is attenuated is shown in Table 1.4 for some typical values of n. Above, we have in effect considered the consequences for two simple wave trains whose wavelengths λ_1 and λ_2 and circular frequencies ω_1 and ω_2 are in the ratio of 2:1 of introducing, in the form of portion B of Fig. 1.29(a), a device which (a) does not at all affect the passage from A to A' of the first and (b) attenuates the other.

TABLE 1.4

n	1	2	3	5	10
T'_T/T_0	1	0·8	0·6	0·38	0·2

For the first wave train the device delays all components reflected and contributed to T_T by exactly a multiple of λ or by $m\lambda$ where m is an integer, or in time by amount $m \cdot (2\pi/\omega_1) = m\lambda_1/c_A$.

For the second wave train the device delays reflected components contributed to T'_T by time $m(2\pi/\omega_2) = m \cdot 4\pi/\omega_1 = m \cdot 2\lambda_1/c_A$.

The components of T_T are all in phase (or out of phase by $2\pi m$) whilst the components of T'_T are out of phase by πm.

For wave trains where the wave length lies between λ_1 and λ_2, the amplitude of the total transmitted wave form will lie between T_T and T'_T; and indeed the same observation applies regardless of initial wave length.

The work above finds application in the 'pulse smoother' used in connection with measurements of torsional impact stresses. A pulse smoother was used by Duffy, Campbell and Hawley[1.6] in a torsional split Hopkinson bar (see p. 59) to study strain rate effects in aluminium and consisted of a short 0·1 in length of *tubing*, 0·030 in thick, placed between the impact end of a recording bar and the specimen. Fluctuations in the magnitude of a torsional input pulse generated using explosives were reduced by the tube and the transmitted pulse was found to be of a lower but more nearly constant amplitude so that the specimen was thus subject to a lower but more nearly constant strain rate. A diagram of the set-up is as shown in Fig. 1.29(b) and it is obviously formally similar to Fig. 1.29(a).

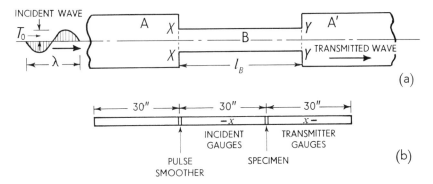

Fig. 1.29.

Stress changes in a bar due to lateral restraint over a finite length

Stress wave reflections and transmissions in a bar, due to changes in area or impedance, have been treated above and in conclusion we indicate that they may be induced similarly by changes in the degree of lateral restraint. Reference 10.21 describes attempts to make practical use of this behaviour.

Consider a long prismatic bar most of which is without any degree of lateral restraint and a finite length of which is wholly restrained against any lateral expansion whatsoever. A rectangular compressive stress wave of intensity σ_0 is then reflected, intensity σ_R, and transmitted, intensity σ_T, at the boundary between the two regions. It is easily shown that,

$$\frac{\sigma_R}{\sigma_0} = \frac{c'/c - 1}{c'/c + 1} \quad \text{and} \quad \frac{\sigma_T}{\sigma_0} = \frac{2(c'/c)}{c'/c + 1}, \tag{1.71}$$

where c is the wave speed in the *free* portion of the bar, c' the wave speed in the restricted portion and (c'/c) is given by (1.24).

On both sides of the plane at which the restriction is introduced the stress thus rises to the same value, i.e. σ_T and $(\sigma_R + \sigma_0)$ which equal to σ_T.

If $v = \frac{1}{3}$, then $\sigma_R = (5 - \sqrt{24})\sigma_0 \simeq \sigma_0/10$ and $\sigma_T = (6 - \sqrt{24})\sigma_0 \simeq 1 \cdot 1\sigma_0$.

If the restraint applies over a finite length of bar, then on emerging from the restraint zone, reflected and transmitted waves will again be generated, of magnitude σ'_R and σ'_T respectively. We have, using (1.71) above with (1.24),

$$\frac{\sigma'_R}{\sigma_T} = \frac{c/c' - 1}{c/c' + 1} \quad \text{and thus} \quad \frac{\sigma'_R}{\sigma_0} = \frac{-2(c'/c)(c'/c - 1)}{(c'/c + 1)^2}$$

Also,

$$\frac{\sigma'_T}{\sigma_T} = \frac{2 \cdot c/c'}{c/c' + 1} \quad \text{and thus} \quad \frac{\sigma'_T}{\sigma_0} = \frac{2(c/c')}{c/c' + 1} \cdot \frac{2(c'/c)}{c'/c + 1} = \frac{4(c'/c)}{(c'/c + 1)^2}$$

Again on *both* sides of the plane at the end of the restriction the stress is σ'_T.

REFERENCES

1.1 KOLSKY, H. *Stress Waves in Solids*. Clarendon Press, Oxford, pp. 211 (1953).
1.2 GOLDSMITH, W. *Impact*. Edward Arnold, London, pp. 379 (1960).
1.3 REDWOOD, M. *Mechanical Waveguides*. Pergamon Press, London, pp. 300 (1960).
1.4 TIMOSHENKO, S. AND GOODIER, J. N. *Theory of Elasticity*. McGraw-Hill, New York, pp. 506 (1951).
1.5 DAVIDS, N. AND KESTI, N. E. Stress wave effects in the design of long bars and stepped shafts. *I.J.M.S.*, **7**, 759–769 (1965).
1.6 DUFFY, J., CAMPBELL, J. D. AND HAWLEY, R. H. *On the Use of a Torsional Split Hopkinson Bar to Study Rate Effects on 1100–0 Aluminum*. Brown Univ. Rep. (Jan. 1970).

2: Applications of elementary one-dimensional stress wave theory

In Chapter 1 the basic, simple equations of elementary one-dimensional stress wave theory were established and in this Chapter they are applied to the discussion of some engineering problems.

Longitudinal impact of a rigid mass on one end of a long uniform bar perfectly fixed at its far end

The situation envisaged is shown in Fig. 2.1 in which a rigid striker of mass M_1 impinges with speed v_0 on the end of a long bar which is perfectly fixed at its distal end. The equation of motion for M_1 is

$$M_1 \frac{dv_1}{dt} = -A_2 \sigma_2 \tag{2.1}$$

where σ_2 is the stress intensity at the interface between the rod and the mass M_1 at time t after first contact; v_1 is the speed of the interface, A_2 is the cross-sectional area of the bar and ρ_2 its density. As previously, from equations (1.7),

$$\sigma_2 = v_1 \sqrt{E_2 \rho_2} \tag{2.2}$$

and substituting into (2.1),

$$\frac{M_1}{A_2} \cdot \frac{dv_1}{v_1} = -\sqrt{E_2 \rho_2}\, dt$$

Integrating and noting that $v_1 = v_0$ at $t = 0$,

$$\frac{M_1}{A_2} \int_{v_0}^{v_1} \frac{dv_1}{v_1} = -\sqrt{E_2 \rho_2} \int_0^t dt$$

or

$$v_1 = v_0 \exp\left(-\frac{A_2}{M_1} \cdot \sqrt{E_2 \rho_2} \cdot t\right) \tag{2.3}$$

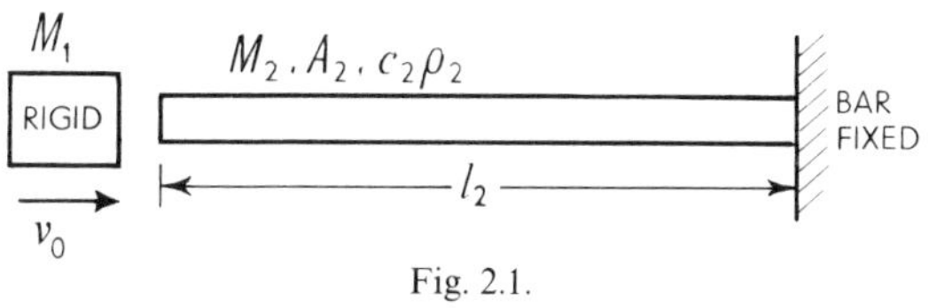

Fig. 2.1.

Alternatively,

$$\left.\begin{aligned}\sigma_2 &= \sigma_0 \cdot \exp\left(-\frac{A_2}{M_1} \cdot \sqrt{E_2\rho_2} \cdot t\right) \\ &= \sigma_0 \cdot \exp\left(-\frac{M_2}{M_1} \cdot \frac{t}{l_2/c_2}\right)\end{aligned}\right\} \tag{2.4}$$

where

$$\sigma_0 = v_0\sqrt{E_2\rho_2}$$

Now, the compressive exponential stress wave, which passes up the bar, is reflected from the fixed end also as a compressive wave. Thus the stress immediately after reflection at the fixed end, i.e. of the head of the wave, is just $2\sigma_0$. Also, after time $t = l_2/c_2$, the stress at the striker σ_2, given by (2.4), will have fallen to,

$$\left.\begin{aligned}\sigma_2 &= \sigma_0 \exp\left(-\frac{A_2}{M_1} \cdot \sqrt{E_2\rho_2} \cdot \frac{l_2}{c_2}\right) \\ &= \sigma_0 \exp(-M_2/M_1)\end{aligned}\right\} \tag{2.5}$$

At the end of time $2l_2/c_2$, i.e. when the head of the reflected wave has arrived back at the striker and is just reflected to provide a compressive stress of $2\sigma_0$, the *total* compressive stress on the striker will be $[2\sigma_0 + \sigma_0 \exp(-2M_2/M_1)]$. Now the striker will be subject to an increased resistance (or compressive force), for $t > 2l_2/c_2$, due to the continuous arrival of the reflected wave from the fixed end of the bar, i.e. σ_2, and hence it will suffer an abrupt change in speed; this in turn will alter the initiating stress. Thus the differential equation (2.1) and expression (2.3) only apply for $0 < t < 2l_2/c_2$. The expression for the stress which is thereafter to replace (2.4) has now to be sought; let it be $\sigma'(t')$ where σ' applies only for $2l_2/c < t < 4l_2/c$, or $0 < t' < 2l_2/c$. The new equation of motion for the striker is,

$$M_1 \cdot \frac{dv'_1}{dt'} = -A_2[2\sigma(t') + \sigma'(t')]$$

or

$$\frac{M_1}{\rho_2 c_2} \cdot \frac{d\sigma'}{dt'} = -A_2[2\sigma(t') + \sigma'(t')] \tag{2.6}$$

using $\sigma' = \rho_2 c_2 v'_1$ and where $\sigma(t') = \sigma_2(t)$,

Simplifying equation (2.6),

$$-\frac{M_1}{A_2\rho_2 c_2} \cdot \frac{d\sigma'}{dt'} = 2\sigma_0 \exp\left(-\frac{A_2}{M_1} \cdot \sqrt{E_2\rho_2} \cdot t'\right) + \sigma',$$

or

$$\exp\left(\frac{A_2}{M_1} \cdot \sqrt{E_2\rho_2} \cdot t'\right) \cdot \frac{d\sigma'}{dt'} + \frac{A_2 \cdot \sqrt{E_2\rho_2}}{M_1} \cdot \exp\left(\frac{A_2}{M_1} \cdot \sqrt{E_2\rho_2} \cdot t'\right)\sigma'$$

$$= -\frac{2A_2\rho_2 c_2\sigma_0}{M_1}$$

and thus,

$$\frac{d}{dt'}\left[\exp\left(\frac{A_2}{M_1}\cdot\sqrt{E_2\rho_2}\cdot t'\right)\sigma'\right] = -\frac{2A_2\rho_2c_2}{M_1}\sigma_0.$$

Hence, integrating,

$$\sigma'\cdot\exp\left(\frac{A_2}{M_1}\cdot\sqrt{E_2\rho_2}\cdot t'\right) = -\frac{2A_2\rho_2c_2}{M_1}\sigma_0 t' + c$$

Now, when $t' = 0$ (or $t = 2l_2/c_2$), $\sigma' = \sigma_0\exp(-2M_2/M_1) = c$. Thus

$$\sigma' = \exp\left(-\frac{A_2\sqrt{E_2\rho_2}}{M_1}\cdot t'\right)\left[\sigma_0\exp\left(-\frac{2M_2}{M_1}\right) - \frac{2A_2\rho_2c_2}{M_1}\sigma_0 t'\right] \qquad (2.7)$$

(i) Reduction to zero of the stress between the striker and the bar

The total compressive stress $_s\sigma_T$, acting on the striker during the second traversal of the bar by the stress wave, is

$$_s\sigma_T = 2\sigma(t) + \sigma'(t')$$

Hence combining (2.4) and (2.7), we have

$$_s\sigma_T = 2\sigma_0\exp\left(-\frac{A_2}{M_1}\sqrt{E_2\rho_2}\cdot t'\right) + \exp\left(-\frac{A_2}{M_1}\cdot\sqrt{E_2\rho_2}\cdot t'\right)\cdot\sigma_0\exp\left(-\frac{2M_2}{M_1}\right)$$

$$-\exp\left(-\frac{A_2}{M_1}\cdot\sqrt{E_2\rho_2}t'\right)\cdot 2\sigma_0\cdot t'\cdot\frac{A_2\rho_2c_2}{M_1}$$

i.e.

$$_s\sigma_T = \sigma_0\exp\left(-\frac{A_2}{M_1}\sqrt{E_2\rho_2}t'\right)\left[2 + \exp\left(-\frac{2M_2}{M_1}\right) - \frac{2t'}{l_2/c_2}\cdot\frac{M_2}{M_1}\right] \qquad (2.8)$$

At $t' = 0$, $_s\sigma_T = (2 + \exp(-2M_2/M_1))\cdot\sigma_0$.

If the stress between the striker and the rod falls to zero then $_s\sigma_T = 0$; and this can, of course, occur in the second wave cycle only for certain values of M_2/M_1. If the stress falls to zero during the second wave cycle, after the greatest permissible time, i.e. $t' = 2l_2/c_2$, then we have, by substituting in (2.8),

$$2 + e^{-2M_2/M_1} = 4M_2/M_1$$

Solving this last equation we find $M_2/M_1 \simeq 0.58$. Of course, for all values of $M_2/M_1 > 0.58$, the stress falls to zero for $l_2/c_2 \le t' \le 2l_2/c_2$. That the stress falls to zero does not imply that contact then ceases.

(ii) Stress between striker and rod for $M_2/M_1 = 1$

Let us examine the case in which $M_2/M_1 = 1$. Then putting $_s\sigma_T = 0$ in (2.8),

$$2 + e^{-2} = \frac{2t'}{l_2/c_2}$$

Hence,

$$\frac{t'}{l_2/c_2} = 1 + \frac{1}{2}e^{-2} = 1.068$$

or

$$\frac{t}{2l_2/c_2} = \frac{t' + 2l_2/c_2}{2l_2/c_2} = 1.534$$

Table 2.1 shows specific values of $_S\sigma_T/\sigma_0$, i.e. the stress acting on the striker/σ_0, at specific times when $M_2/M_1 = 1$.

TABLE 2.1   VALUES OF $_S\sigma_T/\sigma_0$ FOR $M_2/M_1 = 1$

$t/(l_2/c_2)$	0	$\frac{1}{2}$	1	$1\frac{1}{2}$	$2-$	$2+$	$2\frac{1}{4}$	$2\frac{1}{2}$	3	3·068
$0 < t < 2l_2/c_2$	1	0·60	0·37	0·22	0·135	—	—	—	—	—
$\begin{cases} 0 < t' < 2l_2/c_2 \\ 2l_2/c_2 < t < 4l_2/c_2 \end{cases}$	—	—	—	—	—	2·135	1·27	0·685	0·050	0

Figure 2.2(a) shows how $_S\sigma_T/\sigma_0$, i.e. the non-dimensional total stress intensity acting on the striker, varies with a non-dimensional time $t/(l_2/c_2)$ when $M_2/M_1 = 1$.

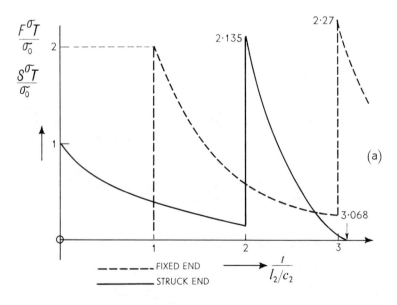

Fig. 2.2(a).

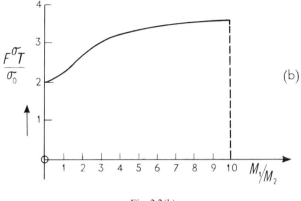

Fig. 2.2(b).

(iii) The stress at the fixed end of the rod when $M_2/M_1 = 1$

The total stress $_F\sigma_T$ at the fixed end of the rod is,
    (i) zero until $t = l_2/c_2$, when it suddenly becomes $2\sigma_0$
    (ii) it falls to $2\sigma_0 e^{-M_2/M_1} = 2\sigma_0 e^{-1} = 0.74\,\sigma_0$ at time $t = 2l_2/c_2$
    (iii) At $t = 3l_2/c_2$, the stress at the fixed end due to reflection of the second wave cycle stress front, originally initiated at the striker at $t' = 0$, is

$$_F\sigma_T = 2(\sigma_0 + \sigma_0 e^{-2}) = 2.27\,\sigma_0$$

Note that for $M_2/M_1 = 1$, though the maximum stress at the striker end is $\sigma_0(2 + e^{-2}) = 2.135\,\sigma_0$, the greatest stress in the rod is created at the fixed end immediately after the second reflection. Figure 2.2(a) shows how $_F\sigma_T/\sigma_0$ varies with a non-dimensional time for this case, i.e. when $M_2/M_1 = 1$.

For small M_2/M_1 ratios, i.e. for M_2/M_1 less than about 0.58, there will be more than two complete passages up and down the rod; thus whilst above $\sigma'(t')$ was calculated for the first reflection at the striker of the initially created wave, in cases when $M_2/M_1 < 0.58$ there will be a need to recalculate σ' at each subsequent reflection there. This is dealt with in ref. 2.1. The smaller is M_2/M_1 the slower the rate of decay of stress intensity. The maximum stress at the fixed end of a rod, impinged upon by a striker at the other end, has been shown to be well summarised by,

$$\frac{_F\sigma_T}{\sigma_0} = 1 + \sqrt{\frac{M_1}{M_2} + \frac{2}{3}};\tag{2.10}$$

equation (2.10) is shown as Fig. 2.2(b).

Rigid striker impinging on one end of a free rod

As above (see p. 51), when a *rigid* striker impinges on one end of a long free rod with speed v_0, a compressive stress σ is propagated along it where at time t

after impact, the stress at the striker-rod interface is

$$\sigma = \sigma_0 \exp\left(-\frac{A_2\rho_2 c_2}{M_1}\cdot t\right) \qquad (2.11)$$

The symbols have the same meaning as before.

(i) The situation at $t = 2l_2/c_2$

Equation (2.11) applies until $t = l_2/c_2$, when the head or front of the compressive wave in the rod is reflected from its free end as a wave of tension. At time $2l_2/c_2$ the stress at the striker-rod interface is $\sigma_0 . \exp(-2M_2/M_1)$, and the particle speed at the struck end of the rod is $v_0 . \exp(-2M_2/M_1)$. Thus the total stress and particle speed near the interface after including the arriving reflected wave is,
    (i) a tensile stress $\sigma_0[1 - \exp(-2M_2/M_1)]$ and
    (ii) a speed of $v_0[1 + \exp(-2M_2/M_1)]$.
Thus separation of the striker and the rod occurs at $t = 2l_2/c_2$; at this instant also, the free end of the struck rod has a speed of $2v_0 . \exp(-M_2/M_1)$. (This speed consists equally of incident and reflected components.)

(ii) The distribution of energy in the bar when $l_2/c_2 < t \le 2l_2/c_2$

The speed of a particle, v, in a section at distance x from the striker during this interval of time, see Fig. 2.3, is given by

$$v = v_0\left[\exp\left(-\frac{M_2}{M_1}\cdot\frac{x-X}{l_2}\right) + \exp\left(-\frac{M_2}{M_1}\left(2-\frac{x+X}{l_2}\right)\right)\right] \qquad (2.12)$$

where X is the distance of the head of the wave from the striker. The normal stress across the same section σ_T is

$$\sigma_T = \sigma_0\left[\exp\left(-\frac{M_2}{M_1}\cdot\frac{x-X}{l_2}\right) - \exp\left(-\frac{M_2}{M_1}\left(2-\frac{x+X}{l_2}\right)\right)\right] \qquad (2.13)$$

Thus the kinetic energy E_B in the bar between X and l_2, where $X \le x$, is,

$$E_B = \int_X^{l_2}\frac{1}{2}(A_2 . \rho_2 . dx)v^2$$

$$= \int_X^{l_2}\frac{1}{2}\cdot\frac{M_2 v_0^2}{l_2}\left[\exp\left(-\frac{M_2}{M_1}\cdot\frac{x-X}{l_2}\right) + \exp\left(-\frac{M_2}{M_1}\left(2-\frac{x+X}{l_2}\right)\right)\right]^2 . dx$$

$$= \frac{1}{4}M_1 v_0^2\left[1 + 4\frac{M_2}{M_1}\exp\left\{-2\frac{M_2}{M_1}\left(1-\frac{X}{l_2}\right)\right\} . \left(1-\frac{X}{l_2}\right) - \exp\left\{-4\frac{M_2}{M_1}\left(1-\frac{X}{l_2}\right)\right\}\right] \qquad (2.14)$$

The strain energy U in the bar between X and l_2 is

$$U = \int_X^{l_2}\frac{A_2\sigma_T^2}{2E_2}dx,$$

and using (2.13)

$$U = \frac{1}{4}M_1 v_0^2\left[1 - 4\frac{M_2}{M_1}\exp\left\{-2\frac{M_2}{M_1}\left(1-\frac{X}{l_2}\right)\right\} . \left(1-\frac{X}{l_2}\right) - \exp\left\{-\frac{M_2}{M_2}\left(1-\frac{X}{l_2}\right)\right\}\right] \qquad (2.15)$$

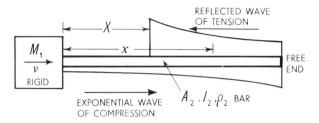

Fig. 2.3.

Hence the total energy in the length of bar between X and l_2 is,

$$U + E_B = \frac{1}{2}M_1v_0^2\left[1 - \exp\left\{-4\frac{M_2}{M_1}\left(1 - \frac{X}{l_2}\right)\right\}\right] \tag{2.16}$$

When $X/l_2 = 0$, i.e. when the head of the stress wave has just returned to the striker,

$$U + E_B = \frac{1}{2}M_1v_0^2\left[1 - \exp\left(-4\frac{M_2}{M_1}\right)\right] \tag{2.17}$$

and the kinetic energy in the striker at this instant E_s is, directly, $\frac{1}{2}M_1 \cdot v_0^2 \exp(-4M_2/M_1)$; and obviously $U + E_B + E_S$ totals $\frac{1}{2}M_1v_0^2$. The energy $\frac{1}{2}M_1v_0^2(1 - \exp(-4M_2/M_1))$ is the kinetic energy lost by the hammer which, by definition is rigid and thus contains no strain energy.

Pile driver and the weight falling vertically onto a collar at the end of a long thin bar

A practical situation which is often discussed is that of the rigid steel monkey of a pile driver, of mass M_1, impinging on the square end of a vertical timber pile. It is required to find, say, the initial retardation of the monkey assuming conditions of simple elastic impact and that no frictional forces are present along the sides of the pile.

Alternatively, if a weight of mass M_1 slides down a long thin rod to impinge on a collar at the bottom end, and induces a tensile stress wave (recall p. 33) then formally the situation is the same as that of the pile driver except that in the latter, a compressive wave is set up in the pile.

The difference between these two cases and that discussed in the previous few pages is minor and only consists in the weight of the monkey, or the falling weight, being taken into account.

The equation of motion of the monkey is

$$M_1\frac{dv}{dt} = M_1g - A_2\rho_0cv \tag{2.18}$$

where v denotes the vertical downward speed of M_1 so that

$$\frac{dv}{dt} = g - \frac{M_2}{M_1}\cdot\frac{c}{l}\cdot v \tag{2.19}$$

The pile mass is $M_2 = A_2l\rho_0$, l is the length of the pile, ρ_0 its density and A_2 its cross-sectional area; the timber is considered isotropic. Integrating (2.19) and assuming $v = v_0$ at $t = 0$,

$$v = \frac{M_1gl}{M_2c}\left[1 - \left(1 - \frac{M_2}{M_1g}\cdot\frac{c}{l}\cdot v_0\right)\exp\left(-\frac{M_2}{M_1}\frac{c}{l}\cdot t\right)\right] \tag{2.20}$$

Using (2.20) in (2.18), the required retardation of the monkey follows.

If the monkey is considered to be elastic and stress wave propagation in it is to be entertained then the total problem is complicated and reference should be made to Fischer's work[2.2].

The situation of the mass sliding down a rod is the same as that of the pile driver except that M_1 and M_2 refer to the mass of the falling weight and the rod respectively.

Reverting to the question raised on p. 33, for which case $v_0 = 0$, equation (2.20) gives

$$v = \frac{M_1 gl}{M_2 c}\left[1 - \exp\left(-\frac{M_2 c}{M_1 l}t\right)\right],$$

the stress in the rod is σ and

$$\sigma = \rho_0 cv = \frac{M_1 g}{A_2}\left[1 - \exp\left(-\frac{M_2}{M_1}\cdot\frac{c}{l}\cdot t\right)\right]$$

which applies for $0 < t < 2l/c$. Thus at $t = 0$, the stress is zero but rises to a value of $M_1 g(1 - e^{-2M_2/M_1})/A_2$ in time $2l/c$.

Momentum traps

Figure 2.4 shows a uniform cyclindrical bar X, of cross-sectional area A_1, to the end of which is lightly attached a bar Y of length l of identical material of cross-sectional area A_2, with $A_1 > A_2$; also $l < l_1$. To the end of X is applied a constant intensity compressive stress pulse of magnitude σ, the pulse length p of which is, say, equal to $2l$. The incident compressive stress is transmitted by the attached bar as a compressive wave, and later reflected from its free end as a tensile wave. It then reaches the plane common to X and Y and immediately contact ceases; Y moves off possessing a certain kinetic energy and having trapped some of the momentum in the incident pulse.

Let us find what fraction of the original impulse delivered to X is carried away by Y. We have, from (1.58) and (1.59),

$$\sigma_T = \frac{2A_1}{A_2 + A_1}\cdot\sigma \quad \text{and} \quad \sigma_R = \frac{A_2 - A_1}{A_2 + A_1}\cdot\sigma$$

The total reflected impulse is $-A_1 . 2l . \rho(\sigma_R/\rho c)$ and the transmitted impulse is $A_2 . 2l . \rho(\sigma_T/\rho c)$. The initial impulse delivered is $A_1 . 2l\rho(\sigma/\rho c)$; this is, of course, just the sum of the last two momenta, i.e.

$$-A_1 . 2l . \rho(\sigma_R/\rho c) + A_2 2l(\sigma_T/\rho c)$$

$$= \frac{2l\rho}{\rho c}(-A_1\sigma_R + A_2\sigma_T)$$

$$= \frac{2l}{c}\left\{-A_1 . \frac{A_2 - A_1}{A_2 + A_1} + A_2 . \frac{2A_1}{A_2 + A_1}\right\}\sigma$$

$$= \frac{2l}{c} . A_1 . \sigma$$

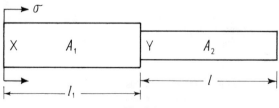

Fig. 2.4.

Hence the fraction of the original impule, f, trapped in the end bar is,

$$f = \frac{A_2 l\rho \cdot 2\sigma_T/\rho c}{A_1 2l\rho \cdot \sigma/\rho c} = \frac{A_2 \sigma_T}{A_1 \sigma} = \frac{A_2}{A_1} \cdot \frac{2A_1}{A_2 + A_1}$$

$$= \frac{2}{(1 + A_1/A_2)}$$

In particular, if $A_1 = A_2, f = 1$.

The addition of a bar lightly attached, as described above, is often used to trap transmitted momentum for either of two reasons:

(i) In order to mitigate the deleterious effects of impact, and

(ii) for use in experimental work for measuring pulse length and applied stress.

To exemplify (ii), we now describe the Hopkinson pressure bar.

Hopkinson pressure bar

In a paper delivered in November 1913[2.3], Bertram Hopkinson described a simple technique whereby "it is possible to measure both the duration of (a) blow and the maximum pressure developed by it". Hopkinson was interested in ascertaining the pressure-time relationship when a "rifle bullet be fired against the end of a cylindrical steel rod or some gun cotton be detonated in its neighborhood". He described his method as follows. "If the (long cylindrical) rod be divided at a point a few inches from the far end, the opposed surfaces of the cut being in firm contact and carefully faced, the wave of pressure travels practically unchanged through the joint. ... At the joint the pressure continues to act until the head of the reflected tension wave arrives there. If the tail of the pressure wave has then passed the joint the end-piece flies off, having trapped within it the whole of the momentum of the blow, and the rest of the rod is left completely at rest. The length of end-piece which is just sufficient completely to stop the rod is half the length of the pressure wave, and the duration of the blow is twice the time taken by the pressure wave to travel the length of the end-piece, ... the momentum trapped in quite short end-pieces will be equal to the maximum pressure multiplied by twice the time taken by the wave in traversing the end-piece. Thus by experimenting with different lengths of end-pieces and determining the momentum with which each flies off the rod as the result of the blow, it is possible to measure both the duration of the blow and maximum pressure developed by it. ... A steel rod is hung up as a ballistic pendulum and the piece is held on to the end by magnetic attraction. A bullet is fired at the other end and the end-piece is caught in a ballistic pendulum and its momentum measured. The momentum of the rod is also measured."

Hopkinson's set-up used a bar several feet long and about an inch diameter suspended horizontally by threads which allowed it to swing in a vertical plane. The end-piece is often called a *time-piece* and, besides its momentum being measured by capturing it in the ballistic pendulum, the momentum in the bar is found from the amplitude of swing of the bar.

The momentum, m, trapped in a time-piece is, $m = A\int_0^T \sigma(t)\,.\,dt$, where A is the bar cross-sectional area, t is time and $T/2$ is the time it takes the stress wave to pass through the time-piece. Experimentally, the time-piece is first made short and its length is increased in steps up to and beyond the point where its momentum reaches a constant value. Alternatively, the shortest time-piece which attains the greatest velocity is sought and any method of velocity measurement can be used.

For a triangular or ramp-type pressure-time wave, such as would be a first approximation for an explosive charge detonated on the end of a bar, a time-piece just long enough would contain the wave as shown in Fig. 2.5a; the pulse length is just twice the time-piece length. The situation for a slightly shorter time piece is as shown in Fig. 2.5b. The difference in the momenta of the two pieces divided by the bar cross-sectional area times the difference in length of the two time-pieces divided by the wave speed c (which is known, or easily found), gives the mean stress in the tail of the pulse. It is easy to imagine how the pressure wave-time curve may now be built up.

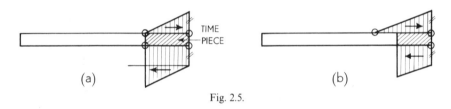

Fig. 2.5.

By using several time-pieces for a sharp fronted pulse it is possible to build up, from a single test, data sufficient for the construction of a complete pressure-time curve, see p. 68 below.

This form of Hopkinson pressure bar is limited (i) because longitudinal elastic waves are distorted to some extent when propagated, (ii) because the stress intensity must not become too large, since the time-piece itself may then scab (or fracture) and (iii) because the decay may be too rapid to provide very useful pressure-time results.

Because torsional waves in circular cyclinders do not distort when propagated, similar methods have been devised to faithfully record torsional pulses of small duration.

Propagation of compressive stress waves in a conical bar

(i) *The coned bar*

Landon and Quinney[2.4] remark that Hopkinson caused "the firing-end of (a cylindrical) rod to be coned-down to a smaller diameter" in the belief that "average maximum pressure could be determined for different areas of cross-section of the end receiving the blow, without having to use bars of small diameter which would have lacked the necessary lateral stiffness.... When using a long time-piece it was observed that the bar instead of moving forward after the time-piece was thrown-off, it actually moved backwards, thus having a negative momentum. The true significance of this does not appear to have been realised. . . ."

In the paper by Landon and Quinney the analysis of pulse propagation down a conical bar is given in an Appendix and in six other sections; they discuss

(a) the effect of coning the firing end of the bar,
(b) the effect of bar length on the distortion of the pressure wave,
(c) the variation of mean pressure with the bar diameter,
(d) the variation of mean pressure with the distance of the charge from the end of the bar,
(e) the maximum pressure produced by the detonation of a charge of gun cotton, and
(f) experiments with a bar of concrete.

"The theoretical investigation of the propagation of a pressure wave along a coned bar shows that, although the pressure applied at the end may be entirely positive, as the wave travels along the bar the rate at which the momentum is transmitted forward gradually increases, and since the total momentum has to remain constant a particle momentum of the opposite direction develops as a negative tail to the wave. . . . In comparing the theory with experiment the main difficulty lies in the fact that the exact shape of the pressure-time curve produced by the detonation is not accurately known."

The authors in their investigations of charges detonated at the end of a bar justify "neglect(ing) the portion of the compressive wave which occurs before the instant of maximum pressure", and then assume that "the pressure on the end of the bar is of the form $\sigma = A \exp (R_0 - at)k$ where t starts at the instant given by R_0/a, a being the velocity of propagation of the wave and R_0 the distance of the apex of the cone from the end of the bar. . . ."

This exponential form for the applied pressure prompts the form of solution in the analysis given below.

Recently Suh[2.5] has used the stress-amplification which accompanies the passage of a pulse along a coned bar, to investigate the dynamic behaviour of an annealed low carbon steel.

(ii) *Analysis*

As remarked above the analysis of how longitudinal pulses are propagated axially down a conical bar was initially carried out by Landon and Quinney[2.4] but is given here in a slightly adapted form following Kolsky[2.6]. To a large extent the results we shall derive have already been foreshadowed by our consideration of the behaviour of an approximated conical bar on p. 40. Two assumptions are made, (i) that the pulse length is large compared with the diameter of the cone in the region of the bar where the wave is being propagated, and (ii) that the angle of the cone is small.

The equation of motion of an element, see Fig. 2.6 parallel to the axis of the cone of solid angle α, is

$$\rho \alpha r^2 \, dr . \frac{\partial^2 u}{\partial t^2} = d(\alpha r^2 \sigma_r), \qquad (2.21)$$

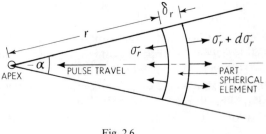

Fig. 2.6.

where u denotes displacement parallel to the cone axis; r and u are measured positively outwards from the apex. Tensile stresses are positive and

$$\sigma_r = E\, \partial u / \partial r \tag{2.22i}$$

Equation (2.21) gives,

$$\rho r \frac{\partial^2 u}{\partial t^2} = 2\sigma_r + r \frac{\partial \sigma_r}{\partial r} \tag{2.23}$$

Substituting in (2.23) from (2.22i)

$$\rho \frac{\partial^2}{\partial t^2}(ur) = E\left(2\frac{\partial u}{\partial r} + r\frac{\partial^2 u}{\partial r^2}\right)$$

or,

$$\frac{\partial^2 (ur)}{\partial t^2} = \frac{E}{\rho} \frac{\partial^2}{\partial r^2}(ur) = c^2 \frac{\partial^2}{\partial r^2}(ur) \tag{2.24i}$$

This is the equation for a spherical wave and obviously its solution is,

$$ur = f(r - ct) + F(r + ct); \tag{2.25}$$

$f(r - ct)$ and $F(r + ct)$ as before, represent waves travelling away from and towards the apex respectively. Up to this point many of the equations are similar to those applying for simple longitudinal wave propagation along uniform section bars, r having been substituted for x.

To describe a pulse moving in the direction of r decreasing, i.e. toward the apex of the cone, we must choose from (2.25), (compare p. 4),

$$u = \frac{1}{r}F(r + ct) \tag{2.26}$$

Thus,

$$\sigma_r = E\frac{\partial u}{\partial r} = \frac{E}{r}.\,F'(r + ct) - \frac{E}{r^2}.\,F(r + ct), \tag{2.27}$$

and the particle speed is given by,

$$v = \frac{\partial u}{\partial t} = \frac{c}{r}.\,F'(r + ct) \tag{2.28}$$

Evidently there is no simple relationship between stress and particle speed—except when r is large, for then the second term on the right of equation (2.27) is negligible and we recover the equation which is already familiar, i.e. $\sigma_r = \rho c v$, where $c^2 = E/\rho$; this is just the expression we derived in connection with plane wave propagation.

For $F(r + ct)$ in (2.26) we choose $C \exp\{-(r + ct)/\lambda\} - 1$; λ is a characteristic length of the pulse which determines its 'sharpness'. This choice is satisfactory because it ensures that, (i) at the pulse head where $u = 0$, $r = -ct$, which is entirely consistent with, (ii), measuring t negatively and taking $t = 0$ to be the instant at which the head of the pulse reaches the apex of the cone. Observe (iii), that when $r < |ct|$ the undisplaced part of the cone is referred to. Thus, specifically in place of (2.26) we write,

$$u = \frac{C}{r}(e^{-(r+ct)/\lambda} - 1) \qquad (2.29)$$

where C necessarily has the dimensions of area.

Using (2.29)

$$\sigma_r = E\frac{\partial u}{\partial r} = -\frac{EC}{r^2}\left[\exp\left(-\frac{(r+ct)}{\lambda}\right) - 1\right] - \frac{EC}{\lambda r} \cdot \exp\left(-\frac{(r+ct)}{\lambda}\right) \qquad (2.30)$$

The pressure at the head of the wave is $-EC/\lambda r$, which is obviously the greater the nearer the pulse head to the cone apex. In regions well behind the head of the pulse, i.e. when $r \gg |ct|$, $\exp\{-(r + ct)/\lambda\} \to 0$ and $\sigma_r \to EC/r^2$, i.e. the stress is *tensile*.

Equation (2.30) is seen to consist of two terms of opposite sign and the change from compressive to tensile stress occurs when $\sigma_r = 0$. Thus,

$$\exp\{-(r + ct)/\lambda\} \cdot \left[\frac{r}{\lambda} + 1\right] = 1 \qquad (2.31)$$

The length of the compression portion of the wave is $(r - |ct|)$ and we may judge how it changes as the pulse approaches the cone apex, by comparing $|r - ct|/\lambda$ with $|ct|/\lambda$, where $|ct|$ is the distance of the pulse head from the cone apex which may be referred to as r'. For values of r'/λ, i.e. r' made non-dimensional, equation (2.31) may be solved and $(r - r')/\lambda$ determined. Typical values are, for $r'/\lambda = 0.25$, 1 and 4, $(r - r')/\lambda = 0.6$, 1.15 and 1.19. Evidently the length $(r - r')/\lambda$ is the shorter, the closer the pulse head is to the cone apex and the longer must be the region of tension. In the limit when $t = 0$, the whole bar is in tension!—but this situation does not subscribe to the original assumptions, see p. 61.

Spalling or scabbing in bars and flat plates

Spalling or scabbing is a form of fracture in a plate of material which occurs near a *free* surface *remote* from the area to which the causative impulsive load is applied; an example is shown in Plate 1.

Perhaps the earliest and first reported work on scabbing and crack formation in plates and cylinders is that of B. Hopkinson[2.3] in his paper of 1912 entitled 'The Pressure of a Blow'. A small quantity of gun cotton was detonated by a 'small quantity of fulminate' after placing it on a $\frac{1}{2}$ in (12·7 mm) plate; it punched out a hole of its own diameter, but placed on a $\frac{3}{4}$ in (19 mm) thick plate it caused scabbing, see Plate 1. Experimenting with a still thicker plate, its effect was only to cause an internal crack, see Plate 2.

If the incident impulse applied is generated by an explosive or by high speed impact, it may be assumed to be a saw-toothed compressive pulse, see Fig. 2.7, and to pass through the plate without change in shape or intensity. If its maximum intensity is MM, or σ_m, then as it is reflected at the rear surface of the plate AA, its sign is changed to become tensile. Fig. 2.8 shows the individual incident compressive and reflected tensile waves and their net effect at times, $t = 0$, $\frac{1}{4}P/c, \frac{1}{2}P/c, \frac{3}{4}P/c$ and P/c where P is the length of the pulse, as they approach the bottom surface of the plate.

As before, the total stress or particle speed in any plane is the sum of that due to the incident compressive pulse and that due to the reflected tensile pulse. Of especial interest is the instant when just one half of the pulse has reached, and been reflected from, the rear face. Figure 2.8(iv) shows that the greatest *tensile* stress first arises at this instant; this greatest tensile stress is σ_m and first occurs at one half the pulse length from the rear face. All the particles in this zone of one half of the pulse length (between the first plane of maximum tensile stress and the rear face) have the same speed, v_N. We have in the usual notation,

$$v_N = v_I + v_R$$

$$= \frac{\sigma_I}{\rho c} + \frac{(\sigma_m - \sigma_I)}{\rho c} = \frac{\sigma_m}{\rho c}$$

Generally, a greatest stress arises on each plane parallel to the bottom face; if a length x of the saw-toothed pulse has reached the bottom face and been reflected, then at a distance x into the plate from the rear face, e.g. see Fig. 2.8(iii), tensile stress σ' in a typical plane, is

$$\sigma' = \sigma_m \left(1 - \frac{P - 2x}{P} \right) = \frac{2x}{P} \cdot \sigma_m \tag{2.32}$$

Equation (2.32) is valid for $x \leq P/2$ and as we have already seen is greatest when $x = P/2$. The particle speed associated with σ' and applying for all parallel planes between it and the bottom face is v', and

$$\rho c v' = \frac{2x}{P} \sigma_m \tag{2.33}$$

Again, v' is greatest when $x = P/2$ and then $v' = \sigma_m/\rho c$.

If a material undergoes fracture when the tensile stress reaches some critical value σ_F, then fracture will occur in a plate in a layer where σ_F is first reached, i.e. where $\sigma' = \sigma_F$. According to the intensity of the input pulse so will fracture occur at a distance of $P/2$ from the rear face, or less, or not at all. If the generated

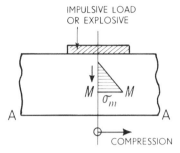

Fig. 2.7.

stress $\sigma_m > \sigma_F$ then fracture occurs at a distance of less than $P/2$ from the back face given by (2.32), if $\sigma_m = \sigma_F$, just at the distance $P/2$ and if $\sigma_m \leq \sigma_F$, no fracture at all would be expected.

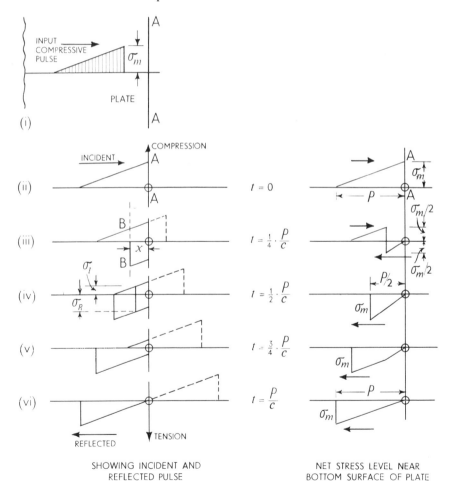

Fig. 2.8.

If fracture occurs, then the material below the fracture surface will have trapped in it an amount of downward momentum equal to the spall mass times v' as given by (2.33); it is this momentum which causes the material to 'fly off' or 'spall' and to do damage.

We have discussed spalling in terms of a saw-toothed pulse but it is not indissolubly associated with it. Pulses of other shape may equally well cause the same phenomenon. For instance, the 'reversed' saw tooth pulse of Fig. 2.9 on reflection from a stress-free rear surface is observed first to start to give rise to tension at a distance $P/2$ from the back face; thereafter the greatest tension on parallel planes increases with the passage of time and reaches a maximum adjacent to the rear surface itself after time P/c.

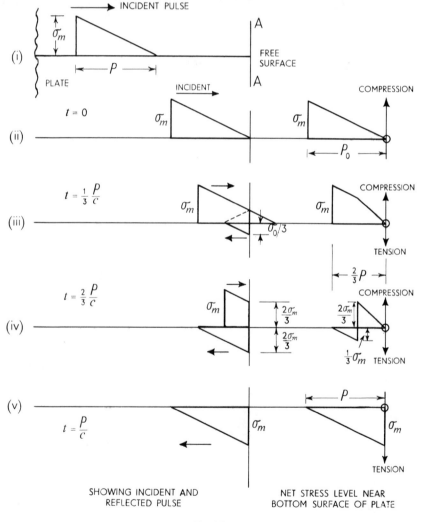

SHOWING INCIDENT AND
REFLECTED PULSE

NET STRESS LEVEL NEAR
BOTTOM SURFACE OF PLATE

Fig. 2.9.

It is straightforward to work out how the stress and particle speed are distributed on reflection from a free surface once the pulse shape is given.

Note that in general then, to predict spalling phenomena the two important requirements are

(i) the shape of the stress pulse, and

(ii) the critical tensile stress, σ_F, required to cause fracture.

Typical values for σ_F as given by Pearson and Rinehart[2.7] are as follows:

TABLE 2.2

	σ_F, lbf/in^2	Differential particle speed, ft/sec
Copper	410 000	264
Brass	310 000	216
4130 Steel	440 000	235
1020 Steel	160 000	84

In the plane in which fracture occurs there will be a theoretical and instantaneous change in particle speed across it of $v_N = \sigma_F/\rho c$. Thus in the Table for the 4130 steel, if we assume

$$\rho c = \left(\frac{0 \cdot 285 \cdot 1728}{32}\right) 16\,800 = 2.56 \times 10^5 \text{ lbf-ft units}$$

then

$$v_N = \frac{440\,000}{2 \cdot 56 \cdot 10^5} \cdot 144 = 248 \text{ ft/sec}$$

When the shape of the compressive pulse and the fracture stress σ_F are known, the thickness of the spalled portion is, as we have seen, easily determined; for a ramp-shaped pulse, if the stress decay after maximum stress σ_m is linear, the thickness of the spall is one half the distance between σ_F and σ_m in the incident pulse, using (2.32).

The account above broadly refers to the case in which the extent of the impulse is about the same as the plate depth. If the extent is much less, see Fig. 2.10, the compressive pulse transmitted through the plate from P, will tend to be spherical. Immediately below P the pulse will be reflected as a wave of tension but further out where it is incident on the bottom surface obliquely, it will be reflected both as a wave of dilatation (or tension) and a distortional wave (see p. 111). The reflected tension wave will appear to be spreading from virtual centre P' so that once a crack has been formed it will spread rapidly and a nearly spherical cap will be flung off. The situation is more complicated than that described earlier in as far as the stress amplitude in the incident pulse from P, and the reflected one from P', are continuously reduced in severity because the pulses are spherical and radiating outwards.

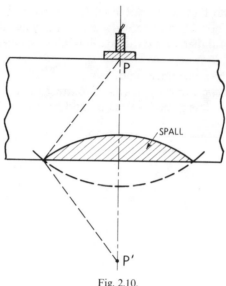

Fig. 2.10.

Multiple scabbing

Once a fracture has occurred, the remainder of the incident compressive impulse in the mass of the plate will be approaching a fresh, new surface and correspondingly will be reflected as a tension wave. Thus further fractures may occur; if no scab is thrown off, the total effect may be a series of more or less parallel cracks[2.7], see Plate 3.

In a metal plate a certain amount of plastic deformation is usually found below the detonated charge (e.g. see Plates 1 and 2) and there the material will generally have been hardened. In some polymeric materials there will have been pulverisation.

Multiple spalling in a concrete bar

Landon and Quinney[2.4] described an experiment in which a concrete bar, resting on a horizontal timber baulk, three feet long and three inches diameter, was subject to the detonation on one end of an 8 oz primer of gun cotton.

The experiment, Fig. 2.11, showed five different lengths of the bar to have been thrown off with different speeds, estimated by measuring the horizontal

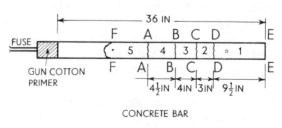

CONCRETE BAR

Fig. 2.11.

and vertical distances they were projected. By assuming the wave front generated by the gun cotton to be vertical and that fracture of a piece occurred when the difference between the propagated pressure wave and the reflected tension wave was equal to the tensile strength of the concrete, it was found possible to deduce an approximate curve for the pressure propagated along the bar, see Fig. 2.12. Piece 5 was scarcely moved and the portion of the bar at the primer end was pulverised by the detonation.

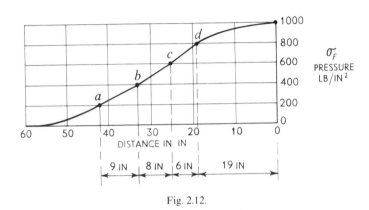

Fig. 2.12.

Static test on the concrete established its tensile strength as 200 lb/in² (1·38 . 10⁶ N/m²) and its compressive strength as 800 lb/in², and with this latter information we shall now deduce the pressure pulse intensity versus distance relation, assuming that this is linear between the points at which the stress may be deduced.

When fracture occurs in plane DD, it will be because the head of the initially compressive stress wave of intensity σ_F, after reflection from free end EE as a tensile wave, exerts a net tensile stress in plane DD of 200 lb/in². The compressive stress in the incident pulse in plane DD at the instant fracture occurs is thus $(\sigma_F - 200)$ and this occurs at distance $(2 \times 9\frac{1}{2})$ in behind the head of the incident pulse. Associated with a distance further back in the pulse of (2×3) in there will have been a further decrease in pulse stress of 200 lb/in², because a second fracture, at CC, occurs. Due to the given information about the location of the further fractures, the diagram in Fig. 2.13 may be constructed. Now, since fracture at FF just occurs, and assuming the compressive stress in the tail of the pulse at FF is effectively zero, the absolute tensile stress in plane FF is 200 lb/in². This stress must have been present in plane AA and reflected with a sign change when fracture in AA occurred. Thus $(\sigma_F - 800) = 200$, or $\sigma_F = 1000$ lb/in². A smooth curve which is a close approximation to the input pulse form may thus be drawn as shown in Fig. 2.12.

Piece 5 will have a forward speed $v_5 = \sigma_5/\rho c$ where σ_5 is 200 lb/in² and ρc is the acoustic impedance of the concrete. If, for concrete $E = 10^6$ lb/in² (6·89 . 10⁹ N/m²) and its specific weight is 0·03 lb/in³ (830 kg/m³), then

$v \simeq 2$ ft/sec (0·61 m/s). Piece 4 will have a forward speed $v_4 = \sigma_4/\rho c = (200 + 400)/\rho c \simeq 6$ ft/sec; and pieces 3, 2 and 1 have speeds of approximately 10, 14 and 18 ft/sec respectively.

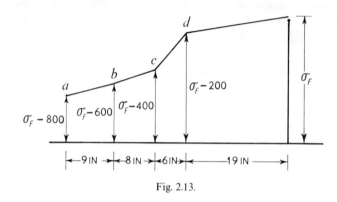

Fig. 2.13.

Parenthetically, it should be remembered that statically-loaded concrete structures which are very rapidly unloaded may fracture due to the unloading pulse and its reflection.

Scabbing in rocks

Rocks are strong in compression and can therefore transmit potentially damaging stresses to regions remote from their source. When compressive stresses are reflected as tensile stresses particularly destructive effects can ensue because the tensile stress of rocks is low—a few hundred lb/in², see Table 2.3— and hence spalling easily takes place. Of course, rocks are inhomogeneous, aelotropic and their stress-strain curves non-linear, so that their stress behaviour can be exceedingly complex; fractures often take place following planes of weakness due to statification, due to heterogeneous structure, and voids or flaws which arise naturally.

The ideas just presented are not limited to small scale phenomena. Rinehart[2.8] has referred to the example of the spalling produced by a 1·7 kilo-ton underground nuclear blast, the 'Rainier' shot; one or more slabs of rock above the blast rose 9 in and then fell, see Fig. 2.14(a). Accelerometers in a vertical hole directly above the blast led to the belief that the stress wave reaching the surface was as shown in Fig. 2.14(b).

The maximum stress in the wave for a maximum particle speed of 5 ft/sec is 560 lb/in² and the wave speed 6000 ft/sec. It is then easy to show that if the pulse length is 780 ft long, a spall of 210 ft thickness would be produced in this material for a tensile strength of 300 lb/in². The spall speed is $[560 + (560 - 300)]/\rho c = \frac{820}{560} \times 5 = 7\cdot3$ ft/sec. A free spall having this speed would rise under gravity to a height of $v^2/2g = 7\cdot3^2/64 = 10$ in.

Rinehart has shown some interesting examples of how stress waves may tear rocks apart. He considers only longitudinal waves and their reflections. The

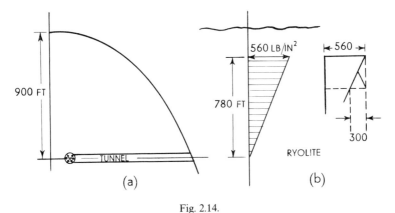

Fig. 2.14.

development of the fractures shown in the examples in Fig. 2.15 and 2.16 is easy to follow, but see pp. 72–78.

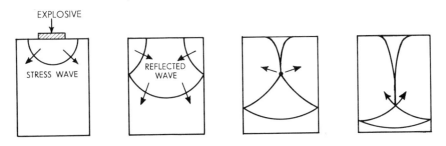

THE GENERATION OF A CENTRAL FRACTURE

Fig. 2.15.

Two interesting examples of scabbing in masonry and brick structures are shown[2.9] in Plates 4(a) and 4(b).

TABLE 2.3[2.8]

	Compressive σ_C, Strength lb/in^2	Tensile σ_T, Strength lb/in^2	σ_C/σ_T	c_L ft/sec	Specific Gravity
Granite	28 000	410	68	10 400	2·7
Sandstone	18 000	310	58	9 600	2·5
Limestone	10 000	400	25	16 200	2·6
Rhyolite	—	—	—	6 000	2·7

EXPLOSIVE

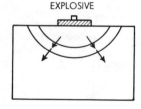 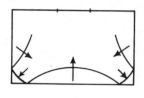 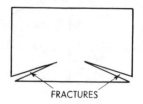

FRACTURES

Fig. 2.16.

Bar fracture: multiple spalling and necking[2.10]

If a bar under impact loading, as in Fig. 2.3, fractures, or alternatively very rapidly necks down when some critical *tensile* stress, S, is reached and so that, effectively, a new free end to the bar is created, the fraction of the length detached may easily be estimated. From Fig. 2.3, the critical net tensile stress S is first reached, say, at a section X_0 from the striker, and will be given by

$$\sigma_T = S = \sigma_0 \left[1 - \exp\left(-\frac{M_2}{M_1} \cdot 2\left(1 - \frac{X_0}{l_2}\right)\right)\right]$$

i.e.

$$\frac{X_0}{l_2} = 1 - \frac{M_1}{M_2}\ln\left(\frac{1}{\sqrt{1 - S/\sigma_0}}\right) \tag{2.34}$$

Writing the fracture stress $S = \rho_2 c_2 v_c$ so that we associate with it a critical particle speed v_c, then the initial striker impact speed to cause fracture (or necking) at a section distant X_0 from the striker is given by

$$v_0 = v_c \left/ \left[1 - \exp\left\{ -2\left(1 - \frac{X_0}{l_2}\right)\frac{M_2}{M_1}\right\}\right]\right. \tag{2.35}$$

Evidently the least speed to cause fracture, which in the limit is at the striker-rod interface, is $v_c/(1 - e^{-2M_2/M_1})$. If for a hard aluminium $S = 20\,000$ lb/in² ($138\cdot10^6$ N/m²), then $v_c = 32$ ft/sec (9·77 m/s), and if $M_2/M_1 = 1$ and $X_0/l_2 = \frac{1}{2}$, then v_0 would be 50 ft/sec (15·2 m/s).

After the far portion of the bar has separated from that contiguous with the striker, it will carry with it a total energy given by (2.16). Also a new tensile stress will be generated in the remaining portion of the bar, from the new free end. (A compressive wave will, of course, be immediately generated in the separated part.) The stress intensity at the head of the wave is $\sigma_0[1 - \exp(-2M_2(1 - X_0/l_2)/M_1)]$. This new wave of tension will now be superimposed on the tail of the striker-initiated compressive wave and thus there will be a tendency to promote another fracture in the portion of the rod between the striker and the first plane of fracture. It is easy to see how successive fractures or spalls, or portions between 'tensile necks', may be created. An indication of how the necessary calculations may be performed may be had by reference to Fig. 2.17.

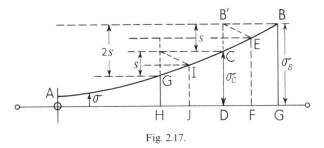

Fig. 2.17.

The striker-initiated stress wave is illustrated as AB, the greatest value of which is reduced from σ_B to σ_C, and $(\sigma_B - \sigma_C) = S$. Taking EF to represent the end of the bar and $B'E$ (dotted) to represent the reflected tensile wave—identical with the incident portion BE—the portion which leaves the original bar on fracture is of length DF where DF is one half of DG. Similarly a second plane of fracture might occur at a distance from the new free end of DJ or HJ. The new or second length of fractured rod would be

$$l_2 \frac{M_1}{M_2} \ln \frac{1}{\sqrt{1 - 2S/l_0}}$$

Generally the nth fracture length is

$$l_2 \cdot \frac{M_1}{M_2} \ln \frac{1}{\sqrt{1 - nS/\sigma_0}} \; ;$$

this is only applicable as long as $S < \sigma_0/n$.

The existence of multiple necking in single bars was apparrently first reported by Thomas in 1948. The formation of several necks in an extruded lead rod[2.10], due to high speed impact, is evident in Plate 6.

Spalling in thin constant cross-section curved bars

Plate 5 shows some of the experimental consequences[2.11] of detonating a small charge of explosive at one end of curved bars of Perspex so that an intense compressive stress pulse is propagated. At the end at which explosion occurs there is always some shattering and comminution of the bar. The three classes of Perspex bar in Plate 5 are
  (a) bars of constant curvature
  (b) L-shaped bars and
  (c) U-shaped bars.
The evident stress induced fractures occupy either or both of two specific locations. Firstly, there are end spall fractures which may be single or multiple and secondly, fractures in the immediate vicinity of a bend in the case of (b) or (c); multiple spall fractures are associated with the relatively large radii of curvature, single spalls with smaller radii and where the radii are small there may be no spall at all. The reduction in number, or disappearance, of spalls is accompanied by the appearance and increase in the number of fractures, in

the case of (b) and (c), the plane of the fracture not often being normal to the bar axis. The results in Plate 5 suggest that it is reasonable to treat a curved bar as a straight one provided the ratio of the radius of curvature to the radial thickness exceeds about six.

Some fracture patterns due to impulsive surface loading

(i) *Conical specimens*

As we have seen in a previous Section a pulse propagated along the axis of a cone from its base increases its amplitude and changes its shape. For a cone in which the longitudinal pulse length is large in comparison with the cross-section diameter, a compressive pulse develops a tension tail; the length of the compression region becomes progressively shorter as the apex is approached and simultaneously the maximum stress amplitude in the tail increases so that fracture at the tip of the cone may follow. An axial fracture—more like a series of bubbles—occurs due to reflection from the curved surface and there is local damage where the charge is detonated at the base; this description is based on work reported by Kolsky[2.6], see Plate 7.

(ii) *Discs or plates*

A blow administered at the centre of a loosely supported square plate, e.g., a ceramic tile, may cause corner fractures[2.12], see Fig. 2.18. As the radiating compression wave moves into each of the four corners between a pair of adjacent sides, it is amplified somewhat as described in (i) with similar consequences. The *amplified* stress is much greater than the *spalling* stress due to reflection from the sides of the plate.

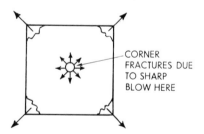

CORNER FRACTURES DUE TO SHARP BLOW HERE

Fig. 2.18.

(iii) *Rectangular slabs*

The following remarks, again due to Kolsky[2.6], are based on observations from experiments carried out on transparent materials, such as Perspex, the explosive pulse being provided by a small live charge of lead azide, P, in Fig. 2.19a which is asymmetrically situated. In this situation the reflected tensile pulse is obtained from the sides of the block. The bottom face will be responsible for a scab while the side faces will tend to give rise to surface fractures parallel to the sides at a

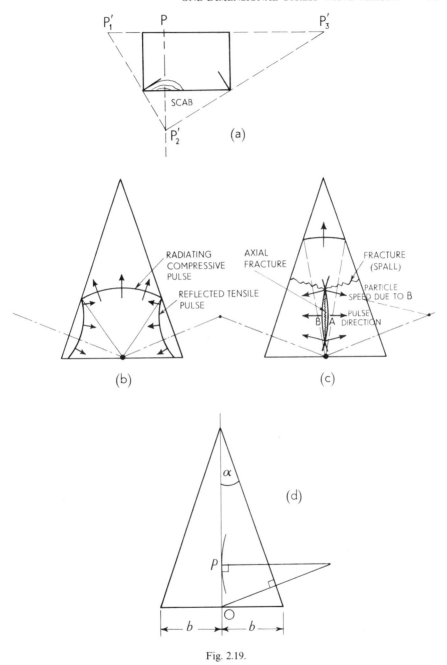

Fig. 2.19.

distance less than one half the pulse length. The reflected tensile pulses will also interfere and reinforce one another and cause corner cracks, whose directions make different angles with the bottom surface. These directions can be estimated with the help of the charge image points P'_1, P'_2 and P'_3, as shown.

(iv) *Straight-sided, thin, flat wedge-shaped plates*

When a charge is detonated *along the whole base* of a flat wedge-shaped plate, multiple spalling near the apex is conspicuous; this is true even for wedge angles which are not small, as Plate 8 shows[2.13]. It is what would be expected by reference to analysis and experiments on small angle cones. It seems that the first spall to occur is that which is furthest from the apex; the tensile tail of the pulse which grows in intensity the nearer the pulse is to the apex of the plate is presumably responsible for the first fracture and subsequent fractures develop from the bottom upwards in the spall tip. This order of development of the spalls is opposite to that which occurs in a uniform bar.

If a point or concentrated charge is detonated at the *centre of the base* of a flat wedge-shaped plate, the consistent fracture patterns which are developed are different from those just described, as the collection of examples in Plate 9 shows. The fracture pattern may be explained as follows. The compressive pulse radiated from the centre of the base is reflected from the sloping sides of the wedge as a predominantly tensile pulse at the same time as the pulse proceeds towards the wedge apex, see Fig. 2.19(b); the reflected waves intersect on the axis of the plate and there tend to tear it apart, see Fig. 2.19(c); this is the reason for the axial crack, as in the case for the cone. It is not difficult to see that if the stress pulse is of sufficient intensity, the axial crack should start on the axis at P and spread upwards and downwards from it, where in Fig. 2.19(d), $OP = b \cdot \sin 2\alpha$. Axial cracking due to reflection from the sloping sides is only possible if $\alpha < 45°$; when $\alpha = 45°$, P is at the apex.

(v) *Cylindrical blocks*

B. Hopkinson[2.3] appears first to have discussed the results of detonating a gun cotton cylinder on one end of a short, thick solid steel cylinder. He records that the cylinder was flattened slightly, that a depression was made under the charge, and that a slight bulge was created on the opposite end. Sawing through the cylinder revealed the cracks shown in Plate 10. Evidently, as well as end-spalling cracks, the applied compression inclined the cylinder to burst on the axis due to radial displacements from reflection at the curved surface.

According to Kolsky[2.6] a charge detonated at the centre of one end of a cylindrical block of Perspex gives rise to fracture patterns which are very similar to those already described in (i) above. Features of these are as follows (see Fig. 2.20).

    (a) Compression damage beneath the charge, and

    (b) a circular crack on the top surface, SS, just inside the outside curved surface; this is due to the reflection of the compressive pulse as a tensile pulse.

    (c) Line fracture extending axially downwards from the charge; this is due to tensile wave reflection, interference and reinforcement from the curved sides of the block. The length of PC is proportional to the weight of charge, and

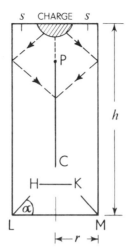

Fig. 2.20.

(d) with short cylinders, a flat region of fracture, HK, occurs; this is similar to scab formation.

(e) A conical corner fracture, LM, arises in a manner similar to that described elsewhere, see pp. 72 and 75.

(vi) *Rectangular blocks*[2.6]

Plates 11(a) and (b), show the results of detonating a charge of explosive at the centre of the top surface of a rectangular block of perspex. The reader should easily be able to interpret the pattern of fractures which are apparent.

(vii) *Fracture in square section thick-walled cylinders internally loaded*

As will have become obvious from the last Section, fracture patterns due to impulsive load often have little resemblance to fractures due to static load. Rinehart and Pearson[2.7] observe that there are two patterns of fracture:

(a) brittle type fractures which occur perpendicular to the greatest tensile principal stress, and

(b) shear fractures.

Consistent fracture patterns are found in the high transient loading of cylinders and, in particular, corner fractures and spalling are again two of the most common types of fractures arising from stress wave interference and reinforcement.

A square cylinder loaded internally is shown in Fig. 2.21 conveying a divergent compressive sharp fronted wave. This is reflected as a tension wave from the free surface, see Fig. 2.22. Tension waves meet on the diagonals, Fig. 2.23, and high tensile stress normal to the diagonals is generated so that corner fractures are caused, see Fig. 2.24. *The cylinder fractures through the thickest part of the section.*

Similarly, fractures through the thickest sections could be expected in the cylinder whose cross-section is shown in Fig. 2.25.

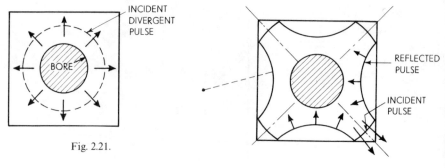

Fig. 2.21.

Fig. 2.22.

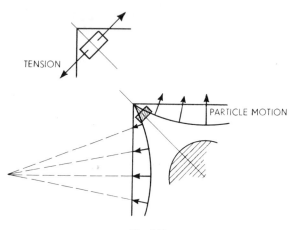

Fig. 2.23.

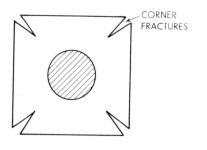

Fig. 2.24.

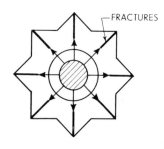

Fig. 2.25.

(viii) *Fractures in hollow circular section cylinders due to internal explosions*

Figures 2.26 and 2.27 respectively show the main fracture features as found by Rinehart and Pearson[2.7] when a thick cylinder of
    (a) annealed mild steel was subjected to internal explosive loading, and
    (b) a 24 ST aluminium alloy was loaded externally using an explosive.

Figure 2.27 indicates shear fractures at the bore due to pulse intensification as it converges on the internal surface and is reflected. Figure 2.26 shows fracture along lines of maximum shear stress near the inner surface and radial fracture due solely to hoop stress further out.

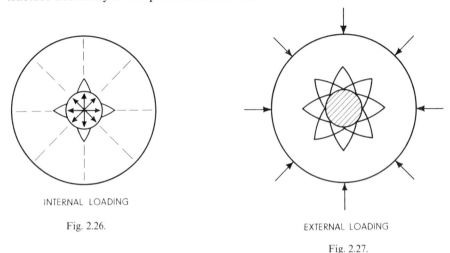

INTERNAL LOADING

Fig. 2.26.

EXTERNAL LOADING

Fig. 2.27.

Fracturing in long thin wires due to tensile impact: The Hopkinsons' early work

B. Hopkinson[2.3] in a paper of 1905, remarks that J. Hopkinson published an account of "An investigation into the effect of a blow by a falling weight on the lower and free end of a wire, the upper end of which is fixed", in 1872. It was stated that when the tension wave is reflected at the fixed end, the stress and strain there are suddenly doubled. "Rough" experiments were carried out by J. Hopkinson which were said to confirm his expectations "that the power of a blow to rupture a wire should be measured rather by the velocity with which it is delivered than by its energy or its momentum, ... also ... that the wire was most likely to break at the upper end". (In fact, the maximum stress occurs at the second reflection, see p. 54.)

B. Hopkinson, in describing the experiment he carried out, writes, "The general result that I have obtained is that iron and copper wires may be stressed much beyond the static elastic limit and even beyond their static breaking loads without the proportionality of stresses and strains being substantially departed from, provided that the time during which the stress exceeds the elastic limit is of the order of $\frac{1}{1000}$ sec or less." This is an early reference to the effects of time on the strength properties of metals and is an example of how caution should be exercised in respect of theoretical prediction.

Fracture patterns in glass

A glass pane firmly held at its periphery, when subject to point impact near its centre and on one side, bends in the direction of the load with the first cracks occurring on the other side and propagating from the edge of the pane and converging towards the centre; later, secondary 'ring' cracks develop. Careful examination of the glass along the cracks shows the existence of striations or hair-line patterns through the thickness. For the primary cracks the striations converge on the point of impact, but for the secondary cracks the striations converge on a point on the rear surface of the pane, opposite to the impact point. This knowledge enables one to decide from the examination of a cracked pane, from which side a blow has been struck, see Fig. 2.28.

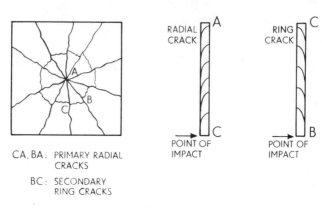

CA, BA : PRIMARY RADIAL
          CRACKS
   BC : SECONDARY
          RING CRACKS

Fig. 2.28.

Glass may be perforated by a high velocity missile, leaving a clean hole and with only general cracking of the pane. When the force on a pane of glass is not concentrated as with a bullet, but is delivered as blast, two main types of failure arise. Severe blast causes circumferential fracture, the central portion being displaced, but with little cracking, see Plate 12(a); less severe blast, see Plate 12(b), is accompanied by radial fractures.

Toughened glass is glass whose surfaces are in compression; it is achieved by a rapid but controlled chilling using air blasts. A fracture at any point in a sheet of toughened glass leads immediately to shattering since the residual stress system is radically disturbed.

Fracture once started in glass is said to spread very rapidly because there are no grain boundaries to interrupt its progress; in bullet-proof glass, plastic glass boundaries are introduced to interrupt spreading fractures.

High speed photography has shown that the maximum speed of crack propagation in glass is less than about $0.4\,c_L$.

Fracture and crack propagation are extensively and clearly discussed in the book by Cottrell.[2.14]

Water hammer[2.15]

A much studied example of longitudinal wave propagation is that which arises when fluid flowing in a pipe line is brought to rest, more or less rapidly by closing a valve; some or all of the momentum of the moving column of liquid is destroyed thereby leading to a pressure rise in excess of that already prevailing in the fluid, which is transmitted from the valve through the column. The effect of the sudden increase in pressure at a valve is often heard as a metallic thud and is known as water hammer.

Analysis of the situation is more complicated than it might seem at first sight since the pressure intensity created is dependent on the rate of valve closure, the elastic properties of the pipe and friction between pipe and water.

(i) For a rigid pipe, in which a liquid flows with uniform speed v, instantaneous arrest at a point by valve closure, gives rise to a pressure in excess of that of the atmosphere of $p = \rho c v$ where $c = \sqrt{K/\rho}$; thus for water $p = 63.7 \cdot v$ lb/in^2, if v is in ft/sec.

(ii) A pressure wave in a liquid travels from the valve when closed, see Fig. 2.29(a) and (b) with speed c towards the open end of the pipe of length l and at time $t = l/c$ the whole of the liquid column

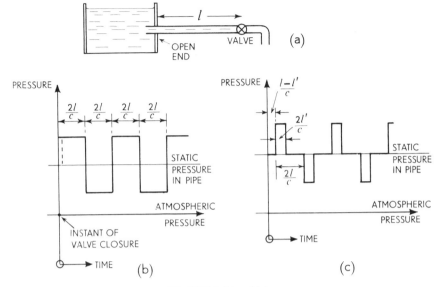

Fig. 2.29(a), (b) and (c).

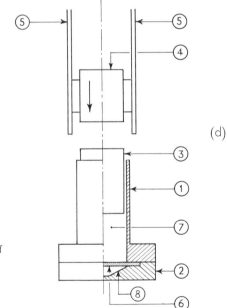

Fig. 2.29 (d) Diagrammatic representation of apparatus for water-hammer forming.
1 Hydraulic cylinder   5 Guides
2 Specimen holder   6 Blank
3 Piston   7 Water column
4 Weight   8 Die: conical

is at rest. The wave reflects from the open end of the pipe and at time $t = 2l/c$, the whole of the pipe contents will have had their speed reversed which will be v towards the open end, and the pipe pressure will have been reduced to atmospheric. The water column cannot leave the valve unless the pressure there drops to zero (or nearly so) and its motion is consequently checked. If the water is completely checked, a wave at $t = 2l/c$ moves towards the open end of the pipe so that at $t = 3l/c$, the pressure is p (or $\rho c v$) below atmospheric. Reflection at $t = 3l/c$ from the open end ensures that by $t = 4l/c$, the pressure is restored to just atmospheric and the column is again moving as a whole, with speed v, towards the valve. Thus conditions are the same as at the beginning of the cycle, which then proceeds to repeat itself. The pressure-time graph at the valve and at a point distant l' from the open end is given in Fig. 2.29(c).

(iii) The process described in (ii) above is, of course, idealised. If the speed of water flow was such as to make p greater than the normal absolute pressure in the pipe, the first reflux wave would tend to reduce the pressure below zero and this is improbable. The pressure, we may assume, can only fall to zero so that the subsequent rise would be correspondingly reduced.

Further, at low pressure, any air dissolved in the water is liberated and the water motion would quickly break down.

(iv) Since the effect of friction in a pipe line is to cause a steady pressure drop along it, it follows that in any real situation the graph of Fig. 2.29(a) is likely to be over-idealised. This subject is discussed in ref. 2.14.

(v) The elasticity of the pipe walls obviously works so as to reduce the water hammer pressure, and in general to complicate the phenomena encountered by contributing to an increase in the rate at which the pressure waves are attenuated.

The arrest of the water column by the valve in a pipe free to stretch longitudinally may not be total; if w is the common speed of movement of the end of the pipe and water column, then the ideal water hammer wave pressure initiated will be $(v - w)\sqrt{K/\rho}$. A pulse will however be transmitted along and *in the metal pipe* at a speed much in excess of $\sqrt{K/\rho}$; after its reflection at the free end of the pipe it will arrive back at the valve and thus allow a rebound of speed w which will produce an auxiliary wave of pressure $w\sqrt{K/\rho}$ in the liquid; this is superimposed on the initial pressure, thus bringing the total idealised water hammer pressure to $v\sqrt{K/\rho}$—exactly as if the pipe was firmly anchored. Without wishing to pursue this complex topic we note then that a subsidiary wave of high periodicity and of magnitude $\pm w\sqrt{K/\rho}$ will be superimposed on the normal pressure wave.

(vi) Further complications arise due to the elasticity of the pipe. Suppose the *increase* in pressure in the portion of pipe through which the pressure wave has travelled is p, then, if the pipe is free to expand axially, the increase in hoop and axial stresses created, σ_θ and σ_z respectively are

$$\sigma_\theta = pa_0/t_0 \quad \text{and} \quad \sigma_z = pa_0/2t_0$$

where a_0 and t_0 denote the mean pipe radius and thickness respectively. Now the change in unit internal volume of the stressed pipe is $\delta V/V$ and

$$\frac{\delta V}{V} = \frac{\delta(\pi a_0^2 z)}{\pi a_0^2 z} = 2\frac{\delta a_0}{a_0} + \frac{\delta z}{z} = 2e_\theta + e_z$$

$$= [2(\sigma_\theta - v\sigma_z) + (\sigma_z - v\sigma_\theta)]/E$$

$$= \frac{pa_0}{2Et_0}(5 - 4v)$$

The volumetric strain of the liquid under pressure p is p/K; the apparent volumetric strain may be denoted however by p/K' and thus,

$$\frac{p}{K} + \frac{pa_0}{2t_0 E}(5 - 4v) = \frac{p}{K'}$$

or

$$\frac{1}{K'} = \frac{1}{K} + \frac{a_0}{t_0 E}\left(\frac{5 - 4v}{2}\right)$$

If the pipe was anchored so that all longitudinal extension was prevented, we should have

$$\frac{1}{K'} = \frac{1}{K} + \frac{a_0}{t_0 E} \cdot 2$$

The pressure rise due to the sudden stoppage of the liquid column is then $v\rho c'$ where $c' = \sqrt{K'/\rho}$.

For water $K = 3 . 10^5$ lb/in^2 ($2{\cdot}06 . 10^9$ N/m^2) so that $c = \sqrt{K/\rho} = 4720$ ft/sec (1438 m/s); for a 3 in dia. pipe, $\frac{1}{4}$ in thick and with $E = 3 . 10^7$ lb/in^2 ($206 . 10^9$ N/m^2), $K' = 2{\cdot}68 . 10^5$ lb/in^2 ($1{\cdot}84 . 10^9$ N/m^2) and $c' = 4460$ ft/sec (1360 m/s).

(vii) Valves are not shut instantaneously but on the assumption that the liquid column is uniformly retarded at a rate f then, provided the closing-down time of the valve is less than l/c, the pressure generated is still ρvc as for instantaneous stoppage. Let the pressure generated by partial valve closure be p', when the head of the wave has travelled distance x from the valve, then

$$p' = \rho f x$$

and

$$f = \frac{v}{x/c}$$

so that

$$p = \rho vc$$

Using these assumptions the law of valve closure is seen to be immaterial. The book by L. Bergeron, "Water hammer in hydraulics and wave surges in electricity", John Wiley & Sons Inc., N.Y., 1961, p. 293, should be consulted for many aspects of the treatment of waves in pipes.

Water hammer forming

A method of sheet metal forming introduced in recent years makes constructive use of the phenomenon of water hammer as shown in Fig. 2.29(d). The aim is to form a given thin circular metal blank into a die to form say a cone; by allowing a weight to fall onto a metal piston, a pressure pulse is generated and propagated in the water column and then allowed to impinge on the metal blank thus communicating momentum to the latter. The kinetic energy acquired by the blank is dissipated in doing plastic work as the metal blank takes up the intended shape: details of the process and its wave analysis are to be found elsewhere[2.16].

High speed liquid impact with a solid surface

When a liquid drop moves at high speed and impinges on a solid surface, very high pressures are developed for about one microsecond after impact. If a square-ended, liquid circular cylinder having a speed v impinges normally on a *rigid* anvil, it gives rise to a pressure, p, whose value is determined by its *compressible* behaviour;

$$p = \rho vc_0. \tag{2.36}$$

c_0 is the elastic wave speed in water.

If impact takes place compressibly against a solid plane surface whose acoustic impedance is $(\rho c)_S$, then the pressure created is taken to be

$$p = v . \frac{(\rho c_0) . (\rho c)_S}{\rho c_0 + (\rho c)_S}; \tag{2.37}$$

this expression is identical with (1.27) and neglects all area considerations.

The pressure, p, applies over the whole area of contact at the instant of impact; its duration depends upon the time taken for unloading waves to move inwards to the axis of the cylinder from the curved surface of the cylinder. The sequence of events is conceived to be as shown in Fig. 2.30; at the moment of impact the whole of the head of the cylinder rises to pressure p but it is only the

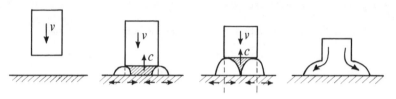

Fig. 2.30.

liquid at the *edges* which is free to flow laterally, the portions of the cylinder near the axis remaining compressed until the pressure release wave from the cylinder edge encompasses it; after this the pressure on the anvil will fall to the steady state flow, incompressible pressure of $\rho v^2/2$. For a jet of diameter 3 mm, the release wave takes a time $t = r/c_0$, i.e. about 1μ sec (10^{-6} secs) to release the compressible flow pressure over the whole of the end section of the cylinder. The steady state pressure is usually one or two orders of magnitude less than the compressible flow pressure. Brunton[2.17], by embedding a bar of titanate crystal in the end of a steel pressure bar, recorded a decay time of about 2μ secs attributing this length of decay to the fact that the jet was unlikely to have been square-ended. A jet having a speed of 1700 ft/sec (520 m/s) would, using (2.36), cause a peak pressure of about 50 ton/in^2 ($0.77 . 10^9$ N/m^2). (This is calculated by taking $c_0 \simeq 5000$ ft/sec (1500 m/s), but the value of c_0 at the pressure level created would be about 9400 ft/sec (2870 m/s) so that $p \simeq 100$ ton/in^2 ($1.54 . 10^9$ N/m^2).) A typical value for the flow stress of mild steel is about 16 ton/in^2 ($0.246 . 10^9$ N/m^2), so it is evident that stresses due to impact can easily give rise to stress wave interaction fractures in brittle materials or plastic deformation in ductile materials. It is especially true that the repeated impact of liquid drops at speeds of even as low as 100 metres/sec will quickly erode hard surfaces. Thus the subject of liquid droplet impact takes on great importance such as at the low pressure end of a steam turbine where water droplets impinge on fast moving blading and cause erosion, or in the front regions of a fast moving aircraft where, for instance, a plastic observation window may be hit by water droplets as it passes through a rain cloud.

A thin plate of hard polymer when subject to normal impact by a jet undergoes compression and causes radial tension outside the peripheral compressed zone, which can promote ring fractures. Liquid flowing radially outwards removes projecting material from the zone of ring fracture. Ring fracture and spalling are clear from a section of a damaged plate, see Plate 13.

In metals which can deform plastically, at speeds of about 2000 ft/sec, shallow craters are formed with wavy elevations and depressions at the periphery. At speeds of about 7000 ft/sec in low flow stress metals, features peculiar to hypervelocity impact arise, see p. 321.

The shape of the leading region of an impinging jet governs the pressure-time history at an interface with other bodies. In the very early stages of the impact of a spherical drop with a rigid plane surface, outward flow is prevented, see Fig. 2.31a. Point P at the junction of the curved surface of the sphere and the anvil is moving radially outwards with speed $\dot{x}$. Now

$$\dot{x} = \frac{d}{dt}(r \sin \theta) = r \cdot \cos \theta \cdot \dot{\theta}$$

and

$$v = \frac{d}{dt}(r \cos \theta) = -r \sin \theta \cdot \dot{\theta}$$

so that

$$\dot{x} = -v \cdot \cot \theta \tag{2.38}$$

The compressible flow pressure can only begin to decay if $\dot{x} < c_0$. The limiting case, as defined by a radius of contact x_0 is, using (2.38),

$$\dot{x} = c_0 = v \cot \theta \simeq v \cdot \frac{r}{x_0}$$

or

$$x_0 = v \cdot \frac{r}{c_0} \tag{2.39}$$

For a sphere of radius 2 mm and with $v = 607$ m/s (2000 ft/sec), $x_0 \simeq$ 0·8 mm.

If a liquid cylinder made dynamic contact with a plane along a line parallel to a generator, see Fig. 2.31(b), the width of contact would be $2x_0$.

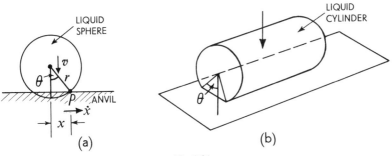

Fig. 2.31.

Expression (2.39) is not exact, but it shows the importance of the curvature of a drop or jet at first impact and that when v is small, x_0 is infinitesimal.

In summary, when a jet or drop collides with a solid surface the sequence of events is usually assumed to be as follows:

First there is the formation of a small central area of first contact, under uniform pressure p given by (2.37). This initial point, or line, or area of contact grows as impact continues with little or no reduction in pressure until appreciable outward flow begins at some critical extent, e.g. as given by equation (2.39) or when the liquid/solid interface angle attains a certain value β. At this stage† a rapid fall in pressure ensues starting from the periphery of the interface, and outward flow follows. As outward flow continues the compression is progressively relieved across the interface until the maximum pressure acting on the surface is only the stagnation pressure for incompressible flow, i.e. $\rho v^2/2$.

A quantity of water having a concave surface, S, contained in a steel nozzle and suddenly subject to a blow delivered through a plug, P, see Plate 14a, will be ejected in the first place as a very fast moving *jet*, followed by a slower main jet or slug of water[2.16], see Plate 14(b). (Compare the phenomenology of lined charges in Chapter 9). The micro-jet shown in Plate 14 was found to have a speed of about 6000 ft/sec (1830 m/s) and would give rise on impact to a pressure of over 500 ton/in^2 (7·7 . 10^9 N/m^2), so that it would be expected to, and indeed can, punch a small deep hole or crater in very hard materials. This deep micro-penetration is usually surrounded by a much larger but shallower diameter crater, due to the late arrival of the main jet. It is not difficult to appreciate that if two spheres collide, that when their angle of contact is small, micro-jets may be formed and a very fast radially outward moving ring of tiny droplets is created.

Brittle fracture in the tensile test: Miklowitz' observation[2.18]

An interesting investigation reported by Miklowitz concerns the tensile testing of brittle materials in which it was noted that fractures were produced at two different cross-sections of the specimen when the rupture load was reached. Experiments were conducted on plexi-glass at a loading rate of 300 lb/min (136 kg/min) and on high speed steel at 2000 lb/min (905 kg/min). The situation was analysed by considering that two types of waves emanate from the initial ruptured section. One is a longitudinal compression wave which is, in fact, an unloading wave associated with the decrease in load in the fracture process. The other is a group of flexural strain waves produced by the moment that develops as the crack propagates across the bar from its origin at a surface discontinuity. It was found that the second fracture usually occurred at a gauge cross-section adjacent to the specimen head farthest from the initial fracture surface. It was shown in the analysis that this second failure is due to the superposition of the longitudinal strain from the unloading wave, which through reflections becomes tension, and the resulting flexural strain, which together total more than the original static tensile fracture strain.

Elastic impact of a short square-ended solid cylinder with a plane elastic semi-infinite medium

(i) *The rigid cylinder*

The equation of motion for a rigid square-ended solid cylinder of circular cross-section, whose height is equal to its diameter and which impinges normally on a semi-infinite medium so that the response of the latter is wholly elastic, is

$$P = -m \cdot \frac{d^2x}{dt^2} \tag{2.40}$$

---

† Experiments show the angle θ as calculated using (2.39) to be too small by almost an order of magnitude.

P is the total elastic resisting force which, in reference 2.1 is shown to be given by

$$P = 2aEx/(1 - v^2) \tag{2.41}$$

where a is the radius and m the mass of the striking cylinder, E is Young's modulus and v Poisson's ratio for the semi-infinite mass; x denotes the current amount of indentation measured from the undisturbed surface and is small by comparison with a.

Equation (2.41) of course implies the existence of a zone of plastic deformation at the periphery of the cylinder; the effect of this quickly reduces to zero with distance from the periphery.

Thus

$$\frac{d^2x}{dt^2} + \frac{2aE}{(1 - v^2)m} \cdot x = 0$$

Substitute $2\pi a^3 \rho_S$ for m where ρ_S denotes the density of the striker and equation (2.41) becomes

$$\frac{d^2x}{dt^2} + \frac{E}{\rho_S(1 - v^2)\pi a^2} \cdot x = 0$$

Thus the total time of elastic contact between the striker and the medium is $T = \pi a \sqrt{[\rho_S(1 - v^2)\pi/E]}$.

This assumes that the time of contact during rebound is the same as for penetration, i.e. as long as $x > 0$.

If a steel striker impinges against a steel target $\rho_S = 0.28$ lb/in^3 (0.775 . 10^4 kg/m^3), $v = 0.3$ and for $a = 0.5$ in (12.7 mm) T is approximately $= 10^{-5}$ secs.

(ii) *The elastic cylinder*

It is reasonable to assume that the order of the time of contact between the elastic cylinder and a relatively hard semi-infinite medium is given by the time taken for the compression wave initiated in the cylinder, to travel up to the far end and to be reflected back to its region of origin.

This is just $T = 2.(2a/c_0)$, which, for the same material circumstances as in (i), gives $T \simeq 10^{-5}$ secs.

Simple elastic wave propagation in helical springs

The impact loading of helical springs is a frequent occurrence in many engineering elements such as vehicle buffers, gun recuperation and valve springs. We shall therefore briefly discuss wave propagation in springs due to impact, first, for close-coiled helical springs and second, for open-coiled helical springs. In the first case we shall find that an axial spring force gives rise to extensional or compressional waves and a torque applied about the axis to a wave of rotation. The second case is more complicated and involves the propagation of *coupled* waves for either axial force or torque.

Throughout the analysis below, we shall proceed by assuming that the helical spring can be replaced by an equivalent elastic rod having the same unloaded or initial axial length l_0 as the spring, the same weight W, and the same moment of inertia about its axis of WR^2/g; R denotes the mean spring radius. The approach presented in this Section largely follows that given in a paper by Wittrick[2.19].

The close-coiled helical spring

(i) *Extensional waves*

By definition, a close-coiled spring has a helix angle, α, which is vanishingly small. If Δ denotes the axial displacement of an element of the spring at initial distance x from the end of the spring to which the impact load is applied at time $t = 0$, the other end of the spring being fixed, and if F is the actual tensile force in the spring at x, then

(a) the force-displacement relationship relating to an element of length dx is

$$F = \frac{GJ}{LR^2} l_0 \frac{\partial \Delta}{\partial x} \tag{2.44}$$

where GJ is the torsional stiffness of the spring and R its mean radius; and

(b) the axial equation of motion of an element is

$$dF = \frac{W}{g} \cdot \frac{dx}{l_0} \cdot \frac{\partial^2 \Delta}{\partial t^2} \tag{2.45}$$

Combining equations (2.44) and (2.45) and eliminating F, we have

$$\frac{dF}{dx} = \frac{W}{g} \cdot \frac{1}{l_0} \cdot \frac{\partial^2 \Delta}{\partial t^2} = \frac{GJ}{LR^2} \cdot l_0 \frac{\partial^2 \Delta}{\partial x^2}$$

or

$$\frac{\partial^2 \Delta}{\partial t^2} = \frac{JGl_0^2}{LR^2 . W/g} \cdot \frac{\partial^2 \Delta}{\partial x^2} \tag{2.46}$$

Thus, as would have been expected, we have derived the usual simple one-dimensional wave equation and hence the *axial* speed of an extensional wave is

$$c_e = \frac{l_0}{R} \left(\frac{JG}{L . W/g} \right)^{1/2} \tag{2.47}$$

The surge time, t_s, which is the time taken for the wave to traverse the length of the spring is,

$$t_s = R \left(\frac{LW/g}{JG} \right)^{1/2} \tag{2.48}$$

Alternatively, putting $W = wL$, where L is the helical length of the spring,

w its weight per unit length, ρ the density and A the cross-sectional area,

$$t_s = RL\left(\frac{A\rho}{JG}\right)^{1/2} \tag{2.49}$$

The wave concerned actually travels along the helix with, say, speed V_H so that

$$V_H = \frac{L}{t_s} = \frac{1}{R}\left(\frac{JG}{A\rho}\right)^{1/2} \tag{2.50}$$

Recalling from (1.10i) that the torsional wave speed in a straight rod is

$$c_T = \left(\frac{GJ}{I}\right)^{1/2} = \frac{1}{k_T}\left(\frac{GJ}{A\rho}\right)^{1/2},$$

where k_T is the polar radius of gyration of the cross-section of the spring wire,

$$\frac{V_H}{c_T} = \frac{k_T}{R}$$

In the particular case of a circular section wire of radius a,

$$\frac{V_H}{c_T} = \frac{a}{R\sqrt{2}}$$

and for a square section wire of side $2b$, for which $k_T^2 = 2b^2/3$

$$\frac{V_H}{c_T} = \frac{b}{R}\cdot\left(\frac{2}{3}\right)^{1/2}$$

(ii) *Rotational waves*

The sudden application of a twisting moment about the axis of a close-coiled spring causes a rotational wave to be propagated along it. Proceeding as before and denoting by ψ and T respectively, the rotation and twisting moment at a section distance x from the end of application of the torque at time $t = 0$, we have at time t,

(a) the torque-rotation equation for an element of initial length dx, as

$$T = EI\cdot\frac{l_0}{L}\cdot\frac{\partial\psi}{\partial x} \tag{2.51}$$

where EI is the flexural rigidity of the wire, and
(b) the rotational equation of motion of the element as

$$dT = \frac{W}{g}\cdot R^2\cdot\frac{dx}{l_0}\cdot\frac{\partial^2\psi}{\partial t^2} \tag{2.52}$$

Eliminating T from equations (2.51) and (2.52)

$$\frac{\partial^2\psi}{\partial t^2} = \frac{EIl_0^2}{LR^2 W/g}\cdot\frac{\partial^2\psi}{\partial x^2}$$

Thus the axial speed of a rotational wave is

$$c_R = \frac{l_0}{R} \cdot \left(\frac{EI}{LW/g}\right)^{1/2} \tag{2.53}$$

and the surge time t_s' is

$$t_s' = \frac{l_0}{c_R} = R \cdot \left(\frac{LW/g}{EI}\right)^{1/2} \tag{2.54}$$

Alternatively,

$$t_s' = RL\left(\frac{A\rho}{EI}\right)^{1/2} \tag{2.55}$$

The speed V_H' of a rotational wave along the helix itself is

$$V_H' = \frac{L}{t_s'} = \frac{1}{R} \cdot \left(\frac{EI}{A\rho}\right)^{1/2} \tag{2.56}$$

Now $I = Ak^2$ and $w/g = A\rho$ where k is the radius of gyration of the section for bending about the vertical axis of symmetry of the section of the wire. Thus,

$$V_H' = \frac{k}{R} \cdot \left(\frac{E}{\rho}\right)^{1/2} \tag{2.57}$$

In the particular case of (a) a circular section wire of radius a, $k = a/2$, so that

$$V_H' = \frac{a}{2R} \cdot \left(\frac{E}{\rho}\right)^{1/2} \quad \text{or} \quad \frac{V_H'}{c_0} = \frac{a}{2R}$$

and (b) for a square section wire of side $2b$,

$$k = b/\sqrt{3} \quad \text{and} \quad \frac{V_H'}{c_0} = \frac{b}{R} \cdot \frac{1}{\sqrt{3}}$$

where $c_0 = \sqrt{E/\rho}$.

(iii) *Piston effect*

The analyses above (and below) and extensions of it to take account of wave reflections, etc., apply as long as any compression undergone by the spring is not such as to bring individual adjacent coils into contact. If a local force greater than some critical force necessary to bring a pair of adjacent coils together is operative, then a 'shock' effect is produced, see Fig. 2.32. According to Dick[2.20] the length of spring in which adjacent coils are in contact forms a 'piston' in which the coils all move with the same speed and there is a 'shock' wave front at one end and in some cases at both ends of the piston. The speeds of propagation of these shock wave fronts are greater than the wave speed given by equation (2.47) and the force-displacement relationships are also different.

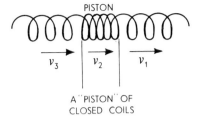

Fig. 2.32.

A "PISTON" OF
CLOSED COILS

Open-coiled helical springs

Consider an axial force F and a torque T acting about the spring axis, see Fig. 2.33(a) to be simultaneously and suddenly applied to an open-coiled spring of helix angle α. We proceed as before, by assuming that the spring can be replaced by an equivalent elastic rod.

The equations of motion for an element of axial length l_0 are given by equations (2.45) and (2.52).

The equations connecting force F, or torque T, with the axial displacement Δ and section rotation ψ, are now derived from first principles.

Referring to Fig. 2.33(b) at any cross-section of the wrire there is a bending moment M_B and a torque M_T. We have

$$M_T = FR \cos \alpha + T \sin \alpha$$

and

$$M_B = T \cos \alpha - FR \sin \alpha$$

(2.58)

Neglecting the contributions to the total strain energy of the wire, U, of the normal force across, and the shear force on each section, we have

$$U = \frac{1}{2} L \left(\frac{M_B^2}{EI} + \frac{M_T^2}{GJ} \right)$$

The extension of the spring due to F and T is Δ and

$$\Delta = \frac{\partial U}{\partial F} = L \left(\frac{M_B}{EI} \cdot \frac{\partial M_B}{\partial F} + \frac{M_T}{GJ} \cdot \frac{\partial M_T}{\partial F} \right)$$

The extension of the spring per unit length is

$$\frac{\Delta}{l} = \frac{\partial \Delta}{\partial x} = \frac{(T \cos \alpha - FR \sin \alpha)}{EI} \cdot (-R \sin \alpha) + \frac{(FR \cos \alpha + T \sin \alpha)}{GJ} \cdot (R \cos \alpha)$$

$$= FR^2 \left(\frac{\sin^2 \alpha}{EI} + \frac{\cos^2 \alpha}{GJ} \right) + TR \left(\frac{1}{GJ} - \frac{1}{EI} \right) \sin \alpha \cos \alpha$$

(2.59)

The rotation of the spring per unit length is

$$\frac{\psi}{L} = \frac{\partial \psi}{\partial x} = \frac{1}{L} \cdot \frac{\partial U}{\partial T} = \frac{M_B}{EI} \cdot \frac{\partial M_B}{\partial T} + \frac{M_T}{GJ} \cdot \frac{\partial M_T}{\partial T}$$

Hence,

$$\frac{\partial \psi}{\partial x} = \frac{(T \cos \alpha - FR \sin \alpha)}{EI} (\cos \alpha) + \frac{(FR \cos \alpha + T \sin \alpha)}{GJ} (\sin \alpha)$$

$$= FR \sin \alpha \cos \alpha \left(\frac{1}{GJ} - \frac{1}{EI} \right) + T \left(\frac{\sin^2 \alpha}{GJ} + \frac{\cos^2 \alpha}{EI} \right)$$

(2.60)

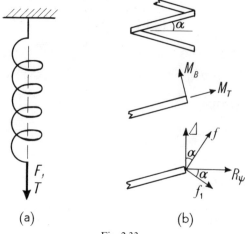

(a)   (b)

Fig. 2.33.

From simultaneous equations (2.59) and (2.60), we find

$$F = \dfrac{\left(\dfrac{\sin^2 \alpha}{GJ} + \dfrac{\cos^2 \alpha}{EI}\right)\dfrac{\partial \Delta}{\partial x} - R\left(\dfrac{1}{GJ} - \dfrac{1}{EI}\right)\dfrac{\partial \psi}{\partial x} \cdot \sin \alpha \cos \alpha}{R^2\left[\left(\dfrac{\sin^2 \alpha}{EI} + \dfrac{\cos^2 \alpha}{GJ}\right)\left(\dfrac{\sin^2 \alpha}{GJ} + \dfrac{\cos^2 \alpha}{EI}\right) - \sin^2 \alpha \cos^2 \alpha\left(\dfrac{1}{GJ} - \dfrac{1}{EI}\right)^2\right]}$$

The denominator of the above equation reduces to $1/EI \cdot GJ \cdot R^2$ so that,

$$FR^2 = (EI \sin^2 \alpha + GJ \cos^2 \alpha)\frac{\partial \Delta}{\partial x} + R \sin \alpha \cos \alpha(GJ - EI)\frac{\partial \psi}{\partial x} \tag{2.61}$$

Similarly, using equations (2.59) and (2.60),

$$TR = \sin \alpha \cos \alpha(GJ - EI)\frac{\partial \Delta}{\partial x} + R(GJ \sin^2 \alpha + EI \cos^2 \alpha)\frac{\partial \psi}{\partial x} \tag{2.62}$$

Substituting for F in equilibrium equation (2.45) using (2.61), and noting that $x = s \cdot \sin \alpha$ where s is measured along the helix from one end of the spring,

$$\frac{\partial^2 \Delta}{\partial t^2} = \frac{l_0}{W/g} \cdot \frac{\partial F}{\partial x}$$

$$= \frac{L}{WR^2/g}\left[(EI \sin^2 \alpha + GJ \cos^2 \alpha)\frac{\partial^2 \Delta}{\partial s^2} + \sin \alpha \cos \alpha(GJ - EI)\frac{\partial^2 (R\psi)}{\partial s^2}\right]\frac{1}{\sin \alpha} \tag{2.63}$$

and using (2.52) and (2.62),

$$\frac{\partial^2 (R\psi)}{\partial t^2} = \frac{L}{WR^2/g}\left[(EI \cos^2 \alpha + GJ \sin^2 \alpha)\frac{\partial^2 (R\psi)}{\partial s^2} + (GJ - EI)\sin \alpha \cos \alpha\frac{\partial^2 \Delta}{\partial s^2}\right]\frac{1}{\sin \alpha} \tag{2.64}$$

Equations (2.63) and (2.64) represent a pair of coupled waves but they may be reduced to two uncoupled wave equations after multiplying both sides of equation (2.64) by some constant ε and adding it to (2.63). This gives,

$$\sin \alpha \cdot \frac{\partial^2}{\partial t^2}(\Delta + \varepsilon R\psi) = \frac{L}{(W/g)R^2}\left[\{EI \sin^2 \alpha + GJ \cos^2 \alpha + \varepsilon(GJ - EI)\sin \alpha \cos \alpha\} \cdot \frac{\partial^2 \Delta}{\partial s^2}\right.$$

$$\left. + \left\{\frac{\sin \alpha \cos \alpha}{\varepsilon}(GJ - EI) + (EI \cos^2 \alpha + GJ \sin^2 \alpha)\right\}\frac{\partial^2 (\varepsilon R\psi)}{\partial s^2}\right] \tag{2.65}$$

If we now choose ε so that the coefficients of $\partial^2 \Delta/\partial s^2$ and $\partial^2(\varepsilon R\psi)/\partial s^2$ in the above equation are equal, we shall have arrived at a simple uncoupled one-dimensional wave equation. Thus,

$$(EI \sin^2 \alpha + GJ . \cos^2 \alpha)\varepsilon + \sin \alpha \cos \alpha(GJ - EI)\varepsilon^2 = \sin \alpha \cos \alpha(GJ - EI)$$
$$+ \varepsilon(EI \cos^2 \alpha + GJ \sin^2 \alpha)$$

The roots of this equation are,

$$\varepsilon = \tan \alpha \quad \text{and} \quad \varepsilon = -\cot \alpha \tag{2.66}$$

Substituting in equation (2.65),
   (i) $\tan \alpha$ for ε, yields

$$\frac{\partial^2}{\partial t^2}(\Delta + \tan \alpha . R\psi) = \frac{G.J}{\rho R^2} . \frac{\partial^2}{\partial s^2}(\Delta + \tan \alpha . R\psi) \tag{2.67}$$

or (ii) $-\cot \alpha$ for ε, yields

$$\frac{\partial^2}{\partial t^2}(\Delta - \cot \alpha . R\psi) = \frac{EI}{\rho R^2} \frac{\partial^2}{\partial s^2}(\Delta - \cot \alpha . R\psi) \tag{2.68}$$

The wave speed indicated by equation (2.67) is V_H as in equation (2.50), and by equation (2.68) is V'_H as in equation (2.56).
   Refer to Fig. 2.33(b) and note that

$$\left.\begin{array}{l} f = \Delta \cos \alpha + R\psi \sin \alpha \\ f' = R\psi \cos \alpha - \Delta \sin \alpha; \end{array}\right\} \tag{2.69}$$

and

f and f' are a pair of orthogonal displacements alternative to Δ and $R\psi$, and at angle α to them. Now reverting to equation (2.58) and evaluating

$$M_T = FR \cos \alpha + T \sin \alpha$$

using equations (2.61) and (2.62), it will be found that

$$M_T = \frac{GJ}{R \sin \alpha}\left[\frac{\partial}{\partial s}(\Delta \cos \alpha + R\psi \sin \alpha)\right] = \frac{GJ}{R \sin \alpha} . \frac{\partial f}{\partial s} \tag{2.70}$$

and similarly,

$$M_B = -\frac{EI}{R \sin \alpha}\left[\frac{\partial}{\partial s}(\Delta \sin \alpha - R\psi \cos \alpha)\right] = \frac{EI}{R \sin \alpha}\frac{\partial f'}{\partial s} \tag{2.71}$$

Now equations (2.67) and (2.68) are,

$$\frac{\partial^2 f}{\partial t^2} = \frac{GJ}{\rho R^2}\frac{\partial^2 f}{\partial s^2} \tag{2.72}$$

and

$$\frac{\partial^2 f'}{\partial t^2} = \frac{EI}{\rho R^2} . \frac{\partial^2 f'}{\partial s^2} \tag{2.73}$$

Differentiating (2.70) twice with respect to t we have

$$\frac{\partial^2 M_T}{\partial t^2} = \frac{GJ}{R \sin \alpha} . \frac{\partial^3 f}{\partial t^2 \partial s} = \frac{GJ}{R \sin \alpha} . \frac{\partial}{\partial s}\left(\frac{\partial^2 f}{\partial t^2}\right)$$

$$= \frac{GJ}{R \sin \alpha} . \frac{\partial}{\partial s}\left(\frac{GJ}{\rho R^2} . \frac{\partial^2 f}{\partial s^2}\right)$$

using (2.72),

$$= \frac{GJ}{R \sin \alpha} . \frac{GJ}{\rho R^2} . \frac{\partial^3 f}{\partial s^3}$$

$$= \frac{GJ}{R \sin \alpha} . \frac{GJ}{\rho R^2}\left(\frac{R \sin \alpha}{GJ} . \frac{\partial^2 M_T}{\partial s^2}\right)$$

using (2.70),

$$= \frac{GJ}{\rho R^2} \cdot \frac{\partial^2 M_T}{\partial s^2} = V_H^2 \cdot \frac{\partial^2 M_T}{\partial s^2}. \tag{2.74}$$

Similarly, it can be shown that,

$$\frac{\partial^2 M_B}{\partial t^2} = V_H'^2 \cdot \frac{\partial^2 M_B}{\partial s^2} \tag{2.75}$$

Now when $f' = 0$, $R\psi \cos \alpha = \Delta \sin \alpha$ and after substituting in (2.61) and (2.62), or otherwise, we find

$$FR = GJ \cot \alpha \cdot \frac{\partial \psi}{\partial x}$$

and

$$T = GJ \cdot \frac{\partial \psi}{\partial x} \quad \text{or} \quad \frac{FR}{T} = \cot \alpha$$

Further, now substituting for F and T in (2.58) it follows that $M_B = 0$. Similarly when $M_T = 0$, $f = 0$. Thus if an open-coiled helical spring has applied to it a load M_T only, then the displacement of each section of the spring wire takes place in the direction of f only, and is propagated according to equation (2.74), with speed V_H along the helix. And correspondingly an applied load M_B only, is accompanied by a displacement f' only and is propagated with speed V_H' along the helix.

When the applied loads give rise to displacements in both the f- and f'-direction, then both extensional waves of speed V_H and rotational waves of speed V_H' are generated. For a circular section wire $V_H/V_H' = (1 + v)^{1/2} = 1 \cdot 14$ if $v = 0 \cdot 3$. For a wire of rectangular cross-section of sides $2a$ and $2b$, where $2b$ is the side normal to the surface of the base cylinder of the helix, then V_H/V_H' depends on the ratio b/a.

Some typical values are, for $v = 0 \cdot 3$,

b/a	0	0·667	1·0	2·0	2·5
V_H/V_H'	0·806	1·051	1·24	1·945	2·35

The practical range of springs is therefore such that,

$$0 \cdot 8 < V_H/V_H' < 2 \cdot 5$$

As developed and discussed above all the waves are considered to be non-dispersive; strictly this is true only for torsional waves propagated along circular section wire for otherwise the theory is subject to the various shortcomings and limitations referred to on p. 2.

It is worthwhile recapitulating the essential points of this analysis for the case in which an axial tension F, only, is suddenly applied at time $t = 0$ at the end $s = 0$, assuming say that $V_H' > V_H$. A wave of constant bending moment $M_B = -FR \sin \alpha$ is initiated and travels along the helix at linear speed V_H' together with a wave of constant torque $M_T = FR \cos \alpha$, moving with a linear speed of V_H. The M_B-wave which moves the faster, causes displacements in the f'-direction only, whilst the following M_T wave produces displacements in the f-direction only. At a particular section in the helix the V_H' or M_B-wave arrives first and, reflections excepted, is subject thereafter to this constant bending moment and a velocity of $FR(\rho EI)^{-1/2} \cdot \sin \alpha$ in the f'-direction. This situation prevails until the slower moving wave of torque arrives when it superimposes on the section both the torque $FR \cos \alpha$ and a component of speed in the f-direction of magnitude, $-FR(\rho GJ)^{-1/2} \cos \alpha$.

The component speeds of the wire are arrived at by noting that the solutions to the wave equations (2.74) and (2.75), (recall p. 3), may be written using functions F_1 and F_2 as,

$$f = F_1(s - V_H t)$$

and

$$f' = F_2(s - V_H' t) \tag{2.76}$$

Then, the speeds in the f- and f'-directions are respectively,

$$\frac{\partial f}{\partial t} = -V_H \frac{\partial f}{\partial s} \qquad (2.77)$$

and

$$\frac{\partial f'}{\partial t} = -V'_H \cdot \frac{\partial f'}{\partial s} \qquad (2.78)$$

But from equations (2.70) and (2.71),

$$\frac{\partial f}{\partial t} = -\frac{V_H R}{GJ} M_T = \frac{-M_T}{(\rho GJ)^{1/2}}$$

and

$$\frac{\partial f'}{\partial t} = -\frac{V'_H R}{EI} \cdot M_B = \frac{-M_B}{(\rho EI)^{1/2}}$$

In the case where F only is applied,

$$\frac{\partial f}{\partial t} = -\frac{FR \cos \alpha}{(\rho GJ)^{1/2}}$$

and

$$\frac{\partial f'}{\partial t} = \frac{FR \sin \alpha}{(\rho EI)^{1/2}}$$

The buckling of rods and tubes due to impact

Slender copper rods when dropped on to a *rigid* anvil buckle; the length of the waves created are the shorter the higher the speed of impact and the deformation is concentrated near to the impact end of the rod. The stress to which such a rod is subjected at impact with speed v is $\sigma = \rho c v$ and recalling the Euler buckling stress formula for a pin-ended strut of length λ i.e. $\sigma = \pi^2 E k^2/\lambda^2$, by eliminating σ, we have

$$\frac{\lambda}{k} = \pi \sqrt{\frac{c}{v}} \qquad (2.79)$$

where k is the radius of gyration of the section.

Figure 2.34 shows a comparison of some experimental results with equation (2.79). Generally, we might expect the impact buckling load to exceed the static buckling load because it requires a finite time for buckling to occur and hence the inertia of the bar contributes to the bar's strength. (Compare p. 105.)

Plate 15 shows a circular tube after being statically compressed between parallel plates. As each new row of buckles forms the axial load rises to a maximum and as the buckles fold flat the load falls to a minimum, both loads oscillating about a mean value, see Fig. 2.35.

When circular tubes are impact loaded on their ends, the ratio of the dynamic to the static crumpling load increases with speed. Macaulay and Redwood[2.21], on whose article this section is based, state that this ratio is a reflection of changes

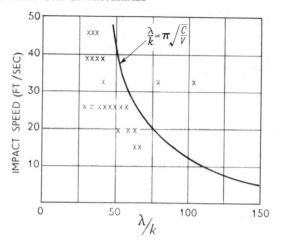

Fig. 2.34.

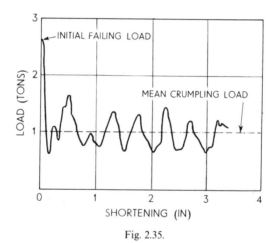

Fig. 2.35.

in buckling mode due to inertia and a consequence of strain rate effect in the material. With mild steel tubes a linear increase in the ratio from 1 to 2·5, as speeds increase from 0 to 125 ft/sec, is reported.

This work was preliminary to studying the design of railway coaches to withstand impact, see Plate 16 for instance; note how the plastic deformation is concentrated in the first diameter of the coach as is mushrooming in bullet impact, see p. 237.

Impact crushing of vehicles

A moving uniform tubular *structure* colliding with a flat, stationary body will experience a resisting force $F = \sigma A$ where σ is the mean crushing stress for the structure and A its cross-sectional area. The mass of the structure is ρAL where

ρ is its *notional* density and L is length. The uniform retardation f is thus $\sigma A/\rho AL = \sigma/\rho L$ and if structures differ only in length, the retardation arising in collisions would, by this idealised approach, be inversely proportional to their length. If passenger injury is assumed to arise from too rapid retardation then this last expression shows that ocean liners are relatively safe, railway coaches somewhat less so and that motor cars are dangerous! This argument has been presented by Pugsley[2.22].

The subject of car collisions as it touches on car and occupant movement, has been discussed by Grime and Jones[2.23], but entirely in terms of rigid body mechanics. Head-on collisions with barriers, or between cars moving with the same speed, in the range 25 to 45 mph, for many British cars shows a time for retardation of about 0·1 sec, with an approximately linear rise to, and fall from a greatest retardation of about 40 g, which occurs after about 0·05 sec, and involves a crushing distance of about 2 ft for each car. The mean crushing strength of a car is probably 30 lb/in^2 of its maximum cross-sectional area (say 16 sq ft).

Some information on ship collisions is given in ref. 2.24.

Dynamic thermal stress

A long, uniform prismatic rod of length l, fixed at one end and subjected to a high time rate of temperature rise β will have a free end speed of movement of $v = \alpha \beta l$, where α is the coefficient of linear expansion. At time l/c, the effect of the rapid expansion will be felt at the fixed end as a normal stress of $\sigma = \rho c v = \rho c \alpha \beta l$; the rapidity with which the thermal expansion occurs gives rise to inertia, wavelike effects. To arrive at stresses equal to a typical yield stress for a typical metal, $\beta \simeq 10^4$ to 10^6 K/sec. These rates of heating are uncommon; they are very much larger than those normally associated with the "thermal shock" of, for example, rapid turbine blade heating or cooling, and are encountered when, for example, large electric currents pass through conductors, or due to impulsive electro-magnetic radiation. A further example arises as when fissile materials are under neutron bombardment and in this connection the development of dynamic thermal stresses in cylinders and slender cones has recently been studied[2.25]. The basic equation requiring solution, which pertains to a cone, is easily arrived at. The fundamental equation of motion of an element is specified by (2.21) or (2.23) except that stress-strain equation (2.22i) is now superseded by

$$e = \frac{\partial u}{\partial r} = \frac{\sigma}{E} + \alpha T \qquad (2.22ii)$$

where T denotes temperature rise in excess of some initial arbitrary zero. After using (2.22ii) to substitute for σ and $\partial\sigma/\partial x$ in (2.23) and simplifying, we arrive at,

$$\frac{\partial^2(ur)}{\partial t^2} = \frac{E}{\rho}\frac{\partial^2(ur)}{\partial r^2} - \frac{E\alpha}{\rho}\left(2T + r\frac{\partial T}{\partial r}\right) \qquad (2.24ii)$$

Solutions of (2.24ii) for certain specific cases are given in ref. (2.25).

Elastic wave propagation in a thin plate

In anticipation of the subject matter of Chapter 3, we consider the propagation of elastic waves in a thin, flat, uniform plate and show that two characteristic waves arise. Figure 2.36 shows the stresses on an element of the plate which

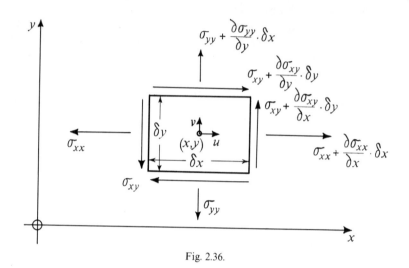

Fig. 2.36.

extends in the Oxy plane and we denote by u and v the displacements of a particle initially at x, y, in the Ox and Oy directions respectively. The equations of motion for an element are,

$$\rho\frac{\partial^2 u}{\partial t^2} = \frac{\partial \sigma_{xx}}{\partial x} + \frac{\partial \sigma_{xy}}{\partial y} \qquad (2.80\text{i})$$

and

$$\rho\frac{\partial^2 v}{\partial t^2} = \frac{\partial \sigma_{xy}}{\partial x} + \frac{\partial \sigma_{yy}}{\partial y} \qquad (2.80\text{ii})$$

The stress strain relationships for the element are,

$$Ee_{xx} = E\frac{\partial u}{\partial x} = \sigma_{xx} - v\sigma_{yy} \qquad (2.81\text{i})$$

$$Ee_{yy} = E\frac{\partial v}{\partial y} = \sigma_{yy} - v\sigma_{xx} \qquad (2.81\text{ii})$$

and

$$G\gamma_{xy} = G\left(\frac{\partial u}{\partial y} + \frac{\partial v}{\partial x}\right) = \sigma_{xy}. \qquad (2.81\text{iii})$$

e and γ refer to direct and shear strain respectively. We may combine (2.81i) and (2.81ii) to write,

$$\sigma_{xx} = \frac{E}{(1 - v^2)}\left(\frac{\partial u}{\partial x} + v\frac{\partial v}{\partial y}\right) \tag{2.82i}$$

and

$$\sigma_{yy} = \frac{E}{(1 - v^2)}\left(v\frac{\partial u}{\partial x} + \frac{\partial v}{\partial y}\right) \tag{2.82ii}$$

Differentiating in (2.81iii) and (2.82i) as appropriate and inserting in (2.80i),

$$\rho\frac{\partial^2 u}{\partial t^2} = \frac{E}{(1 - v^2)}\left[\frac{\partial^2 u}{\partial x^2} + v\frac{\partial^2 v}{\partial x\,\partial y}\right] + G\left[\frac{\partial^2 u}{\partial y^2} + \frac{\partial^2 v}{\partial y\,\partial x}\right] \tag{2.83i}$$

Similarly instead of (2.80ii) we may obtain

$$\rho \cdot \frac{\partial^2 v}{\partial t^2} = G\left[\frac{\partial^2 u}{\partial x\,\partial y} + \frac{\partial^2 v}{\partial x^2}\right] + \frac{E}{(1 - v^2)}\left[v \cdot \frac{\partial^2 u}{\partial y\,\partial x} + \frac{\partial^2 v}{\partial y^2}\right] \tag{2.83ii}$$

For a general disturbance which causes a plane wave to be propagated along the Ox-axis so that the displacement is dependent on x and t only, i.e. $\partial^2 u/\partial y^2 = 0$, $\partial^2 u/\partial x\,\partial y = 0$, $\partial^2 v/\partial y^2 = 0$ and $\partial^2 v/\partial x\,\partial y = 0$, equations (2.83i) and (2.83ii) become respectively,

$$\frac{\partial^2 u}{\partial t^2} = \frac{E}{\rho(1 - v^2)} \cdot \frac{\partial^2 u}{\partial x^2} \tag{2.84i}$$

and,

$$\frac{\partial^2 v}{\partial t^2} = \frac{G}{\rho} \cdot \frac{\partial^2 v}{\partial x^2} \tag{2.84ii}$$

Thus there are in general two wave speeds in the plane of the plate; one causes displacements parallel to Ox and has a value of $c_L = \sqrt{E/\rho(1 - v^2)}$ and the other which causes displacements transverse to Ox, has a speed $c_t = \sqrt{G/\rho}$.

REFERENCES

2.1 TIMOSHENKO, S. and GOODIER, J. N. *Theory of Elasticity*. McGraw-Hill, New York, pp. 506 (1951).

2.2 FISCHER, H. C. New graphodynamical pulse method of computing pile-drawing processes. *Appl. Sci. Res.*, A.9, 93 (1960).

2.3 HOPKINSON, B. *Collected Scientific Papers*. Cambridge Univ. Press (1921).

2.4 LANDON, J. W. and QUINNEY, H. Experiments with the Hopkinson pressure bar. *Proc. R. Soc.*, A.103, 622 (1923).

2.5 SUH, N. P. An investigation of the dyamic behaviour of an annealed low carbon steel by means of stress pulse amplifications. *I.J.M.S.*, 9, 415–31 (1967).

2.6 KOLSKY, H. *Stress Waves in Solids*. Clarendon Press, Oxford, pp. 211 (1953).

2.7 RINEHART, J. S. and PEARSON, J. *Behaviour of Metals under Impulsive Loads*. Dover Publications, New York, pp. 256 (1965).

2.8 RINEHART, J. S. *Stress Wave Propagation in Materials* (edited N. Davids) Interscience, New York, pp. 338 (1960).

2.9   The design of war-time structures: the civil engineer at war. *Proc. Instn civ. Engrs*, **3**, (1948).

2.10 SLATER, R. A. C. and JOHNSON, W. An experimental impact-extrusion machine driven by a linear induction motor, *Proc. Instn mech. Engrs*, **179**, 15 (1964–5).

2.11 NASIM, M., AL-HASSANI, S. T. S. and JOHNSON, W. Stress wave propagation and fracture in thin curved bars, *I.J.M.S.*, **13**, 599 (1971).

2.12 GORDON, J. E. *The New Science of Strong Materials*. Penguin Books, pp. 269 (1968).

2.13 AL-HASSANI, S. T. S., JOHNSON, W. and NASIM, M. *Fracture of triangular plates due to contact explosive pressure*, *J.M.E.S.*, **14**, 1972.

2.14 COTTRELL, A. H. *The Mechanical Properties of Matter*. J. Wiley, New York, pp. 430 (1964).

2.15 GIBSON, A. H. *Hydraulics and its Applications*. Constable, London, pp. 801 (1947).

2.16 VAKIADAKIS, A. P., JOHNSON, W. and DONALDSON, I. S. Deep drawing and water hammer forming. *Proc. Instn mech. Engrs*, **179**, 222 (1964–5).

2.17 A discussion on deformation of solids by the impact of liquids and its relation to rain damage in aircraft and missiles, to blade erosion in steam turbines and to cavitation erosion. Organised by F. P. Bowden, *Phil. Trans. R. Soc.* Series A, No. 1110, vol. 260, 73–315 (1966).

2.18 MIKLOWITZ, J. Elastic waves created during tensile fracture. *Am. Soc. mech. Engrs, J. appl. Mech.*, **20**, 1, 122–30 (1953).

2.19 WITTRICK, W. H. On elastic wave propagation in helical springs. *I.J.M.S.*, **8**, 1, 25–47 (1966).

2.20 DICK, J. Shock waves in helical springs. *Engineer*, **204**, 5298, 193–95 (1957).

2.21 MACAULAY, M. A. and REDWOOD, R. G. Model railway coach impact. *Engineer*, 1041–44 (1964).

2.22 PUGSLEY, A. *The Safety of Structures. Chap. 8: Dynamic Loads on Structures*, Edward Arnold. pp. 156 (1966).

2.23 GRIME, G. and JONES, I. S. Car collisions: the movement of cars and their occupants in accidents. *Proc. Instn mech. Engrs*, AD 5/70 (1970.

2.24 MINORSKY, V. U. An analysis of ship collisions with reference to protection of nuclear power plants. *J. Ship. Res.* **3**, 2, 1–4 (Oct. 1959).

2.25 PARKES, E. W. and CARTER, G. A. Dynamic thermal stresses in a pulsed reactor. *Phil. Trans. R. Soc.*, **270**, 325–347 (1971).

3: Elastic stress waves: more general considerations

For interpreting many aspects of elastic impact behaviour the primitive type of analysis developed in Chapter 1, and used in Chapter 2, is entirely adequate. However, the assumptions made, the limitations imposed and the weaknesses passed over need now to be exposed to some degree. By doing this the engineer will thus be prepared to encounter situations which do not always subscribe to his expectations and, contrariwise, the efficiency of the early work for most practical circumstances will be underscored.

It is also necessary in this Chapter to enlarge the reader's background knowledge of general elastic stress wave behaviour.

Some remarks on the validity of approximate theories

(i) *Longitudinal waves*

The elementary theory described and used above in Chapters 1 and 2 is validated by exact theory only over a limited frequency range—usually the region of very long wavelengths. When a wide band or collection of various frequencies is present in a pulse, approximate theories can be misleading. For longitudinal wave propagation in a circular bar the elementary formulae are valid if the ratio of the diameter of the bar to the wavelength transmitted is small; only by neglecting the radial motion which accompanies longitudinal wave motion can the analysis of reflection at the end of a bar and at discontinuities be treated simply.

An approximate equation, which in fact improves upon equation (1.2i) to allow for transverse radial motion of the elements is due to Love and Rayleigh. If the axial strain in the bar is $\partial u/\partial x$, the lateral strain is $-v\, \partial u/\partial x$ and if the time rate of change of the axial strain is $\partial^2 u/\partial t \,.\, \partial x$, then the time rate of change of the lateral strain is $-v\, \partial^2 u/\partial x \,.\, \partial t$. Thus at radius r, the radial speed of a particle is $vr\, \partial^2 u/\partial x \,.\, \partial t$ and hence the kinetic energy in an element of radial thickness δr and length δx is $\frac{1}{2}(2\pi r \,.\, \delta r \,.\, \delta x)\rho \,.\, (vr\, \partial^2 u/\partial x\, \partial t)^2$. Hence the total kinetic energy due to radial motion for a cylinder of radius a, is

$$\int_0^a \tfrac{1}{2} \,.\, 2\pi r\, dx\rho \,.\, r^2\, dr \,.\, \left(v\frac{\partial^2 u}{\partial x\, \partial t} \right)^2 = \frac{\pi a^4}{4}\rho \left(v\frac{\partial^2 u}{\partial x\, \partial t} \right)^2 dx$$

The energy contained then, in a length of shaft δx, is

$$\frac{1}{2}\rho\pi a^2\, \delta x \left(\frac{\partial u}{\partial t} \right)^2 + \rho \,.\, \frac{\pi a^4}{4} \,.\, \delta x \,.\, \left(v\frac{\partial^2 u}{\partial x\, \partial t} \right)^2 + \frac{1}{2}E\pi a^2 \left(\frac{\partial u}{\partial x} \right)^2 .\, \delta x \qquad (3.1i)$$

The first term is the kinetic energy of the element in the axial direction and the third term is its stored strain energy. The equation of motion for the element may now be derived from (3.1i) using Hamilton's Principle, and is[3.1]

$$\rho\left(\frac{\partial^2 u}{\partial t^2} - \frac{v^2 a^2}{2} \cdot \frac{\partial^4 u}{\partial x^2 \, \partial t^2}\right) = E \cdot \frac{\partial^2 u}{\partial x^2} \tag{3.1ii}$$

An approximate solution of (3.1ii) due to Rayleigh, yields

$$\frac{c_p}{c_0} = 1 - v^2 \cdot \pi^2 \cdot \left(\frac{a}{\lambda}\right)^2, \tag{3.2}$$

where $c_0 = \sqrt{E/\rho}$, and λ is the wavelength. When (3.2) is employed in examining wave propagation in a long bar it transpires that *the predicted speed at which waves are propagated depends on their frequency*; each frequency has its own phase velocity, c_p. A pulse of given initial length which contains a mixture of frequencies will, in view of (3.2), therefore be dispersed. The approximate solution (3.2), shows that the elementary theory is reliable for waves whose length is several times greater than the bar radius. Analyses[3.2,3.3] more rigorous than those embodied in (3.1ii) show (3.2) to be reliable for $0 \lesssim a/\lambda \lesssim 0.7$, but quite discrepant for short wavelengths.

An exact solution for determining how elastic strain waves are propagated in bars of *infinite length* undergoing coaxial impact, has been given by Skalak[3.2], but it is too complicated for use in connection with *finite length bars*. However, using Love's approximate theory, Conway and Jakubowski[3.4] have given an analysis of the co-axial impact of nearly perfect square-ended finite length bars and compared their theoretical results with experimental results obtained on 4 in long, 0.5 in diameter bars. With the help of semi-conductor strain gauges fixed on the curved surface 1 in from the impact end, records of how the axial strain varies with time following the moment of first impact were obtained. Figure 3.1 shows one of their results where the axial strain recording is compared

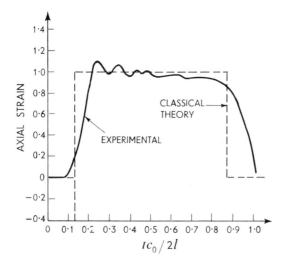

Fig. 3.1   Experimental axial strains in impacted bar, 4 in long × 0.51 dia, 1 in from impacted end.

with the result which would be expected using the elementary wave theory; the experimental curve is characterised by a rapid rise time and an oscillating wake.

The time of impact was found to be slightly greater than $2l/c_0$, the disparity (of order 1%) increasing with the length of a bar; some decrease in duration of impact with increase in impact velocity was also found but was attributed to the cushioning effect of air entrapped between the colliding end faces of the bars.

Figure 3.2 shows a theoretical result given by these authors; it shows an oscillating curve with many well-defined peaks and troughs and a faster rise time than does the curve in Fig. 3.1.

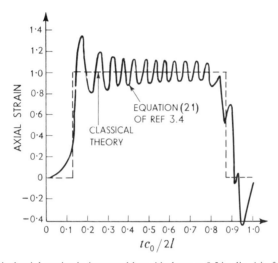

Fig. 3.2   Theoretical axial strains in impacted bar, 4 in long × 0·5 in dia, 1 in from impacted end.

These results emphasise that within about one diameter of a region of impact, conditions are always less uniform than further along the bar.

(ii) *Torsional waves*

The equations and results regarding torsional waves given on p. 7 are exact for the first mode of vibration.

(iii) *Flexural waves*

It was shown on p. 9 that the elastic wave equation for a beam in flexure is,

$$\frac{\partial^2 w}{\partial t^2} = -\frac{EI}{\rho A} \cdot \frac{\partial^4 w}{\partial x^4} \tag{3.3i}$$

and it was noted that no simple expression for the speed of propagation of flexural waves could be derived as for a longitudinal pulse.

Considering a circular bar of radius a, then (3.3i) becomes,

$$\frac{\partial^2 w}{\partial t^2} = -c_0^2 \cdot \frac{a^2}{4} \cdot \frac{\partial^4 w}{\partial x^4} \tag{3.4}$$

where $c_0 = \sqrt{E/\rho}$. Try as a solution

$$w = A \sin \frac{2\pi}{\lambda}(x - c_p t) \tag{3.5}$$

where A denotes the wave amplitude, λ the wavelength and c_p the phase speed. It is found to be a solution to (3.4), if

$$c_p = \frac{c_0}{(\lambda/\pi a)} \tag{3.6}$$

Clearly the wave speed is inversely proportional to the wavelength and infinitely short waves should travel at infinite speed; this is physically unacceptable, of course. Equation (3.4) is only valid as long as the wavelength is much greater than any lateral dimension of the beam; when this is not so it is necessary to include in (3.4), a term allowing for the rotary motion about the neutral axis of elements of the bar. This was first carried out by Rayleigh.

The equation of motion of an element of the beam, see Fig. 1.5a, when its rotary inertia is included is,

$$\left(-F + \frac{\partial M}{\partial x}\right) dx = I_y \cdot dx \cdot \frac{\partial^2 \theta}{\partial t^2} \tag{3.7i}$$

where $I_y \cdot dx$ is the moment of inertia of length dx of the beam about an axis through its centroid parallel to Oy and $\partial^2 \theta / \partial t^2$ its angular acceleration about the same axis.

But

$$\frac{\partial \theta}{\partial t} = \frac{\partial}{\partial t}\left(\frac{\partial w}{\partial x}\right) \quad \text{and} \quad \frac{\partial^2 \theta}{\partial t^2} = \frac{\partial^3 w}{\partial t^2 \partial x}$$

so that (3.7i) becomes, on differentiating with respect to x,

$$-\frac{\partial F}{\partial x} = -\frac{\partial^2 M}{\partial x^2} + I_y \cdot \frac{\partial^4 w}{\partial t^2 \partial x^2} \tag{3.7ii}$$

Again, since

$$\frac{\partial F}{\partial x} = -\rho \cdot A \cdot \frac{\partial^2 w}{\partial t^2}$$

and

$$\frac{\partial^2 M}{\partial x^2} = EAk^2 \cdot \frac{\partial^4 w}{\partial x^4}$$

where Ak^2 is the second moment of area of the cross-section about an axis parallel to Oy. Equation (3.7ii) becomes, for a circular section beam, with $I_y = A\rho a^2/4$,

$$c_0^2 \cdot \frac{a^2}{4} \cdot \frac{\partial^4 w}{\partial x^4} - \frac{a^2}{4} \cdot \frac{\partial^4 w}{\partial x^2 \partial t^2} + \frac{\partial^2 w}{\partial t^2} = 0 \tag{3.7iii}$$

A solution to (3.7iii) is again given by (3.5) except that,

$$c_P = \frac{c_0}{1 + \left(\dfrac{\lambda^2}{\pi^2 a^2}\right)^{1/2}} \tag{3.7iv}$$

This expression for c_P represents a better solution than does (3.6); for very short wavelengths $a/\lambda \to \infty$ and (3.7iv) shows that $c_P/c_0 \to 1$, not infinity, as does (3.6).

A feature still unaccounted for in the above analysis is the distortion of cross-sections (or elements) due to the presence of shear force. Inclusion of a term to accommodate this feature was first made by Timoshenko and results in 'exact' expressions for c_P/c_0 versus a/λ. There is very considerable discrepancy between (3.6), (3.7iv) and Timoshenko's results, when $a/\lambda > 0.1$.

(iv) Elastic columns under impact compression

An infinite, straight, uniform, elastic column subject to a compressive thrust P instantaneously applied and maintained constant has an equation of motion similar to (1.15) or (3.3i), i.e.

$$\rho A . \frac{\partial^2 w}{\partial t^2} = -EI\frac{\partial^4 w}{\partial x^4} - \frac{\partial}{\partial x}\left(P\frac{\partial w}{\partial x}\right) \tag{3.3ii}$$

The second term on the right hand side of the equation is the net transverse force due to P, $\partial w/\partial x$ being the local slope of the column centre line; thus,

$$EI\frac{\partial^4 w}{\partial x^4} + P\frac{\partial^2 w}{\partial x^2} + \rho A\frac{\partial^2 w}{\partial t^2} = 0 \tag{3.3a}$$

Small disturbances may be represented by

$$w = a . \exp\left[2\pi i(\mu x - vt)\right]$$

where the wavelength $\lambda = 1/\mu$. Substitution of the above equation into (3.3ii) yields, for v which has the dimension $(\text{time})^{-1}$,

$$v^2 = \frac{4\pi^2 EI\mu^4 - P\mu^2}{\rho A}$$

For sufficiently small values of λ (or large values of μ) disturbances are propagated with speed v/μ but a critical situation is reached when $\mu_c^2 = P/4\pi^2 EI$ or $\lambda_c = 2\pi\sqrt{EI/P}$, which critical wavelength is not propagated. Perturbations where $\lambda > \lambda_c$ are not propagated and amplitude is increased without limit. For a solid circular shaft of diameter d, $\lambda_c = \pi d\sqrt{E/2\sigma}$ where σ is the compressive stress; this is the wave length of the most unstable wave so that at the onset of instability, waves of length λ_c are to be expected.

The impulsive compression end-on of two identical elastic columns each moving with speed v, gives for the instability wave length $\lambda_c = \pi d\sqrt{c/2v}$.

[If $v > Y/\rho c$, elastic-plastic waves are propagated along a column and in this case the most unstable wave length is given by $\lambda_c = \pi d\sqrt{E_k/2\sigma}$ where E_k is the Karman reduced modulus given by $E_k = 4EE'/(\sqrt{E} + \sqrt{E'})^2$, E', being the slope of the non-linear stress-strain curve of the material of the column at stress level σ. (See p. 174, ref. 4.10.)]

Elastic waves in an isotropic extended medium: body waves

In examining stress wave propagation in previous sections, the body or bar through which the waves pass has usually had one dimension very much larger than the other two, and the wave has been transmitted entirely in the 'extended' dimension. In this section the propagation of a disturbance is considered where the body concerned is extended to the same degree in all directions. The treatment and analysis leading to the basic wave equation is of course fundamentally the same as hitherto, i.e. the equations of motion of a small element are established and then related to the stress and strains in the body through Hooke's law: the strains, as before, are small and are easily related to particle displacement.

Equations of motion in Cartesian coordinates

The equation of motion for an element of a body in the Ox direction, where X is the component body force per unit mass acting in the Ox direction, ρ is the density and u, v, and w the displacements parallel to Ox, Oy, and Oz at time t, is, see Fig. 3.3,

$$\frac{\partial \sigma_{xx}}{\partial x} + \frac{\partial \tau_{yx}}{\partial y} + \frac{\partial \tau_{zx}}{\partial z} + X\rho = \rho \frac{\partial^2 u}{\partial t^2} \qquad (3.8)$$

Now

$$Ee_{xx} = \sigma_{xx} - v(\sigma_{yy} + \sigma_{zz}) = (1 + v)\sigma_{xx} - v(\sigma_{xx} + \sigma_{yy} + \sigma_{zz}) \quad \text{(i)}$$

$$Ee_{yy} = \sigma_{yy} - v(\sigma_{zz} + \sigma_{xx}) = (1 + v)\sigma_{yy} - v(\sigma_{xx} + \sigma_{yy} + \sigma_{zz}) \quad \text{(ii)} \qquad (3.9)$$

and

$$Ee_{zz} = \sigma_{zz} - v(\sigma_{xx} + \sigma_{yy}) = (1 + v)\sigma_{zz} - v(\sigma_{xx} + \sigma_{yy} + \sigma_{zz}) \quad \text{(iii)}$$

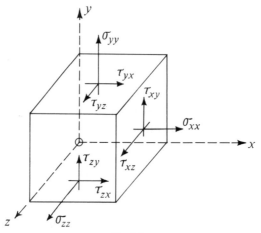

Fig. 3.3.

Adding the above three equations,

$$Ee = (\sigma_{xx} + \sigma_{yy} + \sigma_{zz})(1 - 2v), \tag{3.10}$$

where

$$e = e_{xx} + e_{yy} + e_{zz} = \frac{\partial u}{\partial x} + \frac{\partial v}{\partial y} + \frac{\partial w}{\partial z} \tag{3.11}$$

e is called the *dilatation*, i.e. the change in volume of a unit volume of material. Hence from (3.9) introducing $(\sigma_{xx} + \sigma_{yy} + \sigma_{zz})$ from (3.10)

$$\sigma_{xx} = \frac{Ee_{xx}}{1 + v} + \frac{v}{1 + v} \cdot \frac{E}{1 - 2v} \cdot e$$

or

$$\sigma_{xx} = 2G \cdot \frac{\partial u}{\partial x} + \lambda e, \tag{3.12}$$

denoting $vE/(1 + v)(1 - 2v)$ by λ.

λ and G (often designated as μ in this part of the subject) are known as Lamé's constants. The shear stresses are related to the shear strains through the displacements, thus

$$\tau_{xy} = G\gamma_{xy} = G\left(\frac{\partial u}{\partial y} + \frac{\partial v}{\partial x}\right)$$

$$\tau_{xz} = G\gamma_{xz} = G\left(\frac{\partial w}{\partial x} + \frac{\partial u}{\partial z}\right) \tag{3.13}$$

Now substitute from (3.12) and (3.13) in equation (3.8) to find,

$$\frac{\partial}{\partial x}\left(2G\frac{\partial u}{\partial x} + \lambda e\right) + G \cdot \frac{\partial}{\partial y}\left(\frac{\partial u}{\partial y} + \frac{\partial v}{\partial x}\right) + G\frac{\partial}{\partial z}\left(\frac{\partial w}{\partial x} + \frac{\partial u}{\partial z}\right) + X\rho = \rho \cdot \frac{\partial^2 u}{\partial t^2}$$

Simplifying,

$$2G \cdot \frac{\partial^2 u}{\partial x^2} + \lambda\frac{\partial e}{\partial x} + G\left(\frac{\partial^2 u}{\partial y^2} + \frac{\partial^2 v}{\partial y \, \partial x}\right) + G\left(\frac{\partial^2 w}{\partial z \, \partial x} + \frac{\partial^2 u}{\partial z^2}\right) + X\rho = \rho \cdot \frac{\partial^2 u}{\partial t^2}$$

or

$$G\left(\frac{\partial^2 u}{\partial x^2} + \frac{\partial^2 v}{\partial y \, \partial x} + \frac{\partial^2 w}{\partial z \, \partial x}\right) + \lambda\frac{\partial e}{\partial x} + G \cdot \nabla^2 u + X\rho = \rho\frac{\partial^2 u}{\partial t^2} \tag{3.14}$$

where

$$\nabla^2 = \frac{\partial^2}{\partial x^2} + \frac{\partial^2}{\partial y^2} + \frac{\partial^2}{\partial z^2}$$

Differentiating in (3.11) with respect to x,

$$\frac{\partial e}{\partial x} = \frac{\partial^2 u}{\partial x^2} + \frac{\partial^2 v}{\partial x \, \partial y} + \frac{\partial^2 w}{\partial x \, \partial z}$$

and hence (3.14) becomes

$$(G + \lambda)\frac{\partial e}{\partial x} + G \cdot \nabla^2 u + X\rho = \rho\frac{\partial^2 u}{\partial t^2} \tag{3.15}$$

Similar expressions can be obtained for the Oy- and Oz-directions.

Application to wave propagation

For the work which follows it is assumed that no body forces are operative, i.e. $X = Y = Z = 0$, and we remember that only small strains are considered; thus equation (3.15) becomes

$$(G + \lambda)\frac{\partial e}{\partial x} + G \cdot \nabla^2 u = \rho\frac{\partial^2 u}{\partial t^2} \tag{3.16}$$

Equivoluminal waves

Assume that the equation (3.16) involves deformation in which there is no change of volume with x so that straining therefore involves only distortion and rotation. Thus with $\partial e/\partial x = 0$ in (3.16) we have

$$\frac{\partial^2 u}{\partial t^2} = \frac{G}{\rho} \cdot \nabla^2 u \tag{3.17}$$

For an arbitrary plane wave to be propagated with a speed c, write

$$u = f_1(lx + my + nz - ct);$$

where l, m and n are the direction cosines of the normal to the plane. Then,

$$\frac{\partial u}{\partial t} = -cf'_1; \qquad \frac{\partial^2 u}{\partial t^2} = c^2 f''_1$$

and also

$$\frac{\partial u}{\partial x} = lf'_1 \quad \text{and} \quad \frac{\partial^2 u}{\partial x^2} = l^2 f''_1$$

Similarly,

$$\frac{\partial^2 u}{\partial y^2} = m^2 f''_1 \quad \text{and} \quad \frac{\partial^2 u}{\partial z^2} = n^2 \cdot f''_1$$

Hence adding,

$$\nabla^2 u = f''_1 = \frac{\rho}{G} \cdot \frac{\partial^2 u}{\partial t^2} = \frac{\rho}{G}c^2 f''_1$$

and thus $c_t = \sqrt{G/\rho}$. Equation (3.17) is then a wave equation and represents an *equivoluminal body wave* propagated with a speed of $c_t = \sqrt{G/\rho}$.

Irrotational or dilatational waves

Consider the formal modification to equation (3.15) when the straining propagated is irrotational, i.e. when $\omega_x = \omega_y = \omega_z = 0$ or

$$\frac{\partial v}{\partial x} - \frac{\partial u}{\partial y} = 0, \quad \frac{\partial w}{\partial y} - \frac{\partial v}{\partial z} = 0 \quad \text{and} \quad \frac{\partial u}{\partial z} - \frac{\partial w}{\partial x} = 0 \qquad (3.18)$$

Now from (3.14),

$$\frac{\partial e}{\partial x} = \frac{\partial}{\partial x}\left(\frac{\partial u}{\partial x} + \frac{\partial v}{\partial y} + \frac{\partial w}{\partial z}\right)$$

$$= \frac{\partial^2 u}{\partial x^2} + \frac{\partial^2 v}{\partial x\,\partial y} + \frac{\partial^2 w}{\partial x\,\partial z}$$

$$= \frac{\partial^2 u}{\partial x^2} + \frac{\partial}{\partial y}\left(\frac{\partial v}{\partial x}\right) + \frac{\partial}{\partial z}\left(\frac{\partial w}{\partial x}\right)$$

and using (3.18),

$$= \frac{\partial^2 u}{\partial x^2} + \frac{\partial^2 u}{\partial y^2} + \frac{\partial^2 u}{\partial z^2} = \nabla^2 u.$$

Hence substituting in (3.16) gives,

$$(\lambda + 2G).\nabla^2 u = \rho\frac{\partial^2 u}{\partial t^2}$$

or

$$\frac{\partial^2 u}{\partial t^2} = \left(\frac{\lambda + 2G}{\rho}\right)\nabla^2 u \qquad (3.19)$$

This is a wave equation; the waves transmitted are irrotational or dilatational waves and their speed is, $c_d = \sqrt{(\lambda + 2G)/\rho}$.

Thus only two types of body waves are propagated in an isotropic elastic solid and any general disturbance is evaluated by their superposition. Each of these two types, equivoluminal and irrotational, propagates with its own characteristic velocity. Note that $c_d/c_t = \sqrt{2 + \lambda/G}$ so that $c_d > c_t$.

These two kinds of waves once in the interior of an infinite body, remain separate and distinct for all time and they not only have distinctly different velocities of propagation but also have distinctly different particle motions associated with them.

In seismology, equivoluminal waves are referred to as S or shake waves, and irrotational waves as P or push waves.

For a fluid medium $G = 0$ and thus $c_t = 0$; obviously an inviscid fluid cannot transmit S or shear waves, and only P, or dilatational waves at a speed $c_d = \sqrt{\lambda/\rho}$.

Lord Kelvin in 1899 apparently first applied the terms irrotational and equivoluminal to describe these kinds of waves; knowledge that two kinds of waves each moving with a different speed dates back to Poisson. The recognition of the different characters of the two waves is attributed to Stokes.

The above remarks apply to isotropic materials and for a given direction there are just the wave speeds c_t and c_d; but for a general aelotropic material, i.e. a material like wood whose properties depend on a selected direction, there are three distinct wave speeds associated with any given direction.

Surface waves: Rayleigh waves

Whilst the waves discussed immediately above are body waves, there are well investigated surface waves; a simple example is a surface sea wave. It was shown by Rayleigh in 1887 that waves may propagate along the surface of an unbounded or semi-infinite solid at a speed, for $v = \frac{1}{4}$, of 0·92 c_t or for $v = \frac{1}{2}$, 0·96 c_t. The waves rapidly decrease, exponentially, in amplitude with depth below the surface and their speed is always slightly less than c_t. The motion of a particle in the surface of the body, is elliptical, the ratio of the horizontal to the vertical displacement being 0·681, when $v = \frac{1}{4}$; the amplitude of vibration increases and reaches a maximum at a depth of 0·076 λ and thereafter decreases; λ is the wave length. At a depth of 0·19 λ below the surface the horizontal displacement changes sign, or, at this depth there is no motion parallel to the surface. At a depth of λ the amplitude is 0·19 of that at the surface. *Rayleigh waves* of high frequency are attenuated more rapidly with depth than low frequency waves—a kind of skin effect.

The normal stress (perpendicular to the surface) is greatest at a depth 0·32λ (for $v = 0.29$) whilst the normal stress parallel to the surface changes sign at a depth z of about 0·252 λ.

Earthquake wave sequence: Love waves

Broadly, it is found that P-waves are first recorded by a seismograph, followed by S-waves; later Rayleigh waves arrive. Since from a given initiating source, Rayleigh waves travel only in two dimensions, their intensity falls off more slowly than either the P- or S-waves and thus they tend to be of considerable importance in an earthquake. The Rayleigh waves are not 'pure' because their vertical component is often absent; also the horizontal component tends to be parallel to the wave front and not parallel to the direction of wave movement. Love showed that these phenomena can be accounted for by properly assuming that the elasticity and density of the earth's crust varies with depth. An analysis based on this assumption leads to *Love waves*—another kind of surface wave.

Interesting photographs[3.5] showing the plastic deformation which occurred due to strong shaking by earthquakes together with roof gravity effects are shown in Plates 17 and 18. Reference 3.6 may be consulted for a short account of seismology.

Reflection and refraction of waves at an interface

Stress waves propagated through any real body must at sometime encounter free surfaces or interfacial boundaries. Their behaviour thereafter is relatively complex and we shall thus confine our attention simply to describing how they are reflected and refracted. Detailed mathematical treatment necessary for analysing these situations can be found in refs. 3.2 and 3.3. The results outlined below apply for *plane waves* and *plane surfaces*.

(1) *Fluid-vacuum interfaces*

The stress boundary or interfacial condition to be fulfilled in this circumstance is obviously that of zero normal stress at all times. Since wave propagation in a fluid is considered, only a plane dilatational wave may be propagated into it and a plane dilatational wave reflected, see Fig. 3.4a; the wave speed is fixed at $c_d = \sqrt{\lambda/\rho}$ and the angle of incidence is equal to the angle of reflection. The (incident) disturbing wave initiates the reflected wave and since it also has a speed of c_d, this implies that the angle of reflection must be the same as that of incidence. There is also a change of phase of π radians on reflection for sinusoidal waves, i.e. the amplitude or intensity of the incident wave is reversed in sign on

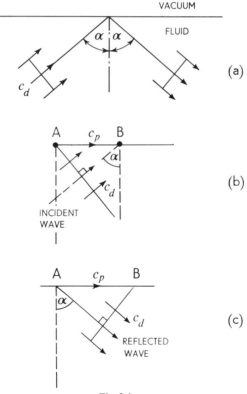

Fig. 3.4.

reflection. (Recall the 'sign change' when a longitudinal pulse is reflected from the free end of a long rod). Together the incident and reflected plane waves give the propagated wavefront and an 'interference' or 'standing wave' pattern is found for the direction normal to the plane of Fig. 3.4(a), of periodicity $\omega/c_d \sec \alpha$, where ω is 2π. frequency of the incident wave and α the angle of incidence.

Phase velocity. The phase speed at a boundary is the rate at which a point of constant phase travels along the interface, e.g. from A to B in Fig. 3.4(b) and (c), and an analogy is that of sea waves striking a straight wall at an angle. The rate at which the point of intersection of, say, a crest of a wave and the wall, moves along the wall is the boundary phase velocity, $_B c_p$; obviously $_B c_p = c_d/\sin \alpha$.

(2) *Solid-vacuum interfaces*

A vacuum may here be taken to include the case of a gas, say air, at low (atmospheric) pressure, into which any energy radiated is negligibly small.

The stress conditions to be fulfilled at the interface are that both normal and shear stresses on the boundary are everywhere zero.

(i) *Reflection of a dilatation wave.* A plane P-wave incident on a plane boundary produces both reflected plane P-waves and plane S-waves, see Fig. 3.5(a). Since a disturbance at the interface is propagated with speed $c_d/\sin \alpha$, due to the

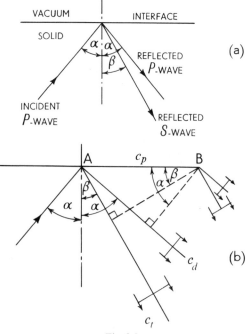

Fig. 3.5.

incident P-wave and since, as in (1) above, the angle of reflection of the reflected wave must equal that of the angle of incidence of the incident P-wave, and because both of the reflected waves, i.e. S and P, are initiated concurrently from the surface, then see Fig. 3.5(b),

$$_Bc_p = \frac{c_d}{\sin \alpha} = \frac{c_t}{\sin \beta} \qquad (3.20)$$

In general the energy of the incident wave is distributed between the reflected S- and P-waves. Further, using (3.20), note that if $\alpha = 90°$, a condition of grazing incidence is arrived at, and $\sin \beta = c_t/c_d$; certainly if $\alpha = 0°$ there can obviously be no reflected S-wave. For further detailed discussion of the many curious cases which can arise, the reader is referred to refs. 3.2 and 3.3.

(ii) *Reflection of an equivoluminal or S-wave.* The discussion of S-wave reflection follows the detailed treatment given in (3ii) below.

(3) *Interfaces between two semi-infinite solids*

In Fig. 3.6 two semi-infinite homogeneous media A and B are shown possessing a plane interface. We suppose A and B to be 'welded' together at the interface so that on either side of the boundary the following four conditions must be satisfied:

   (i) equality of normal displacements,
   (ii) identical tangential displacements,
   (iii) equality of (or continuity in) normal stresses, and
   (iv) equality of (or continuity in) shear or tangential stresses.

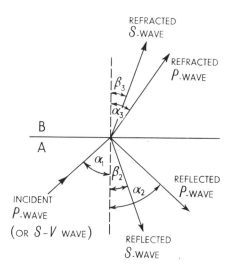

Fig. 3.6.

(i) *Incident dilatational or P-waves: see Fig. 3.6.*
If the angle of incidence is α_1, incident dilatational waves give rise to reflected and refracted waves in both A and B; also the following set of relations holds

$$\frac{\sin \alpha_1}{c_{d_A}} = \frac{\sin \alpha_2}{c_{d_A}} = \frac{\sin \beta_2}{c_{t_A}} = \frac{\sin \alpha_3}{c_{d_B}} = \frac{\sin \beta_3}{c_{t_B}}. \tag{3.21}$$

c_d and c_t refer to the P- and S-wave speeds and suffices A and B the corresponding medium. The first three equations are effectually the same as those in (3.20) and apply here for the same reason as there; by allowing for different c_d and c_t values in medium B and using the same argument as before—that only one speed of disturbance prevails at the interface—angles α_3 and β_3 follow. Again the relations are clearly similar to those prevailing for geometrical optics. Expressions can be found for the amplitudes of the reflected and refracted waves in terms of the incident dilatation wave amplitude.[3.2,3.3]

(ii) *Incident equivoluminal or S-waves.*
The behaviour of plane S-waves at a boundary can be resolved in terms of S-waves which are horizontally polarised or vertically polarised with respect to the plane boundary; the former are referred to as SH-, and the latter as SV-waves. For an SH-wave, particle motion occurs parallel to Oy only; i.e. $u = 0$ and $w = 0$, see Fig. 3.7, and gives rise only to two S-waves, in particular,

$$\frac{\sin \alpha_1}{c_{t_A}} = \frac{\sin \beta_3}{c_{t_B}} \tag{3.22}$$

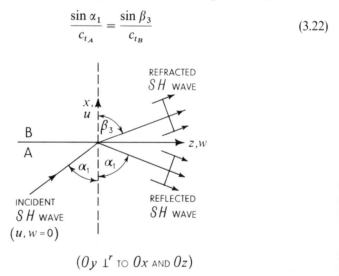

$(Oy \perp^r \text{ TO } Ox \text{ AND } Oz)$

Fig. 3.7.

Since there is only motion parallel to Oy, there is thus no particle motion normal to the interface and hence no P-waves can result.

Alternatively, in SV-waves, particle movement occurs parallel to the Oxz plane only, i.e. $v = 0$ and Fig. 3.6 applies in this instance; the same relation between the various angles and speeds applies as before.

Other cases such as behaviour at a solid-liquid interface can easily be deduced as special cases of the solid–solid interface instance discussed above.

Vibrations in cylindrical bars

It is convenient to recognise a stressed body as being subject to one of three loading conditions, because, when loaded, various elements of it accommodate themselves slowly or rapidly, according to the loading rate.

(i) Static

(ii) Vibrational, and

(iii) Impact

We have not concerned ourselves at all with (i), and as earlier stated intend mainly to discuss (iii). Statement (ii) enters into our considerations because along with (iii) it is concerned, among other things with the propagation of stress waves. For (ii), we usually have in mind cyclical non-destructive loading; cyclical, repetitive deformation and consequently cyclical stressing is undergone by structural elements which have generally, a very frequently and identically repeated history of loading. Impact, by contrast, focuses attention on the transient aspects of material behaviour; usually one pattern of loading is once imposed on a structure and we seek to analyse the consequences. Obviously there are common features in (ii) and (iii), since in both cases stress is conducted or propagated throughout the body. For this reason some small attention is given to the vibrational aspects of the behaviour of bodies. Since impact has been studied less than vibration it follows that many useful ideas—even if only for use as background knowledge—may be acquired from it and used to facilitate understanding impact behaviour. We have, in fact, already adopted this approach above without explicitly stating it; but in view of the topics presented in the next few sections, this explanation is called for.

Pochhammer equations for cylindrical bars

The purpose of this section is to give the reader an acquaintanceship with the very well known Pochammer–Chree equations as usually applied to the study of vibrations in cylindical bars. It is desirable that engineering students of stress propagation be aware of them in themselves, because they illustrate how difficult it can be to find mathematically rigorous solutions for relatively practical problems. Also they introduce concepts not encountered in the elementary approaches already presented at length above and enlarge our appreciations of the complexity of the problems met. It is essential, too, that in applications of our elementary approaches we should constantly have in mind an awareness of the approximate nature of our formulae and of their limitations.

With a view to determining the speeds of wave propagation along a cylindrical bar associated with various frequencies subject to different modes of vibration, the equations of motion for an element of elastic solid obviously require to be available in cylindrical co-ordinates; the equations of motion in Cartesian co-ordinates have been obtained on p. 108 and equation (3.15) was derived in particular for the Ox-direction. The three equations for the cylindrical situation are, see Fig. 3.8,

$$\rho\frac{\partial^2 u}{\partial t^2} = (\lambda + 2G)\frac{\partial e}{\partial r} - \frac{2G}{r}\frac{\partial \omega_z}{\partial \theta} + 2G.\frac{\partial \omega_\theta}{\partial z}$$

$$\rho\frac{\partial^2 v}{\partial t^2} = (\lambda + 2G)\frac{1}{r}.\frac{\partial e}{\partial \theta} - 2G\frac{\partial \omega_r}{\partial z} + 2G\frac{\partial \omega_z}{\partial r} \qquad (3.23)$$

and,

$$\rho\frac{\partial^2 w}{\partial t^2} = (\lambda + 2G).\frac{\partial e}{\partial z} - 2G\frac{\partial}{\partial r}(r\omega_\theta) + \frac{2G}{r}\frac{\partial \omega_r}{\partial \theta}$$

where u, v and w denote the displacement of a particle in the r-, θ- and z-directions; the axis of the bar is designated Oz. The symbol e is the dilatation and, compare (3.11), in cylindrical co-ordinates,

$$e = \frac{1}{r}.\frac{\partial}{\partial r}(ru) + \frac{1}{r}\frac{\partial v}{\partial \theta} + \frac{\partial w}{\partial z}. \qquad (3.24)$$

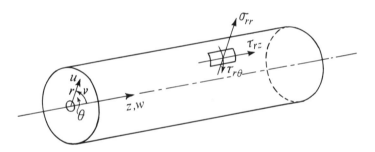

Fig. 3.8.

ω_r, ω_θ and ω_z are the rotations about the three orthogonal axes, and

$$\omega_r = \frac{1}{2}\left(\frac{1}{r}.\frac{\partial w}{\partial \theta} - \frac{\partial v}{\partial z}\right)$$

$$\omega_\theta = \frac{1}{2}\left(\frac{\partial u}{\partial z} - \frac{\partial w}{\partial r}\right) \qquad (3.25)$$

and

$$\omega_z = \frac{1}{2r}\left(\frac{\partial(rv)}{\partial r} - \frac{\partial u}{\partial \theta}\right)$$

On the surface of the bar, supposedly located in vacuum, all three components of the stress are zero, i.e.

$$\sigma_{rr} = \tau_{r\theta} = \tau_{rz} = 0 \qquad (3.26)$$

These stresses are related through Hooke's Law to the displacements—compare (3.12) and (3.13)—thus

$$
\sigma_{rr} = \lambda e + 2G \cdot \frac{\partial u}{\partial r}
$$

$$
\tau_{r\theta} = G\left[\frac{1}{r}\frac{\partial u}{\partial \theta} + r \cdot \frac{\partial}{\partial r}\left(\frac{v}{r}\right)\right]
$$

and

$$
\tau_{rz} = G\left[\frac{\partial u}{\partial z} + \frac{\partial w}{\partial r}\right]
$$

(3.27)

The equations above can be satisfied by using displacement equations due to Pochhammer (1876) and Chree (1889) which represent an infinite train of waves thus,

$$
u = U \cdot \exp\left[i \cdot \frac{2\pi}{\lambda}(z + c_p t)\right]
$$

$$
v = V \cdot \exp\left[i \cdot \frac{2\pi}{\lambda}(z + c_p t)\right]
$$

and

$$
w = W \cdot \exp\left[i \cdot \frac{2\pi}{\lambda}(z + c_p t)\right]
$$

(3.28)

λ and c_p denote wavelength and phase speed respectively, and U, V, W, are functions of r and θ only. By choosing an appropriate form of U, V and W the equations of motion (3.23) and the surface stress conditions (3.26) may be satisfied, to represent longitudinal, transverse and torsional wave propagation in the cylinder.

(i) *Longitudinal waves*

To investigate longitudinal waves, i.e. periodic extensions and contractions of parts of the bar, it is assumed that particles of the cylinder move in an rOz plane only, i.e. $V = 0$, and also that functions U and W are independent of θ. Introducing these conditions into the various equations of the previous section, a very complex equation for the frequency of wave transmissions which includes wavelength, cylinder radius and λ, G and ρ, is arrived at; this equation is long and is written in terms of Bessel functions J_0 and J_1. By expanding the latter for the case when the bar radius to wavelength ratio is relatively small, Rayleigh arrived at the equation,

$$
f\lambda = \left(1 - \frac{1}{4}v^2\frac{\pi^2}{\lambda^2} \cdot a^2\right)\sqrt{\frac{E}{\rho}} = c_p
$$

or

$$
c_p/c_L = 1 - v^2\pi^2(a/\lambda)^2
$$

(3.29)

where again c_p is the phase speed.

In a bar which propagates very long waves, $a/\lambda \to 0$ and $c_p \to c_L = \sqrt{E/\rho}$; this is the condition we have repeatedly stated must apply if the elementary theory is to be applicable.

The second term in (3.29) shows that a band of waves propagated in accordance with the assumptions chosen is, in fact, *dispersed*; short wavelength waves travel slower than long wavelength waves and hence, as time passes, the extent of a wave train is progressively increased.

The results quoted only apply for a cylinder of infinite length; any specific requirements that the ends of a cylinder should satisfy prescribed displacement or stress boundary conditions at the end of infinite or semi-infinite bars cannot be fulfilled by the solutions described. However, for a cylinder whose length is very large compared with its radius we may assume that the end effects are negligible.

The solution given by (3.29) is only adequate approximately for $0 < a/\lambda < 0.7$, see ref. 3.3.

(ii) *Torsional waves*

To transmit torsional waves, longitudinal and lateral displacements must be zero, i.e. $u = w = 0$, and motion about the cylinder axis must be symmetrical so that V must be independent of θ.

The principal result which transpires is that $c_p = \sqrt{G/\rho}$ as arrived at by elementary theory; in this fundamental mode dispersion is absent. Other more complex modes of torsional vibrational, involving 'nodal' cylinders[3.3], may occur however.

(iii) *Flexural waves*

The displacement functions (3.28), adapted for flexure, with the axis of the cylinder having a purely lateral motion, i.e. where there is periodic bending and stretching of parts of the centre line are,

$$
\left.
\begin{array}{l}
u = U . \cos\theta . \exp\left[i . \dfrac{2\pi}{\lambda}(z + ft) \right] \\[2ex]
v = V . \sin\theta . \exp\left[i . \dfrac{2\pi}{\lambda}(z + ft) \right] \\[2ex]
\text{and} \\[2ex]
w = W . \cos\theta . \exp\left[i . \dfrac{2\pi}{\lambda}(z + ft) \right]
\end{array}
\right\}
\qquad (3.30)
$$

where U, V and W are functions of r only. Since any account of the treatment for this case is lengthy we shall not pursue discussion but simply refer to Love's treatment[3.1], observing that results for this case sufficient for many purposes have already been presented in pp. 103–105.

(iv) *General remarks*

Starting from the Pochhammer–Chree equations, for each of the three cases or modes of vibration discussed, a frequency equation is arrived at and each of them has an infinite number of roots; each root corresponds to a particular mode of vibration (or deformation pattern) referred to as a first, second, third, . . . mode, and for each mode there is a particular relation between c_p/c_L and a/λ.

The inability of the Pochhammer–Chree type solutions to admit realistic end conditions for stress and displacement, and the complicated frequency equations to which they give rise, augurs ill for the analysis of impact problems. For these reasons less rigorous theories have to be admitted for simplifying mathematical solutions and facilitating a realistic analysis of engineering or physical problems.

The simplest form of approximate wave transmission theory which envisages only a single mode of propagation for each kind of vibration is really only acceptable for long waves and when short wavelengths are considered 'correction factors' are best introduced. Fortunately it transpires that experimental evidence shows approximate theories to provide a reasonably valid description of the principal stress and displacement features frequently encountered.

Pulse distortion due to dispersion in a solid cylinder

A single pulse propagated along a bar cannot generally be accommodated by 'exact' theory (Pochhammer–Chree solutions). To analyse a pulse it requires to be analysed into sinusoidal components in terms of a Fourier integral which is generally intractable.

However, it has been shown[3.2] that a trapezoidal pulse, e.g. Fig. 3.9, disperses with time or distance from the source; i.e. sudden changes of shape are smoothed, linear parts of the original pulse become oscillatory and slope changes are modified so that pulse rises are slowed.

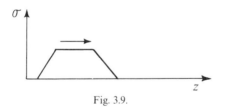

Fig. 3.9.

Propagation of a short pulse through a short cylinder

Kolsky[3.3] has demonstrated that the propagation of a pulse through a short solid cylinder is complex. A small explosive charge was used to produce a pulse at the centre of one end face of a short steel cylinder, the pulse duration being about 2 μsec.

Both P- and S-waves were created by the explosive and spread out spherically from it. Waves arriving at a detector at the centre of the lower face can travel by a number of paths of different length, so that the detected signal has many components corresponding to the different routes through the cylinder.

The first signal to arrive is a P-wave following route 1 and then the same P-wave is reflected from the sides of the cylinder, i.e. via route 2. The reader should easily be able to appreciate the routes followed in Fig. 3.10. The observed signals were found to correspond somewhat to the theory; only the first few pulses of the explosive are clearly recognisable and separate. A propagated pulse obviously is difficult to interpret for there are then many paths producing similar time delays.

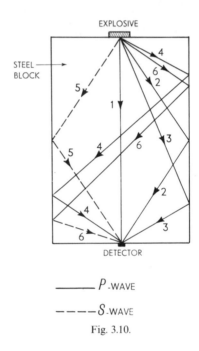

Fig. 3.10.

REFERENCES

3.1 LOVE, A. E. H. *The Mathematical Theory of Elasticity*. Cambridge Univ. Press, pp. 551 (1906).

3.2 REDWOOD, M. *Mechanical Waveguides*, Pergamon Press, London, pp. 300 (1960).

3.3 KOLSKY, H. *Stress Waves in Solids*, Clarendon Press, Oxford, pp. 211 (1953).

3.4 CONWAY, H. D. and JAKUBOWSKI, M. Axial impact of short cylindrical bars. *J. appl. Mech.* **36**, 809 (1969).

3.5 JENNINGS, P. C. and HUSID, R. Collapse of yielding structures during earthquakes. *Proc. Am. Soc. civ. Engrs*, 94, No. EM5, Pap. 6154, 1045–65 (1968).

3.6 BULLEN, K. E. *Seismology*, Methuen, pp. 132 (1954).

4: Plasticity theory and some quasi-static analyses

This chapter reviews many of the basic ideas of plasticity theory and emphasises those parts of it which are later to be used. The principal terms and concepts are indispensible for the proper study of processes which involve plastic deformation. Most of the applications presented are quasi-static, i.e. are statical treatments of dynamic problems; they are however chosen both for their own intrinsic and novel interest and in order to exemplify the use of some of the methods of plasticity theory.

A short bibliography of books likely to be of use to students of engineering plasticity is given at the end of this chapter.[4.1-4.22]

Tensile stress, strain and strain-rate

A portion of a uniform homogeneous bar of metal of length l_0 and cross-sectional area A_0 in the unloaded state is subjected to a slowly applied axial force F which increases its length to l and reduces its cross-sectional area to current value A, see Fig. 4.1. Over a cross-section of the bar transverse to the direction of F, the *true* stress, σ, is uniform and $\sigma = F/A$. The quantity $\sigma_0 = F/A_0$ is defined as the *nominal* or *engineering stress* on the section. The engineering tensile strain is

$$e = (l - l_0)/l_0 \qquad (4.1)$$

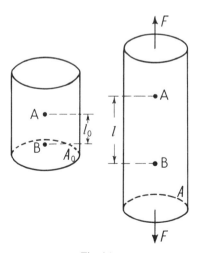

Fig. 4.1.

and an increment of tensile strain is

$$de = dl/l_0 \qquad (4.2)$$

If in place of l_0 in equation (4.2) we write l, then

$$d\varepsilon = dl/l \qquad (4.3)$$

and $d\varepsilon$ is defined as an increment in *natural* or *logarithmic strain*. The natural strain ε imposed on the bar is

$$\varepsilon = \int_0^\varepsilon d\varepsilon = \int_{l_0}^l dl/l = \ln l/l_0 \equiv \ln(1 + e) \qquad (4.4i)$$

or

$$d\varepsilon = \frac{de}{1 + e} \qquad (4.4ii)$$

In dealing with large deformations there are advantages in working in terms of natural strain and these will become apparent as we proceed. Note that for small strains $\varepsilon \simeq e$.

Tensile engineering strain rate $\dot{e}$ is the time rate of increase in tensile strain, so that from (4.2)

$$\dot{e} = \frac{de}{dt} = \frac{dl/dt}{l_0} = \frac{v}{l_0} \qquad (4.5)$$

where t denotes time and v is the speed of separation of the points A and B at the ends of the chosen portion of the bar of length l_0. The tensile natural strain rate is, using (4.3),

$$\dot{\varepsilon} = \frac{d\varepsilon}{dt} = \frac{dl/dt}{l} = \frac{v}{l} \qquad (4.6)$$

In the conventional engineering laboratory tension test, an 8 in length of bar may typically be stretched at a rate of between 0·05 and 5 in per minute so that by reference to equation (4.5), $\dot{e}$ lies between 10^{-2}/sec and 10^{-4}/sec.

In discussing the quasi-static tension test it should always be kept in mind that the tensile strain rate is of order 10^{-3}/sec.

Engineers are familiar with creep strain rates which usually lie in the region between 10^{-9}/sec and 10^{-12}/sec. For very fast impact loaded bars $\dot{\varepsilon}$ may be about 10^3/sec. *In discussions on strain-rate it is usually only the order of magnitude which carries importance.*

The tension test: yield stress, flow stress, tensile strength

A conventional slowly applied load, F—extension, Δ, curve for a relatively long, uniform non-ferrous metal bar is shown diagrammatically in Fig. 4.2(a). The curve is convex towards the extension axis and displays a maximum M, i.e. shows a greatest load which can be withstood; fracture of the bar occurs at T.

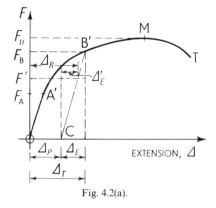

Fig. 4.2(a).

Point M serves to distinguish between two distinct classes of bar behaviour; from O to M the bar extends *uniformly* under tension, but after M a distinct single neck forms which, with continued extension at reducing load, is accentuated until fracture occurs. Examples of the kind of neck formed in circular and non-circular section bars when fracture occurs are shown in Plate 19.

The early part of the curve in Fig. 4.2(a) shows a linear, elastic relation between load and extension extending as far as load F_A, point A'; unloading, i.e. removal of the extending force F_A when it has any value less than F_A, allows the bar to completely elastically recover its original length. If the bar was extended significantly, i.e. beyond point A' to say, B', and then fully unloaded, it would be found to have acquired a permanent increase in length; the bar would have suffered plastic deformation. A plot of load versus extension during unloading appears as a substantially straight line $B'C$, which is parallel to the elastic line OA'. At B' the total extension is Δ_T, but complete unloading reduces the extension to Δ_P, i.e. length Δ_E is recovered.

If an axial tensile force was re-applied to the specimen, so that the load became F', then the total extension would become Δ_R; it would consist of Δ_P and Δ'_E; removing load F' would enable the bar to elastically recover the amount of extension Δ'_E. Reloading to any degree takes place first along CB' and then along $B'M$; if unloading occurs along $B'C$ then reloading along substantially the same curve, i.e. CB', takes place and both are associated with linear elastic behaviour.

Thus at any load F_B, the extension undergone by a tension specimen consists of permanent plastic extension Δ_P and recoverable elastic extension Δ_E. The further is B' along the load extension curve, the greater is Δ_P in relation to Δ_E. In particular, F_A for which Δ_P first becomes sensibly positive as measured using conventional engineering instruments, is referred to as the yield load for the material; this load divided by the cross-sectional area of the bar A_0 is designated Y and is the *tensile yield stress* of the material. For all points on the curve beyond A', the load divided by the current cross-sectional area is known as a *tensile flow stress*.

Load-extension curves may easily be converted to stress-strain curves, σ_0/e, σ/e or σ/ε. The slope of these curves in the elastic region is Young's

Modulus, E, and $E = Fl/A_0\Delta$. The material ceases to be completely elastic at stress level Y and is substantially uniformly elastic-plastic until the tensile strength $\sigma_0 = F_U/A_0$ is attained. For most metals at about room temperature E is of order 10^7 lb/in^2 and Y of order 10^4 lb/in^2, so that Y/E is of the order of $\frac{1}{1000}$. The tensile strain at the onset of yield is given by $\sigma/E = e$ or Y/E so that plastic deformation begins for many metals when the tensile strain exceeds about $\frac{1}{1000}$. Typical strains at the tensile strength are 0·25, so that in Fig. 4.2(a) the horizontal scale is heavily distorted.

In the region of the curve from A' to M, the material is said to *strain-harden* because increasing stress or load is required to enforce further strain.

A load-extension curve for annealed mild steel bar appears as in Fig. 4.2(b); it differs from Fig. 4.2(a) in that it possesses an upper, Y_u, and a lower Y_L, yield stress. In fact, over a small region before Y_u is reached the material may have a slightly non-linear elastic behaviour. When stress Y_u is attained, the tensile load on a specimen suddenly reduces and the operative stress becomes Y_L; the bar continues to extend at constant load and this prevails until the strain is about $\frac{1}{100}$, after which the material strain-hardens. If instead of a cylindrical bar a thin uniform strip of annealed mild steel which has been polished is pulled in simple tension, it will show dark bands of plastically-yielded material at about 55° (*not* 45°; see p. 127) to the tension axis, intermingled with lighter zones of unyielded or elastic material. As the extension continues the proportion of yielded material increases until, when strain-hardening begins, the whole strip has assumed a dark colour. Other features of the load-extension curve for anneal mild steel are as described in connection with Fig. 4.2(a).

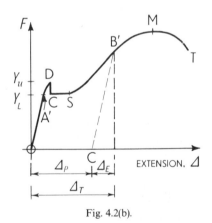

Fig. 4.2(b).

The tensile stress-strain curve

That there is no volume change during *plastic* deformation is made use of in relating tensile stress-strain curves through $A = A_0 l_0/l$. Then

$$\sigma = \frac{F}{A} = \frac{F}{A_0 l_0/l} = \frac{F}{A_0} \cdot \frac{l}{l_0} = \sigma_0(1 + e) \tag{4.7}$$

The relative position of the σ/e and the σ_0/e curves in Fig. 4.2(c) is therefore clear; the ordinate σ for a given value of e, is easily obtained by multiplying the corresponding ordinate σ_0 by $(1 + e)$ and evidently the disparity between σ and σ_0 is the greater the greater is e.

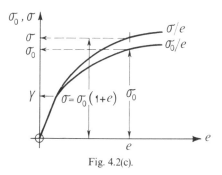

Fig. 4.2(c).

In engineering tensile tests on uniform bars the transverse strains ε_2 and ε_3 are equal and if ε_1 is the uniaxial tensile strain, then anticipating (4.10i) because

$$\varepsilon_1 + \varepsilon_2 + \varepsilon_3 = 0$$

therefore

$$\varepsilon_2 = \varepsilon_3 = -\tfrac{1}{2}\varepsilon_1 \tag{4.8}$$

Metals are said to be *isotropic* if the stress-strain properties of test specimens are independent of the direction from which they are cut from the original block of material. If they show direction dependent properties they are said to be *anisotropic*. Some strip specimens when pulled in tension undergo different transverse strains; this is often due to the manner in which the strip was processed, e.g., by rolling.

Logarithmic or natural strain: Equations for a no-volume change

A unit cube of material subject to principal stress σ_1 which causes only elastic behaviour, gives rise to three principal strains e_1, e_2 and e_3 where $e_1 = \sigma_1/E$ and $e_2 = e_3 = -\nu\sigma_1/E$ and ν is Poisson's ratio.

The new volume of the cube becomes $(1 + e_1)(1 + e_2)(1 + e_3)$ and since e_1, e_2 and e_3 are each very small, the volume alteration ΔV is, approximately,

$$\Delta V = e_1 + e_2 + e_3 = \sigma_1(1 - 2\nu)/E \tag{4.9}$$

Taking $\nu = \tfrac{1}{3}$ and putting $\sigma_1 = Y$, $\Delta V = Y/3E$; thus for typical elastic stress conditions, changes in volume are certainly very small—less than $\frac{1}{1000}$. Measurements show that in the tensile test, the more plastic does the specimen become the more nearly does ν approach $\tfrac{1}{2}$. Putting this value into equation (4.9), $\Delta V = 0$, i.e. there is no volume change.

Frequently, in calculations concerning extensive plastic deformation, it is assumed that there is no change in volume of the material. For no change in volume of a unit cube,

$$1.1.1 = (1 + e_1)(1 + e_2)(1 + e_3),$$

i.e.

$$\ln(1 + e_1) + \ln(1 + e_2) + \ln(1 + e_3) = 0$$

or

$$\varepsilon_1 + \varepsilon_2 + \varepsilon_3 = 0 \qquad (4.10\text{i})$$

where ε_1, ε_2 and ε_3 are the three natural strains imposed. Alternatively, instead of a cube, a cylindrical block of initial length L_0 and diameter D_0 might have been considered to be uniformly extended by principal stress σ_1 to become a cylinder whose dimensions are L and D. The equation for no volume change is then,

$$\frac{\pi}{4} . D_0^2 L_0 = \frac{\pi}{4} D^2 L$$

i.e.

$$2 \ln D/D_0 + \ln \quad L/L_0 = 0$$

or

$$2\varepsilon_\theta + \varepsilon_l = 0 \qquad (4.11)$$

The expression $\varepsilon_\theta = \ln D/D_0$ denotes the natural or logarithmic hoop strain and ε_l the natural or logarithmic axial strain. Equation (4.11) merely states what is intuitively obvious, namely that the strains in orthogonal directions, in a plane perpendicular to the uniaxial stress axis are equal and in magnitude are one half of the natural axial tensile strain.

Alternatively, for an annulus of a circular block,

$$\pi D_0 . (dD_0) h_0 = \pi D . (dD) . h$$

where h_0 and h are the original and current height of a block in, say, simple compression. Then,

$$\ln D/D_0 + \ln (dD)/(dD_0) + \ln h/h_0 = 0,$$

or

$$\varepsilon_\theta + \varepsilon_r + \varepsilon_z = 0 \qquad (4.10\text{ii})$$

ε_r denotes natural radial strain and ε_z natural compressive strain.

Equation (4.10ii) is of course similar to (4.10i) and taken together with (4.11) we find, for the particular case considered,

$$\varepsilon_\theta = \varepsilon_r \qquad (4.10\text{iii})$$

Applied to a thin circular ring of mean radius r, radial width dr and thickness t, when strained so that it has a mean radius $(r + u)$ a radial width $dr + d(dr)$

and a thickness $t + dt$, the equation for no volume change is,

$$2\pi r \cdot dr \cdot t = 2\pi(r + u)(dr + d(dr))(t + dt)$$

i.e.

$$\frac{r + u}{r} \cdot \frac{dr + d(dr)}{dr} \cdot \frac{t + dt}{t} = 1$$

or

$$\ln \frac{r + u}{r} + \ln \frac{dr + d(dr)}{dr} + \ln \frac{t + dt}{t} = 0$$

i.e.

$$\varepsilon_\theta + \varepsilon_r + \varepsilon_t = 0; \tag{4.12}$$

ε_θ is the logarithmic circumferential strain, ε_r the logarithmic radial strain and ε_t the logarithmic thickness strain.

Equivalent expressions (4.10), (4.11) and (4.12) are extremely important in plasticity calculations and represent nearly precise behaviour for plastically deformed metals subject to ordinary engineering levels of stress.

Upper yield point: Lüder's bands[4.3]

If annealed mild steel strip as referred to above is strained just to the upper yield point, D, see Fig. 4.2(b), and a further strain increment applied, then across particular sections yielding will occur and Lüder's bands appear. These are visible as grey-black bands inclined at a particular angle to the direction of the tensile stress. The material inside a Lüder's band is plastic and that on either side of it, elastic. *The plastic flow is constrained by the two elastic regions and does not allow plastic strain in the direction of the length of the band.* Thus the direction along which bands lie is that of zero extension in the plane of the strip, see Fig. 4.3(a).

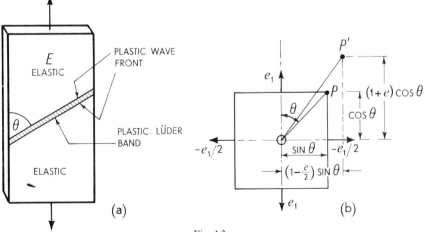

Fig. 4.3.

Recall that in the plastic range, if the principal strain in the direction of the tensile stress is e, that $-e/2$ is the strain in each of the transverse directions. Thus, if in an element of the strip as in Fig. 4.3(b), OP, is of unit length, then in straining P moves to P', and the condition for zero extension is $OP' = OP$, so that we have,

$$(1 + e)^2 . \cos^2 \theta + (1 - e/2)^2 . \sin^2 \theta = 1$$

(4.13)

Neglecting terms in e^2, equation (4.13) reduces to

$$\tan^2 \theta = 2 \quad \text{or} \quad \theta = 54°44'$$

The Lüder bands thus form at $\sim \pm 55°$ to the specimen axis.

As the amount of tensile extension is increased more and more Lüder bands appear. Material inside the bands undergoes a finite amount of strain of about $\frac{1}{100}$ whilst neighbouring material remains elastic; this phenomenon is discontinuous yielding. The mixture of elastic and plastic zones alters with increase in extension until eventually the whole specimen becomes plastic. When all the material is elastic, the total extension is that prevailing at point D, see Fig. 4.2(b). As more and more Lüder bands form, each to have a strain of about $\frac{1}{100}$, the total measured extension of the strip increases, which quantity is recorded by progression from C to S. At S all the material is plastic and the total impressed strain is about $\frac{1}{100}$.

On either side of an individual Lüder's band is a very thin wave-front of thickness s which advances at an extremely low speed v, and as material is encompassed by it, an increment of strain Δe is undergone. Effectively there is a strain discontinuity at the wave-front or at the head of this plastic wave. The strain rate $\dot{e}$ is given by

$$\dot{e} \doteqdot \frac{\Delta e}{s/v} ;$$

(4.14)

Δe is imposed in time s/v. If $v = 1$ cm/sec, $\Delta e = 0.01$ and $s = 0.01$ cm (i.e. a magnitude typically a grain size in diameter) then the strain rate $\dot{e} = 1/\text{sec}$—which is relatively high for a standard tensile test.

When the bulk of the material has attained a strain of about $\frac{1}{100}$ it may then harden. The difference in magnitude between the upper and lower yield point stress is sensitive to the rate of loading and depends on moving dislocations from 'pinning' nitrogen atoms.

The form of the decrease from D to C depends on the testing machine stiffness.

Ductile and brittle metals

The behaviour of metals is generally classified as *ductile* or *brittle* according to their performance in the simple slow speed tensile test. A metal which fractures after only a few per cent elongation with little change in cross-sectional area would be classified as brittle and the fracture as a cleavage fracture. A specimen which can be drawn out to have, say, more than 10% extension is ductile; the final stage of deformation would be concentrated in a neck and the final fracture would be typically 'cup and cone'.

Brittleness can often be removed and ductility substituted by applying a sufficient increase in temperature or by the imposition of equal 'all-round' hydrostatic stress[4.32]; material behaviour also depends on strain rate and the method of testing.

Stress-strain-strain-rate temperature

How stress and strain are related thoroughout a body during dynamic situations is obviously a matter of considerable importance especially in the context of the title of this book. The behaviour of metals which is dependent on their rate of loading and the testing temperature level in a complex way is determined by metallurgical factors as much as by the principles of mechanics. For over half a century these four factors have been studied without any very clear quantitative perception of their inter-relationship having been established. It requires a book in itself to attempt to discuss this confusing and controversial subject, see for instance, "Physics of Large Deformation of Crystalline Solids" by J. F. Bell (Springer-Verlag, New York Inc., 1968). In view of the state of this field it is intended below only to describe in broad outline some of the principal features concerning these factors which the author believes will help students orient themselves. To the writer it appears that there is little to indicate that any considerable simplification will emerge in this field in the course of the next few years. The effort is made in the next few pages, however, to provide the background for some systemisation of the major ideas which are presently evident. It is well to keep in mind that knowledge of the phenomena in this field is called for by engineers for use in two particular fields. These are,

(i) In designing structures, where concern is often with yield stress at room temperature since, generally, plastic deformation must not occur, i.e. concern is with strains of the order of 10^{-3} to 10^{-2} at most, and

(ii) In metal processing where concern is with flow stress often at high temperatures and strains of order unity.

'Strain-rate effect' to workers in these two fields often implies different things. Alterations in yield stress of a few per cent may be important to structural designers but are hardly worth noting by those engaged in practical metal deformation. The latter would tend only to become interested and to regard strain rate as seriously deserving of attention when alterations of say 50% and more begin to become apparent.

There are four aspects of strain-rate which should always be kept in mind when discussing its effect. To do this reduces the possibility of misunderstanding and to some extent aids clarification and classification of results. These are,

(i) Define clearly the *amount of strain* over which any stress alteration occurs.

(ii) Identify the *temperature level* of the experimental process in terms of homologous temperature, see below.

(iii) Tend to discuss strain rate in *order of magnitude* terms.

(iv) Bear in mind that, strictly, the behaviour of material in plasticity is dependent on its *history* and not on its momentary or final state.

Cold working: hot working

Metals are said to be cold worked if they become permanently harder during the working process, e.g. as in the common tensile test, though conventionally, cold working refers to room temperature working. Strain-hardening occurs at room temperature with most metals but pure lead, tin and cadmium only permanently strain-harden below typical room temperature. If these latter metals are strained and left at room temperature they become softer, or self-anneal with the passage of time.

During plastic deformation there is a generation, movement and interlocking of dislocation. The greater the degree of deformation the larger the number of dislocations produced, and due to their mutual interaction larger stresses are required to enforce their movement and hence cause further plastic flow; broadly, this explains strain-hardening.

Recrystallisation

Above a somewhat indefinite temperature called the recrystallisation temperature T_r, a metal may be worked and after a certain small strain, cease to harden with increasing strain. A balance would have been established between the tendency to strain-harden and the tendency to soften due to thermal activation. These two competing tendencies are first seriously concurrent over a narrow range of temperature near T_r; below this range the material perceptibly hardens during straining, but above it the yield stress is constant, though highly strain-rate dependent. The softening processes are recovery, recrystallisation and grain growth, and they are all thermally activated.

Figure 4.4(a) and (b) shows curves for metals compressed at slow strain-rate[4.23,4.24] in a compression testing machine, ($\sim 10^{-3}$/sec) and at high strain rates[4.25], Fig. 4.4(c), in a cam-plastometer ($\sim 10^0 - 10^2$/sec) at temperatures above and below the recrystallisation temperature.

Recrystallisation and homologous temperature

A very useful means of facilitating the interpretation of the stress-strain-strain-rate temperature behaviour in metals is via the homologous temperature, T_H; this is defined as

$$T_H = \frac{\text{Testing temperature } T\,(\text{K})}{\text{Melting point temperature } T_M\,(\text{K})} \tag{4.15}$$

Comparisons between metals which have different melting point temperatures are by this measure reduced to a common scale.

The recrystallisation temperature expressed in this non-dimensionalised way is usually found to be between 0·4 and 0·55 but is dependent on the strain and strain-rate imposed and the above figures are only given as a guide.

Hardness testing is fundamentally related to the stress-strain properties of a material, and thus indentation tests may be conducted for the purpose of

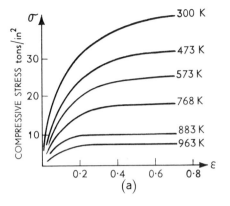

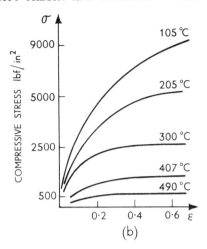

Fig. 4.4 Quasi-static (compression) stress–strain curves at various temperatures and $\dot{\varepsilon} \simeq 10^{-3}/\text{sec}$,
(a) copper, and
(b) super pure aluminium.
(c) Showing the compressive stress–strain curve for EN 52 steel at 1000 °C at various rates of strain.

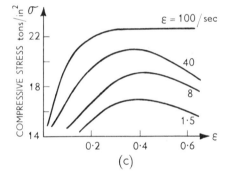

illuminating material behaviour generally. Indentation pressure is, in effect, a mean yield stress for a given mean strain. In Figs. 4.5(a) and 4.5(b) the logarithm of the *static indentation pressure*, using a lubricated cone of 90° angle, is plotted against temperature and it is observed that in (a) there is a discontinuity of slope, or as in (b) a hiatus at about the recrystallisation temperature. The pivotal role thus played by the recrystallisation temperature is clearly evident.

The compressive stress after various amounts of compressive strain at different *absolute temperatures* is shown in Fig. 4.5(c) and again the recrystallisation temperature region is well defined by the discontinuity.

A distinction between cold and hot working can be usefully based on the recrystallisation temperature, T_r, *cold working* occurring if the temperature at which it starts is less than T_r but if the temperature of working exceeds T_r it is *hot working*. The term 'warm working' is sometimes used to refer to working at a temperature which is intermediate between typical room temperatures and a recrystallisation temperature.

An account of the mechanical behaviour of metals at less than room temperature will be found in the paper by Conrad[4.26].

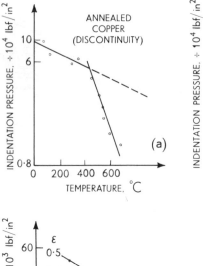

(a)

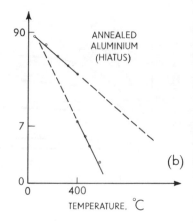

(b)

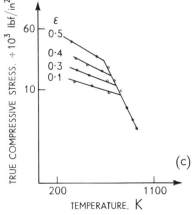

(c)

Fig. 4.5.

The ratio of dynamic to static flow stress

It is very useful to consider how the ratio of the dynamic, σ_D, to the static, σ_S, simple compressive flow stress of a metal at a specified strain varies with temperature. Static flow stress is referred to the strain rate 10^{-3}/sec—a typical slow speed compression test—and dynamic flow stress is associated with an impact test, e.g. that due to a falling hammer, which is likely to be about 10^2/sec. Thus σ_D/σ_S refers to a strain-rate ratio of about 10^5. Figures 4.6(a) and 4.6(b) show how σ_D/σ_S varies with temperature and homologous temperature for two steels and copper[4.27] and is very typical of the behaviour of most metals.

When strains imposed are large, say between 0·05 and 0·5,

   (i) strain-rate effects below the recrystallisation temperature are not pronounced and approximately, $1 < \sigma_D/\sigma_S < 2$;

  (ii) above T_r, σ_D/σ_S is very sensitive to strain rate; when $T_H \simeq 0.6$ or 0·7. for many metals the ratio is 10, more or less.

These simple facts are not widely recognised. Point (ii) is important because it implies that when deforming hot metal at temperatures exceeding T_r, at a

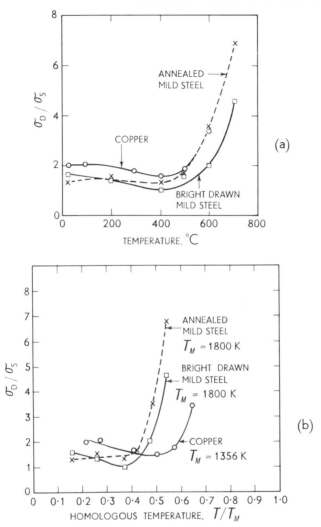

Fig. 4.6 (a) Showing variation of dynamic/static mean yield stress ratios with temperature.
(b) Showing variation of dynamic/static mean yield stress ratios with homologous temperature
(T/T_M).

fast rate, its 'stiffness' is, vis-à-vis σ_S, greatly increased. As Figs. 4.6(a) and (b)
show, fast worked mild steel at temperatures slightly in excess of $T_H = 0.5$,
are nearly as strong as they would be if slowly worked at room temperature.

The yield stress[†] of steel at about 15 °C

An extensive summary of work on this topic will be found in the book by
Goldsmith[1.2]; this is worthy of special mention as it bears heavily on the
design of structures to withstand impact loading at everyday temperature levels.

---

† See the recent extensive experimental results of Cl. Leblois and Ch. Massonet, *I.J.M.S.*, **14**, 72,
1972.

(i) *Yield stress: tension and compression*

From the work of Hopkinson[2.3] in 1905 to that by Taylor, Campbell and others in the 1950's, and including the findings of Russian workers, the conclusion which seems to emerge fairly clearly from quasi-static and impact tension tests (strain rates 10^{-3} to 10^2 or 10^3/sec) is, that the ratio of dynamic to static *yield stress* in mild steel is in excess of unity, is usually about two and sometimes as high as three. If instead of yield stress, *flow stress* is considered, this ratio is the smaller, the larger the plastic strain at which the comparison is made. Flow stress for a given strain is, generally, the larger the more rapid is the load application. The above ratio concerning yield in mild steel can fall from about 2·5 to 1·3 when the time available for loading increases from 10^{-5} to 10^{-2} secs; also this ratio is the smaller the higher the absolute value of the static yield stress.

(ii) *Delay times*

There is a clear delay in time between load application and the onset of plastic flow in low carbon steels; it is associated with the existence of a distinct yield point and yield mechanism.

The time to yield is the shorter the higher the load; the maximum delay period at 25 °C is of order 1 sec; for a delay period of only 10^{-6} sec the yield stress may have to be 2·5 times as great as its normal value. At -60 °C, with this ratio unaltered, the delay time may increase to more than 10 sec; however, at 121 °C, the time may be reduced to between 10^{-2} and 10^{-3} sec. At high temperatures, e.g. 1600 °F (872 °C), the delay time does not decrease rapidly with necessary tensile stress.

Some proposed formulae for correlating stress, strain, strain-rate and temperature[†]

(i) Ludwik[4.28] (1909) proposed a semi-logarithmic dependence of tensile yield strength on strain-rate, and subsequent work for certain metals in certain ranges of strain have satisfied it. The form of the equation is,

$$\sigma = \sigma_1 + \sigma_0 \ln \dot{\varepsilon}/\dot{\varepsilon}_0 \qquad (4.16)$$

Symbols σ_0, σ_1 and $\dot{\varepsilon}_0$ are constants. Constant strain-rate tests were used to give σ/ε curves for given ε and T.

Equation (4.16) seems to be generally satisfactory provided σ does not increase rapidly with $\dot{\varepsilon}$.

Manjoine and Nadai[4.29] (1940) found that tensile strength at elevated temperature varied nearly linearly with the logarithm of strain-rate.

(ii) Alder and Phillips[4.30] (1954) in work on copper at up to 600 °C, on aluminium at up to 500 °C and on steel at up to 930 to 1200 °C, were best able to summarise their results in the strain-rate range 1 to 40/sec by

$$\sigma = \sigma_0 \cdot \dot{\varepsilon}^n, \qquad (4.17i)$$

[†] See, 'On relating the flow stress of aluminium and copper to strain, strain-rate and temperature,' by S. K. Samanta, *I.J.M.S.*, **11**, 433 (1969).

where σ_0 and n are constants. These authors found that the power law provided "a slightly better interpretation" of their data than did the Ludwik type of equation. Sokolov, from earlier tests in compression over the range 20 °C to melting temperature, has advanced the same opinion as Alder and Phillips.

Note that equation (4.17i) is dimensionally invalid; $\dot{\varepsilon}$ is not non-dimensional but has dimensions (time)$^{-1}$. Properly then, (4.17i) should be replaced by

$$\frac{\sigma}{\sigma_0} = \left(\frac{\dot{\varepsilon}}{\dot{\varepsilon}_0}\right)^n \tag{4.17ii}$$

where σ_0 is the flow stress at strain rate $\dot{\varepsilon}_0$.

(iii) Macgregor and Fisher[4.31] (1946) introduced the idea of a "velocity modified temperature", T_m, so that

$$T_m = T(1 - m \ln \dot{\varepsilon}/\dot{\varepsilon}_0) \tag{4.18}$$

T is the test temperature (absolute) and m and $\dot{\varepsilon}_0$ are constants. This form gives the expected qualitative result that an increase in strain-rate is equivalent to a decrease in temperature. Equation (4.18) is only acceptable as an approximation at less than the recrystallisation temperature.

(iv) Inouye has used the expression

$$\sigma = \sigma_0 \varepsilon^n \cdot \dot{\varepsilon}^m \exp\left(A/Tk\right) \tag{4.19}$$

where σ_0, n, m, A and k are constants.

(v) Malvern[4.33] (1965) introduced an equation of the form

$$\dot{\varepsilon} = \frac{\dot{\sigma}}{E} + F(\sigma - \sigma_0(e)) \tag{4.20}$$

if $\sigma > \sigma_0(e)$; $\sigma_0(e)$ is the static stress at strain ε. Special forms of (4.20) are

$$\dot{\varepsilon} = \frac{\dot{\sigma}}{E} + D\left(\frac{\sigma}{\sigma_0} - 1\right)^p \tag{4.21}$$

and

$$\dot{\varepsilon} = \frac{\dot{\sigma}}{E} + A\left[\exp\left(\frac{\sigma}{\sigma_0} - 1\right)^q - 1\right], \tag{4.22}$$

where A, D, p and q are empirical constants and σ_0 is the static yield stress.

Equation (4.20) is satisfactory in that it gives an apparent increase in initial yield stress at high rates of strain and it allows plastic strain increments to be propagated at elastic wave speeds along bars initially stressed into the plastic range, see p. 218. Both these features are experimental facts.

(vi) Ripperberger[4.34] (1965) has maintained and shown that his experimental data in plastic wave propagation work can be best summarised by adapting Malvern's equation to

$$\dot{\varepsilon} = \frac{1}{\tau}\left[\frac{\sigma - \sigma_0(\varepsilon)}{\sigma_0(\varepsilon)}\right]^m \tag{4.23}$$

τ is the relaxation time of the material, $\sigma_0(\varepsilon)$ the static stress at strain ε, and thus $\{\sigma - \sigma_0(e)\}$ is the 'over stress', or the 'excess stress' to which the material is subject at the given strain-rate. For Armco iron $\tau \sim 1\cdot2$ m sec and $m \sim 1\cdot18$.

(vii) Other formulae will be found and are discussed in the book by Thomsen, Yang and Kobayashi[4.14].

(viii) From dynamic wave propagation studies Bell[4.35] claims to have demonstrated the "wide and remarkable generality" of the following stress-strain function,

$$\sigma = \left(\frac{2}{3}\right)^{r/2} . \mu(0) . B_0 \left(1 - \frac{T}{T_M}\right) . e^{1/2} \qquad (4.24)$$

where $\mu(0)$ is the zero-point isotropic linear elastic shear modulus; B_0 is a dimensionless universal constant having the value $B_0 = 0\cdot0280$ and r is an integral index, $1, 2 \ldots$ etc. Equation (4.24) is said to be "applicable over the entire temperature scale from $4\,°K$ to within $20°$ of the melting point of crystalline solids and is known experimentally to apply for strain rates $\dot{e} = 10^{-9}/\text{sec}$ to $\dot{e} = 10^4/\text{sec}$".

Bell determines the stress-strain function from

$$\sigma = \int_0^e \rho_0 . c_p^2(e) . de \qquad (4.25)$$

where ρ_0 denotes density and $c_p(e)$ is the plastic wave speed, see Chap. 5. Records of the non-linear wave front generated in uniaxial impact experiments after the front is more than one specimen diameter from the impact face are used.

Bell uses a diffraction grating technique to determine "large strain in microsecond time".

To emphasise that flow stress is history-dependent it is necessary to point out that experiments relating strain and flow stress are normally carried out at constant rate of strain. However, tests carried out in which, after a given amount of strain ε at a rate of $\dot{\varepsilon}_1$, there is a sudden change in rate of strain to $\dot{\varepsilon}_2$, show the flow stress to be immediately changed also. The tendency is for the σ/ε curve to shift significantly from the constant $\dot{\varepsilon}_1$ curve *towards* the constant $\dot{\varepsilon}_2$ curve, see Fig. 4.7; but it does not proceed along the $\dot{\varepsilon}_2$ curve which originates at $\varepsilon = 0$.

Strain-rate in relation to recrystallisation temperature

As remarked above, Alder and Phillips[4.30] particularly, have shown that the logarithm of compressive stress for up to 50% compression in the range 1 to 40/sec varies with logarithmic strain-rate at specific temperatures, for aluminium, copper and mild steel.

Using the equation

$$\sigma = \sigma_0 . \dot{\varepsilon}^n \qquad (4.26)$$

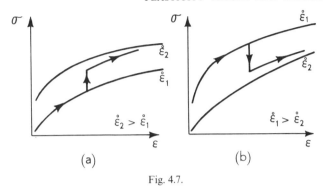

Fig. 4.7.

σ is the compressive stress, which is equal to σ_0 at a logarithmic strain-rate of unity and n is a constant. In summary, the experimental data for compressive strains up to 0·5, shows the exponent n to vary with homologous temperature, thus,

   (i) for $T_H < 0.55$, $n \simeq 0.055$ and
   (ii) for $T_H > 0.55$, $n \simeq 0.43$.

A point of reversal in compression: strain-softening

During the working of a metal, work is done on the specimen which manifests itself as a temperature increase and over a substantial range of temperature, any temperature increase, and hence softening tendency, due to working seems not to be too influential; however it is evident that a point will be reached when the contribution of the latter to the softening tendency will be decisive. It may be expected that a region of behaviour will exist in which the effects of the softening rate will predominate over the effects of the hardening rate. Experiments using a cam plastometer show that after sufficient high constant rate of strain, at a sufficiently elevated temperature, the flow stress of metal may indeed be found to decrease with increasing strain[4.25], see Fig. 4.4(c).

As the temperatures of testing move closer to the melting temperature of a metal, resistance to deformation—a quantity that would be measured as a mean flow stress—also becomes increasingly dependent on the inertia of the metal which is being deformed.

Idealised stress-strain, strain-rate independent behaviour

To facilitate analysis and understanding in many cases, it is usual to conceive of model materials which possess idealised stress-strain curves and which are independent of any rate of strain effects. The six most common ones are shown in Fig. 4.8 and they represent respectively in simple tension terms:

   (a) the linear elastic material of Strength of Materials with a modulus E;
   (b) the rigid-perfectly plastic or non-hardening material: the material

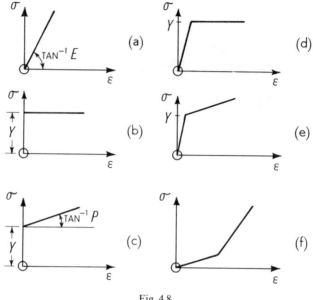

Fig. 4.8.

suffers no elastic strain, i.e. is rigid (or $E \to \infty$) until the yield stress Y is reached when plastic flow takes place without any hardening;

(c) the rigid-linear strain hardening material which has a yield stress Y and a plastic modulus P;

(d) the linear elastic-perfectly plastic or non-hardening material;

(e) the linear elastic-linear strain hardening material with yield stress Y;

(f) the idealised bi-linear locking material which is concave to the strain axis. This finds especial use in stress wave propagation work because it implies that true shock waves can be generated.

Perforation of a thin plate

Figure 4.9 shows a conical-ended drift which completely perforates a thin plate to create a lip of height H and leave behind a hole of its own diameter. Neglecting all elastic and frictional effects, the height of the lip may be estimated by a method due to Taylor[4.36] in which each element of the lip attains its final position by the simple process of 'hoop' stretching and rotation from its initial position in the plate; all bending and shear force effects are neglected. The solution is an example of the use of the equation for no change in the volume of the metal involved in the process. Each element in the plate at initial radius r, is conceived as being subject to circumferential stress only—as in a tensile test—whilst being stretched to final radius R_0, and the element thickness changes from t_0 to h and the radial length from dr to dz. For the volume of the element to remain constant,

$$2\pi r \,.\, dr \,.\, t_0 = 2\pi R_0 \,.\, dz \,.\, h$$

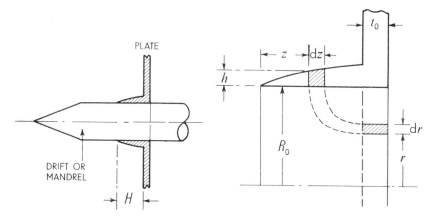

Fig. 4.9.

or

$$\frac{R_0}{r} \cdot \frac{dz}{dr} \cdot \frac{h}{t_0} = 1 \qquad (4.27)$$

Equation (4.27) in terms of natural strain is similar to equation (4.12) and is just,

$$\varepsilon_\theta + \varepsilon_r + \varepsilon_t = 0$$

Since only hoop stress prevails, then the thinning strains in the two transverse directions are equal, i.e. $\varepsilon_r = \varepsilon_t$, and following (4.8) each is equal to one half of ε_θ in magnitude. Particularly then,

$$\varepsilon_\theta = -2\varepsilon_r \quad \text{or} \quad \frac{R_0}{r} = \left(\frac{dr}{dz}\right)^2$$

Thus,

$$\int_0^H \sqrt{R_0} \cdot dz = \int_0^{R_0} \sqrt{r} \cdot dr$$

and

$$H = \tfrac{2}{3}R_0 \qquad (4.28)$$

If the drift creates a lip starting from a hole in the plate of radius R_1, it may be shown as above that,

$$z = \frac{2}{3}R_0\left[\left(\frac{r}{R_0}\right)^{3/2} - \left(\frac{R_1}{R_0}\right)^{3/2}\right], \qquad (4.29)$$

and thus that the lip height is

$$H = \frac{2}{3}R_0\left[1 - \left(\frac{R_1}{R_0}\right)^{3/2}\right] \qquad (4.30)$$

Also, that,

$$h = t_0 \left[\frac{3}{2} \cdot \frac{z}{R_0} + \left(\frac{R_1}{R_0} \right)^{3/2} \right]^{1/3}$$ (4.31)

An assumption on which this analysis is based is that the plate material is sufficiently ductile for the mode of deformation assumed to be possible. In fact, cold-formed plate generally shows several axial fractures, see Plate 20. We assume in the analysis, in effect, that plate material initially located along the drift axis undergoes infinite hoop strain, or if perforation starts from a hole of radius R_1, that the maximum hoop strain is $\ln R_0/R_1$. Punch-displacement/punch load diagrams for a perforation are nearly triangular in shape, see the experimentally obtained diagrams[4.37] in Fig. 4.10. Note in Plate 20 that there is considerable evidence of bending even some distance away from the lip and out into the plate[†].

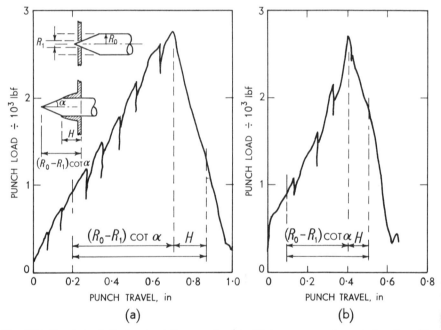

Fig. 4.10   Punch load-displacement diagrams for $\frac{1}{8}$ in thick copper specimens using $R_0 = \frac{1}{4}$ in radius punch with a nose semi-angle of $22\frac{1}{2}°$, (a) initial hole radius $R_1 = \frac{1}{32}$ in, (b) initial hole radius $R_1 = \frac{1}{8}$ in.

Empirical equations for uniaxial stress-strain curves

Many authors have given equations relating uniaxial stress and strain for a strain-hardening material, but only a small number of these will be referred to here

(i) $$\sigma = B\varepsilon^n \quad \text{or} \quad \sigma = B'e^m$$ (4.32)

---

† See, 'Penetration and perforation processes in metal targets at and above ballistic velocities', by W. Goldsmith and S. A. Finnegan, *I.J.M.S.*, **13**, 843 (1971).

(ii) $$\sigma = Y + P\varepsilon \qquad (4.33)$$

(iii) $$\sigma = B(C + \varepsilon)^n \qquad (4.34)$$

(iv) $$\sigma = Y_0 \tanh^{-1}(E\varepsilon/Y_0) \qquad (4.35)$$

B, B', m, Y_0, P and C are empirically determined constants. The most frequently used form is (4.32).

Empirical equations can only be made to describe the real stress-strain curve of a material over a limited range of strain and whilst they are frequently used for deriving simple analytical results, the latter should always be regarded with circumspection. A plot of $\ln \sigma$ versus $\ln \varepsilon$ following equation (4.32) would appear as a straight line, but experiments provide curves slightly concave to the axis of $\ln \varepsilon$.

B is typically of the order of 10^5 lb/in² (10^8 N/m²) and n and m about 0·25; $n \simeq 0·5$ for stainless steel and this is unusually large.

Tensile instability

At the maximum load when a prismatic bar is subject to an axial force F, see Fig. 4.2, $dF = 0$, so that because $\sigma = F(1 + e)/A_0$, using equation (4.7),

$$d\left(\frac{A_0\sigma}{1 + e}\right) = 0$$

i.e.

$$\frac{d\sigma}{1 + e} - \frac{\sigma \cdot de}{(1 + e)^2} = 0$$

or

$$\frac{d\sigma}{de} = \frac{\sigma}{1 + e} = \sigma_0 \qquad (4.36)$$

using (4.7), or, alternatively,

$$\frac{d\sigma}{d\varepsilon} = \sigma \qquad (4.37)$$

using (4.4ii).

If empirical equation (4.32) is given, then, in conjunction with equation (4.37),

$$\frac{d\sigma}{d\varepsilon} = Bn \cdot \varepsilon^{n-1} = \sigma = B\varepsilon^n$$

Thus, at the maximum load, the strain

$$\varepsilon = n \quad \text{or} \quad e = [\exp(n) - 1];$$

correspondingly, using equations (4.32) and (4.36) or (4.37),

$$e = \frac{m}{1 - m} \quad \text{or} \quad \varepsilon = \ln(1/(1 - m)) \qquad (4.38)$$

In physical terms, as extension of a bar proceeds, its capacity to carry load is reduced in as far as its cross-section reduces. However, the act of stretching the bar strengthens or hardens it, so that up the maximum load an equilibrium is maintained, the two competing factors being a geometrical one—the reducing area, a feature which depends on the specimen shape and how it is loaded—and a metallurgical one, the multiplication of interacting dislocations, due to the applied stress and a basic factor disclosed by the form of the true stress-strain curve. At maximum load, a further slight extension causes a reduction in area and hence a reduced capacity to carry load, which cannot be sufficiently offset by a further increment in hardness. Thus, equilibrium is not maintained and depending upon the manner of loading or unloading the specimen, a concentrated or localised straining occurs, soon followed by fracture.

The argument just presented applies qualitatively to the radial expansion of spheres and cylinders, and to sheet metal in equal biaxial tension. Continued and increasing tensile stress in material, due to increasing load (e.g. the internal pressure in a spherical shell), causes expansion, area reduction and an increase in the hardness of the material. Equilibrium between these two factors persists only until a critical 'load' is reached, after which the rate of the increase in strength of the material can no longer compensate for the reduction in area suffered. These maximum loads are often referred to as loads causing tensile instability.

When a thin ring is expanded with a sufficiently high radial speed, e.g. by explosives[4.38] or a pulsed-magnetic field, a neck will form somewhere around the circumference, so that the hoop *force* there then begins to fall and in the unnecked portion of the ring the stress begins to decrease; this reduction is communicated circumferentially in opposite directions from the neck at the elastic wave speed, see Fig. 4.11. It is possible, if the radial speed is large enough for a second (or third, etc.) neck to form (as indeed is found in some experiments), in the unnecked portion of the ring, because the release wave from the first neck has not yet passed through it. From the second neck, new elastic release waves are propagated. Reductions in area in necks, impart both circumferential speed and acceleration to the material at each side of the neck and thus give rise to inertia forces, with a consequent true stress reduction. Inertia thus provides a stabilising influence and hence in the high speed expansion of a ring there is reason to expect multiple necks and stable straining to a higher degree than in the corresponding quasi-static process. Most of these points were made by Mott[4.39].

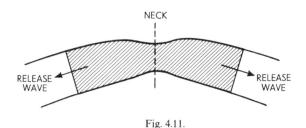

Fig. 4.11.

Homogeneous compression

If a stress-free cylindrical block of metal is compressed so that every small element of it is deformed to the same degree at the same instant, it is said to be homogeneously compressed, see Fig. 4.12. A cylindrical block whose height is less than about twice its diameter if plastically compressed between rigid, parallel and substantially frictionless plates is a case of homogeneous compression. Buckling becomes a feature when the block height is about three time the diameter. As the plates approach one another, every transverse cross-section of the block remains circular and increases in diameter at the same rate as every other cross-section; the block remains prismatic. No bulging of the cylindrical vertical sides occurs—these remain straight and vertical.

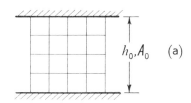

h_0, A_0 (a)

Fig. 4.12 (a) A diametral section of a cylindrical block on which a square grid of lines is marked. (b) Homogeneous deformation; all squares after compression have become identical rectangles.

h, A (b)

Recall that homogeneous extension has, in fact, already been described in connection with the simple tension test conducted until the tensile load is a maximum.

If a cylindrical block of non-hardening material of yield stress Y, see Fig. 4.12, initial height h_0 and cross-sectional area A_0 is homogeneously compressed, the force necessary to initiate plastic compression is $A_0 Y$. When the height of the block is reduced to h, the cross-sectional area is $A_0 h_0/h$ and the force to cause further deformation is $A_0 h_0 Y/h$; this compressive force thus increases hyperbolically.

If the current height of the block is h and it is compressed a further amount $-dh$, then the axial compressive logarithmic strain increment $d\varepsilon_c$, is

$$d\varepsilon_c = -dh/h \tag{4.39}$$

The total compressive strain in reducing the height of the block from h_0 to h is thus,

$$\varepsilon_c = \int_{h_0}^{h} -\frac{dh}{h} = \ln \frac{h_0}{h} \tag{4.40}$$

Since the block is isotropic, the two transverse strains must be equal and the magnitude of each is $\varepsilon_c/2$.

To compress the block an amount $-dh$, an amount of plastic work dW must be performed and

$$dW = F.(-dh) = \frac{A_0 h_0}{h} . Y . (-dh)$$

Thus the total work done in compressing the block from h_0 to h is W and

$$W = A_0 h_0 Y \int_{h_0}^{h} -\frac{dh}{h} = A_0 h_0 Y \ln \frac{h_0}{h}, \qquad (4.41)$$

The work done per unit volume of the material is

$$w = \frac{W}{A_0 h_0} = Y \ln \frac{h_0}{h} \quad \text{or} \quad w = Y . \varepsilon_c \qquad (4.42)$$

As no energy is used in overcoming friction between the compressing platens and the metal, and since every element is identically strained, it follows that the alteration in *shape* of the block is achieved with maximum efficiency; homogeneous straining, or shape-changing, is the most efficient method of securing deformation and is the criterion by which all other methods of securing the same final shape are judged. Homogeneous deformation is an idea of great value in the study of metal deformation processes.

A bar of non-hardening material of length l_0 homogeneously stretched in tension to length l, i.e. on which a logarithmic strain $\varepsilon_l = \ln l/l_0$ is imposed, has an amount of work done on it per unit volume of

$$w = Y \ln l/l_0 = Y\varepsilon_l \qquad (4.43)$$

Similarly, for a thin ring of non-hardening material given a simple principal hoop strain ε_θ, the plastic energy required is $w = Y . \varepsilon_\theta$ per unit volume.

Temperature rise in the adiabatic compression or stretching of a strain-hardening material

The work done in frictionlessly and homogeneously compressing a cylindrical block from height h_0 to h, when its true stress-natural strain curve is $\sigma = B\varepsilon^n$, is

$$W = \int_{h_0}^{h} - A\sigma . dh = \int_{h_0}^{h} - A_0 h_0 \sigma . \frac{dh}{h} .$$

But $dh/h = d\varepsilon$, and thus,

$$W = -\int_0^\varepsilon A_0 h_0 . \sigma . d\varepsilon$$

$$= -\int_0^\varepsilon A_0 h_0 . B\varepsilon^n . d\varepsilon, \qquad (4.44)$$

or

$$w = \frac{W}{A_0 h_0} = B \left[\frac{\varepsilon^{n+1}}{n+1} \right]_0^\varepsilon$$

i.e.,

$$w = B \cdot \frac{[\ln h_0/h]^{n+1}}{n+1} \tag{4.45i}$$

The right hand side of the last expression is just the area under the appropriate true stress-logarithmic strain curve from zero to the imposed final strain, ε.

Experimentally it is found that about 90% of the energy supplied to effect plastic compression reappears as heat and causes a rise in temperature of the material. An estimate of the greatest possible temperature rise may be arrived at if adiabatic compression is assumed with complete conversion of plastic work to heat. If there is no change in the material properties of the metal with increase in temperature, if ρ denotes density, c specific heat, J the mechanical equivalent of heat and $\Delta\theta$ the *uniform* temperature rise in unit mass of the metal, then

$$\rho c \cdot \Delta\theta \cdot J = w$$

where w is the plastic work done on a unit volume of the metal; or

$$\Delta\theta = \frac{w}{J\rho c} \tag{4.45ii}$$

w is given by equations (4.43), (4.45i) or (4.45ii). A bar of mild steel ($<0.35\%$ C), which, at an ultimate strength of about 45 ton/in² ($0.692 \cdot 10^9$ N/m²), had a strain of 0.3 would, if adiabatically stretched, undergo a uniform temperature rise of about 57 °C. An alternative approach is given on p. 208.

Energy calculations in the penetration of a plate by a drift

Refer to the analysis of this problem on p. 138. The work done in creating the lip is the sum of the work done on each element. Each element of circumferential length $2\pi r$ and cross-sectional area $t_0 \cdot dr$, is subject to hoop strain $\varepsilon_\theta = \ln R_0/r$ so that, if the plate is of non-hardening material, the work done on it is, using equation (4.43), $(2\pi r t_0 \, dr) \cdot Y \cdot \ln R_0/r$. The total work done W in creating the lip is,

$$W = \int_0^{R_0} 2\pi t_0 \, Yr \ln R_0/r \cdot dr = \tfrac{1}{2}\pi R_0^2 t_0 Y \tag{4.46}$$

If the material of the plate is linear strain-hardening, then the work required to be done in order to form the lip is, using equations (4.33) and adapting equation (4.44)

$$\int_0^w dW = \int_0^R (2\pi r t_0) \cdot \sigma \cdot \ln R_0/r \cdot dr$$

i.e.

$$W = 2\pi t_0 \int_0^{R_0} r\left(Y + \frac{P}{2}\ln \frac{R_0}{r}\right) \ln \frac{R_0}{r} \cdot dr$$

$$= \tfrac{1}{2}\pi R_0^2 t_0 (Y + \frac{P}{2}) \tag{4.47}$$

If, instead of a drift we consider a projectile, and assume that all dynamical effects may be neglected, we may estimate the change in speed of the projectile in order to achieve penetration by equating the kinetic energy loss of the projectile to the plastic work done in perforating the plate. Thus, if the projectile weight is W, if its initial speed is v_0 and its speed on emerging from the plate is v, then

$$\frac{1}{2} \cdot \frac{W}{g}(v_0^2 - v^2) = \tfrac{1}{2}\pi \cdot R_0^2 t_0 \cdot Y \tag{4.48}$$

Reference 4.40 discusses the incorporation of 'dynamical work', or allowing for the inertia of plate material in equation (4.48); this term is the more important the closer is v/v_0 to unity.

The explosive forming of thin rings

By detonating a charge of explosive in a tank of water[4.41] as shown in Fig. 4.13, a radially moving pressure wave is generated which, with various reflections, acts on a given circular ring causing each element of it to acquire a radial speed v_0. If the stress-strain curve for the ring material is known, e.g. as in equation (4.32), and assuming that strain rate effects are negligible, the magnitude of v_0 in order that the ring be expanded from diameter D_0 to D is easily estimated by assuming that all the plastic work which is required to be done on the ring is acquired initially as kinetic energy. The work to be done per unit volume of the ring is

$$\int_0^{\varepsilon_0} B\varepsilon^n \, . \, d\varepsilon = B\varepsilon_0^{n+1}/(n+1)$$

where $\varepsilon_0 = \ln D/D_0$ and the kinetic energy acquired per unit volume is $\rho v_0^2/2$.

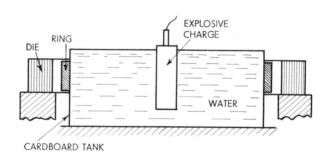

CARDBOARD TANK

Fig. 4.13.

Thus,

$$v_0 = \left\{ \frac{2B(\ln D/D_0)^{n+1}}{\rho(n+1)} \right\}^{1/2} \tag{4.49}$$

Plates

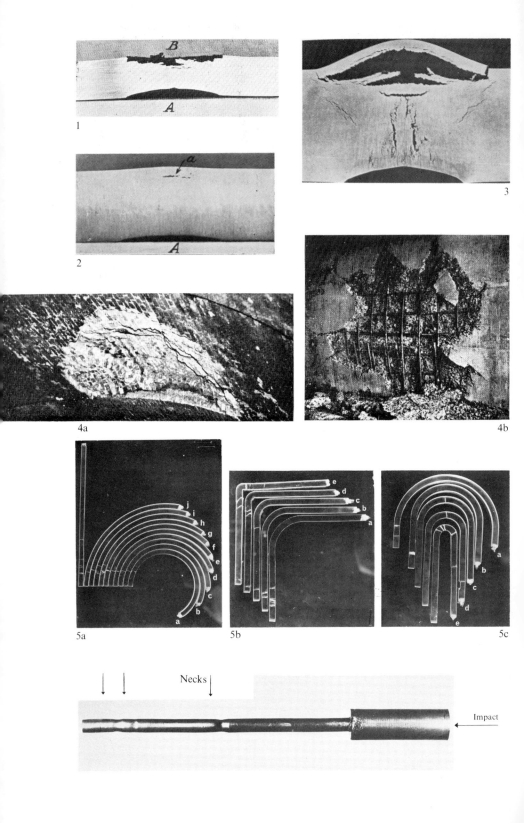

1

2

3

4a

4b

5a

5b

5c

Necks

Impact

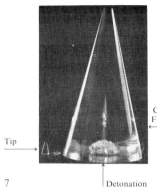

Tip

Central Fracture

7

Detonation

8

10

late 1   Section of a mild steel plate, $\frac{3}{4}$ in thick, after[2.3] the detonation of gun-cotton in contact with the side A. Scab torn off from B.

late 2   A section of a mild steel plate, $1\frac{1}{4}$ in thick, after[2.3] the detonation of gun-cotton in contact with the side A. Crack formed at a.

late 3   Cross-section of mild steel plate showing multiple[2.8] scabbing (6 in dia by 3 in thick plate, 3 in diameter by 2 in explosive).

late 4   (a) Scabbing from the soffit of a brick arch.[2.10]
          (b) Scabbing from the inside face of a 39 in thick reinforced concrete wall caused by a bomb exploded in contact with outer face.

late 5   Fractures in curved Perspex bars after detonator explosion at one end.

late 6   Extruded rod showing necks due to impact.[2.11]

late 7   Fractures in a Perspex cone produced by 0·4 g of lead azide.[2.6]

late 8   Plaster of Paris wedge-shaped plates explosively loaded along the *whole* of the base.[2.12]

late 9   Plaster of Paris wedge-shaped plates explosively loaded at the *centre* of the base.[2.12]

late 10 Axial sections of steel cylinders, after the detonation[2.3] of gun-cotton in contact with one end.

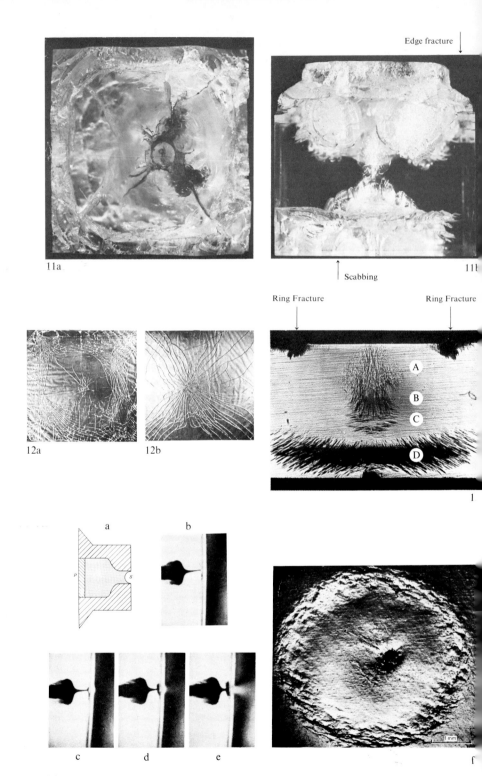

11a

11b

↑ Scabbing

Ring Fracture   Ring Fracture

12a   12b

A
B
C
D

1

a   b

P   S

c   d   e

f

14

15   16

17   18

Plate 11   A rectangular block of Perspex after detonation of an explosive[2.12] charge.
             (a) View on to top of block.
             (b) Side view.
Plate 12   Fracture patterns in glass.
             (a) Severe blast causing circumferential fracture.
             (b) Less severe blast: radial fracture.
Plate 13   Cross section through a 3·5 mm thick polymethylmethacrylate plate.[2.16]
             A: shear fractures
             B: due to tangential shear stresses
             C, D: scabbing fractures.
Plate 14   (a)–(e) Crater formation by liquid impact on stainless steel.[2.16]
             (f) Near its centre a second small but deep crater (0·3 mm dia) has been formed by the
             microjet.
Plate 15   Crumpled circular tube due to end impact.[2.21]
Plate 16   Damaged coach model due to end impact.[2.21]
Plate 17   Garage structure after Alaska earthquake[3.5]: column heads displaced $10\frac{5}{8}$ in.
Plate 18   Canopy damaged in July 1967 Caracas earthquake.[3.5]

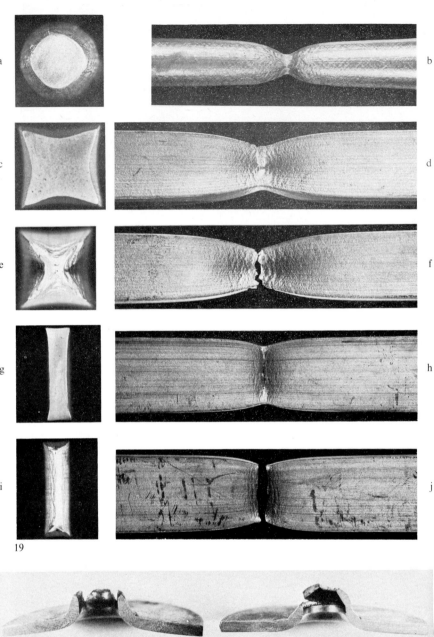

19

20

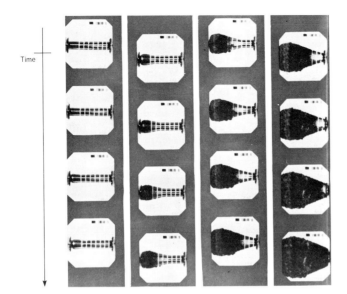

21

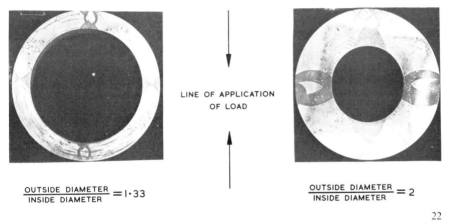

LINE OF APPLICATION
OF LOAD

$$\frac{\text{OUTSIDE DIAMETER}}{\text{INSIDE DIAMETER}} = 1 \cdot 33$$

$$\frac{\text{OUTSIDE DIAMETER}}{\text{INSIDE DIAMETER}} = 2$$

22

Plate 19   Bars of super-pure aluminium of, (a) and (b) circular, (c) to (e) square and (g) to (j) rectangular cross-section, which have necked-down in tension. Note, in transverse views (c), (e), (g) and (i), how the centre of each plane face of the bar is drawn-in whilst the corners or edges are relatively little displaced. Views (a), (c) and (g) are taken a little to one side of the imminent fracture section: (e) and (i) are taken in the fracture plane.

Plate 20   Showing the perforation of some copper plates by a conical drift passing into a hole in the plate, see caption to Fig. 4.10. Note the lip fractures and that plate bending extends beyond the lip deformation.[4.37]

Plate 21   A sequence of photographs showing an exploding tubular bomb; detonation from left hand end[4.44]. Framing speed, 200 000/sec.

Plate 22   Showing plastic hinges at the quarter points in rings under diametral load.[4.52]

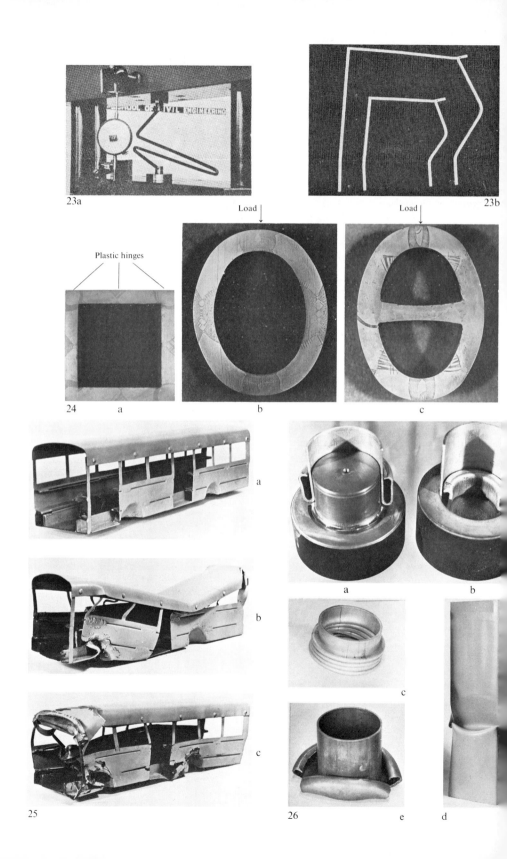

23a

23b

Load ↓

Load ↓

Plastic hinges

24   a

b

c

a

b

c

25

a

b

c

d

e

26

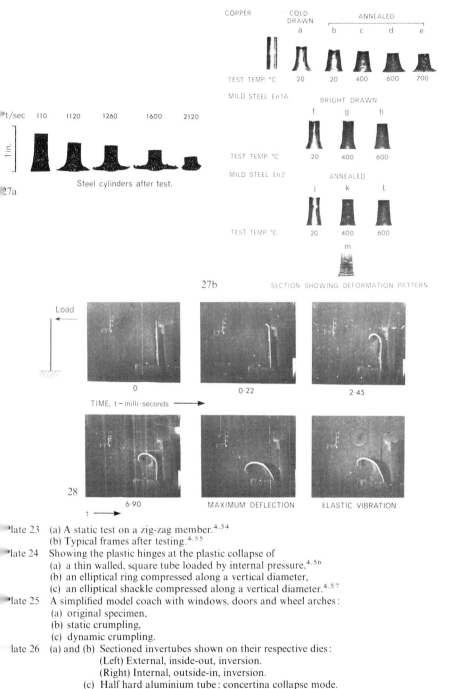

Plate 23 (a) A static test on a zig-zag member.[4.54]
(b) Typical frames after testing.[4.55]

Plate 24 Showing the plastic hinges at the plastic collapse of
(a) a thin walled, square tube loaded by internal pressure,[4.56]
(b) an elliptical ring compressed along a vertical diameter,
(c) an elliptical shackle compressed along a vertical diameter.[4.57]

Plate 25 A simplified model coach with windows, doors and wheel arches:
(a) original specimen,
(b) static crumpling,
(c) dynamic crumpling.

Plate 26 (a) and (b) Sectioned invertubes shown on their respective dies:
(Left) External, inside-out, inversion.
(Right) Internal, outside-in, inversion.
(c) Half hard aluminium tube: concertina collapse mode.
(d) Thin steel tube: static diamond mode type buckling.
(e) Tearing failure in a mild steel invertube.

Plate 27 (a) Showing the shape of solid steel cylinders after impact at various speeds.[5.2]
(b) Showing 'mushrooming' when hot bullets are fired against a rigid anvil at about 600 ft/s.[5.4]

Plate 28 Showing the movement with time of a plastic hinge generated at the tip of a vertical cantilever (trapezoidal in plan), loaded with a transverse impulsive point (magneto-motive) load.[6.18]

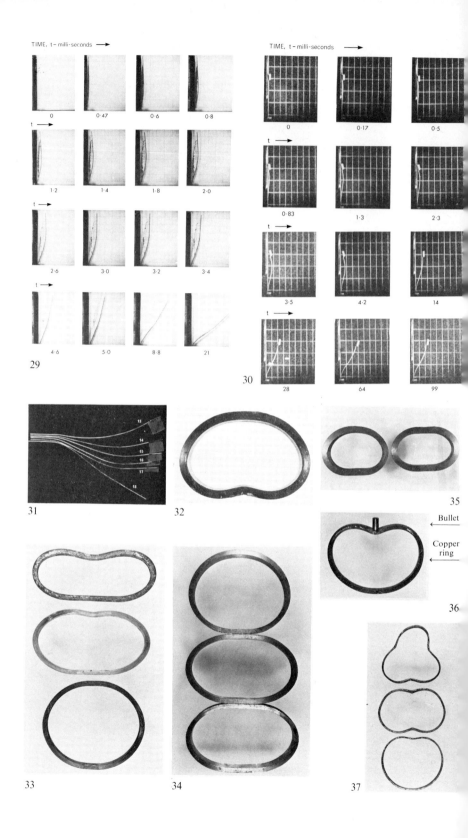

TIME, t – milli-seconds ——→

0   0·47   0·6   0·8

t ——→

1·2   1·4   1·8   2·0

t ——→

2·6   3·0   3·2   3·4

t ——→

4·6   5·0   8·8   21

29

TIME, t – milli-seconds ——→

0   0·17   0·5

t ——→

0·83   1·3   2·3

t ——→

3·5   4·2   14

t ——→

28   64   99

30

31

32

35

Bullet

Copper
ring

36

33

34

37

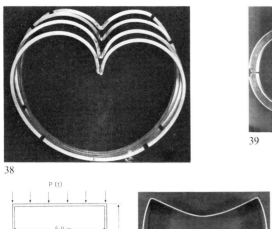

38

39

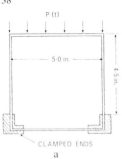

a

b

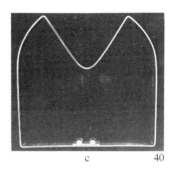

c   40

Plate 29   High speed photographs of the instantaneous profile of a cantilever subjected to a magneto-motive impulse along its length.[6.18]

Plate 30   High speed photographs of the instantaneous profile of a cantilever subjected to a magneto-motive impulse along 0·58 of its length and having attached to it a tip mass.[6.18] (Ratio of cantilever mass to twice tip mass is 0·13).

Plate 31   Photograph of terminal shapes of specimens subject to a full length beam loading (same in all cases) but with various attached tip masses.[6.18]

Specimen No.	13	14	15	16	17	18
Cantilever mass / Twice tip mass	0·065	0·074	0·129	0·222	0·258	∞

Plate 32   A typical terminal profile of a 5·0 in o.d., 0·475 in radial thickness lead ring which has fallen freely on to a sharp indenter.[7.2]

Plate 33   Typical terminal profiles of (top) Copper, (middle) Aluminium, and Mild Steel stationary rings struck by a freely falling sharp indenter, all having the same input kinetic energy.[7.2]

Plate 34   A photograph of the profiles of three 5·0 in o.d., 0·25 in radial thickness lead rings after the top ring has been allowed to impinge upon the other two stationary rings.[7.2]

Plate 35   The final profiles of two lead rings subjected to the same kinetic energy input; (i) Left: freely falling on a flat anvil and (ii) Right: struck by a freely falling flat hammer.

Plate 36   Showing the final profile of a 5·0 in o.d., $\frac{1}{4}$ in radial thickness copper ring, subjected to the impact of a 0·370 in diameter and 0·75 in long mild steel bullet moving with a speed of 695 ft/sec. The ring was freely supported.[7.2]

Plate 37   The final profiles of 5·0 in o.d, $\frac{1}{8}$ in radial thickness and $\frac{3}{8}$ in width annealed copper rings subjected to; (a) Top: three point explosive loading, (b) Middle: two point explosive loading and (c) Bottom: one point explosive loading. All rings were freely supported.[7.2]

Plate 38   Showing the final profiles of 6·5 in o.d, $\frac{1}{8}$ in radial thickness and $\frac{1}{4}$ in width aluminium rings explosively loaded at one point. Each ring had two $\frac{1}{4}$ lb weights attached at the locations marked in black. All rings were subjected to the same explosive charge.[7.2]

Plate 39   Perspex rings: (i) Right: 5·5 in o.d, $\frac{1}{4}$ in radial thickness and $\frac{3}{8}$ in width loaded explosively, (ii) Left: 5·0 in o.d, $\frac{7}{16}$ in radial thickness and $\frac{1}{4}$ in width loaded under a drop hammer with a freely falling sharp indenter.[7.2]

Plate 40   (a) Magnetomotive loading[7.3] of square frames by applying a uniform impulse to the top side. (b) Showing the final profile of a 5·0 × 5·0 in square frame loaded as shown with a discharge energy of 1·44 · 10³ J. (c) As for (b) but a discharge energy of 2·55 · 10³ J.

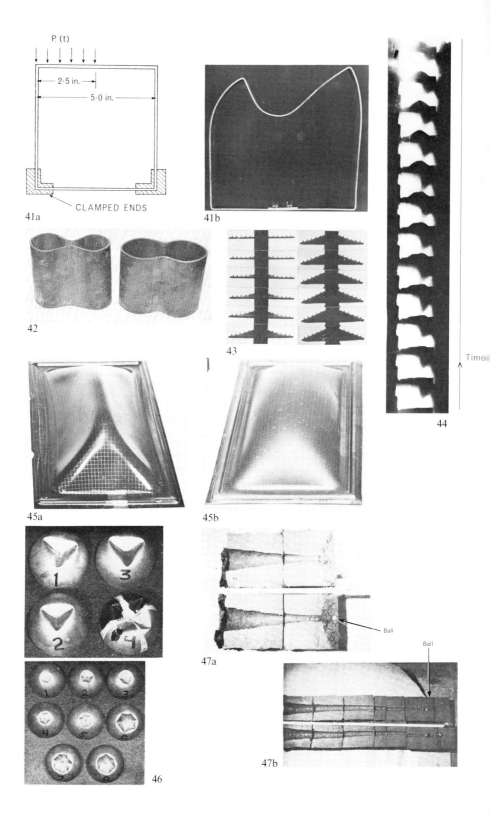

P. (t)

2·5 in.

5·0 in.

CLAMPED ENDS

41a

41b

42

43

44

Time

45a

45b

46

47a

Ball

Ball

47b

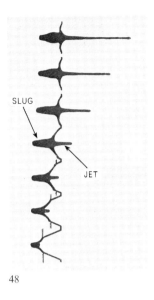

SLUG

JET

48

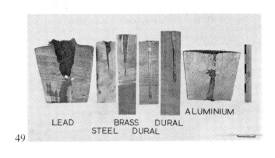

LEAD   BRASS   DURAL   ALUMINIUM
    STEEL   DURAL

49

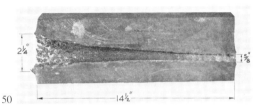

$2\frac{1}{4}''$ $\frac{5}{8}''$

$14\frac{1}{2}''$

50

51

52

Plate 41   Showing[7.3] the final profile of a square, 0·5 in wide thin aluminium frame loaded magneto-motively (asymmetrically) at a discharge energy of 2·554 · 10³ J.

Plate 42   Constrained and free deformation[7.4] to form an impeller (mild steel, original diameter = 160 mm, height H = 160 mm).

Plate 43   The deformation process in a circular blank fixed to a central boss and freely formed by an impulsive transverse pressure[8.3]. Time interval between frames, 0·118 m sec.

Plate 44   Silhouette high speed photographs of a thin lead[8.3] plate undergoing explosive deformation: note the emergence of a frustum shape leading to a cone.

Plate 45   Thin copper plates free-formed[8.6] through a 2:1 aspect ratio rectangular die, by
    (a) magnetic forming,
    (b) hydrostatic forming.

Plate 46   Deformation modes—hemispherical shell[8.7] under static tests (top) and dynamic tests (bottom).

Plate 47   Showing the cavity shape created when a small fast-moving spherical ball projectile penetrates a block of clay[9.6]: (a) aluminium (b) steel.

Plate 48   A model of the sequence of events when a lined cavity collapses.[9.8]

Plate 49   Penetrations into various metals achieved by lined cavity charges.[9.8]

Plate 50   Penetration by a hollow charge.[9.8]

Plate 51   Showing the damage to a stainless steel plate caused by a micro-meteorite weighing about 10^{-7} g and travelling at 10–40 km/second. Plate was exposed by the Gemini 8 crew.

Plate 52   Barringer crater, Arizona.

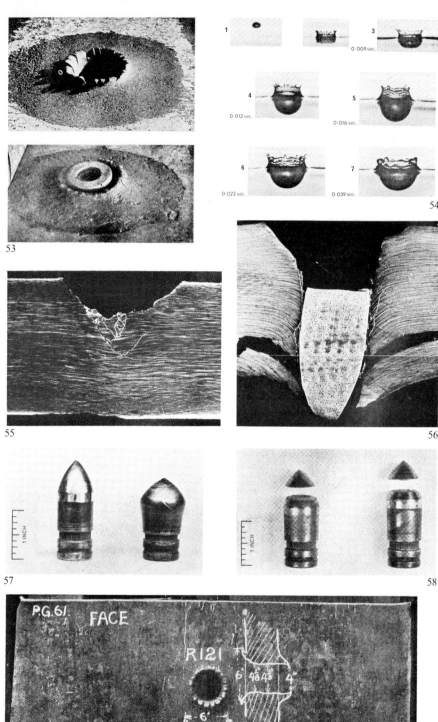

53

54

55

56

57

58

59

1. TRIAL OF HADFIELD'S "ERA" STEEL HARD-FACE ARMOUR PLATE, 4 ft. × 4 ft. × 4¼ ins.
2. TRIAL OF HADFIELD'S "HECLON" 10·5 cm. (4¼ in.) ARMOUR-PIERCING SHELL OF 32¼ LBS.

TEST OF PLATE

1. Round 583. Hadfield's Cast Steel A.P. Shot (British Standard) Uncapped

Striking Velocity	Energy—Foot-tons	Factor of Penetration
2010	920	2·32

Round 588. Hadfield's Cast Steel A.P. Shot (British Standard) Uncapped

Striking Velocity	Energy—Foot-tons	Factor of Penetration
1920	840	2·18

TEST OF PROJECTILE

2. Round 587. Hadfield's "HECLON" Cast Steel A.P. Shell. Capped

Striking Velocity	Energy—Foot-tons	Factor of Penetration
1920	840	2·18

No. 872

60

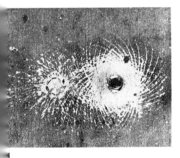

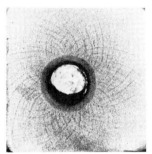

62

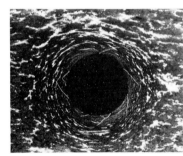

63

Plate 53   Permanent 'splashes' left where a projectile has entered an armour-plate.[9.16]
Plate 54   The splash of a globule.[9.16]
Plate 55   Showing armour plate which has shattered a projectile on impact. Note the net of white lines beneath the cavity.
Plate 56   Showing incomplete penetration by a bullet. Note the white lines and the perforated spall.
Plate 57   Swelling produced during penetration.
Plate 58   Projectile fracture which occurred after penetration.
Plate 59   A plate of wrought iron after penetration by an armour-piercing shell.[10.1]
Plate 60   Showing the change in behaviour in a plate which is very hard on its front face and tough and ductile at the rear, when the projectile tip is capped.[10.1]
Plate 61   Scale blown off rear side of a steel plate to show logarithmic spiral nature and extent of deformation.
Plate 62   Lüder lines in a plate around a penetration, as found some distance below the plate surface.
Plate 63   White martensitic spirals in a plate, radiating from the bullet–plate interface.

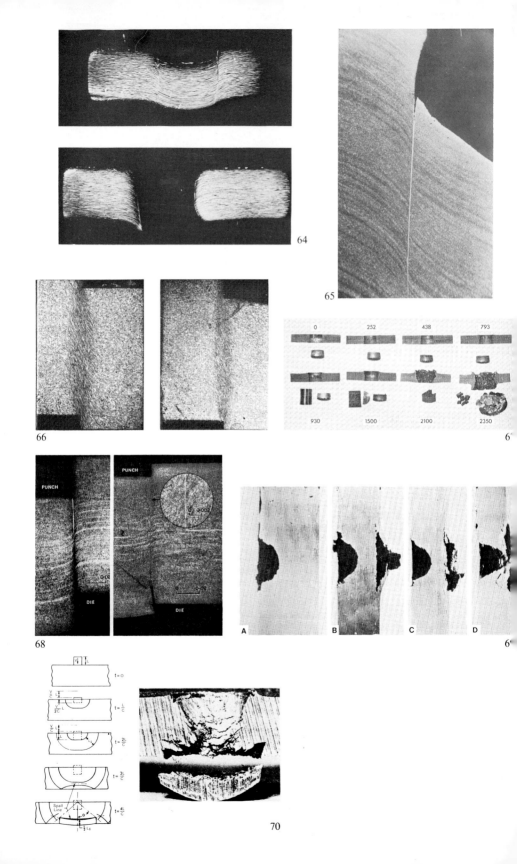

64

65

66

67

| 0 | 252 | 438 | 793 |

| 930 | 1500 | 2100 | 2350 |

68

A   B   C   D

69

70

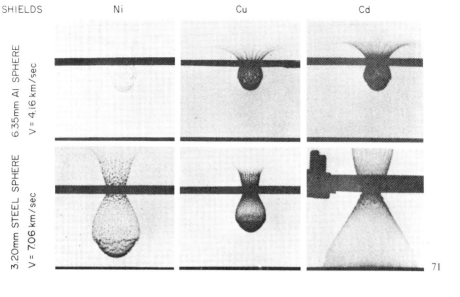

SHIELDS   Ni   Cu   Cd

6.35mm Al SPHERE V = 4.16 km/sec

3.20mm STEEL SPHERE V = 7.06 km/sec

71

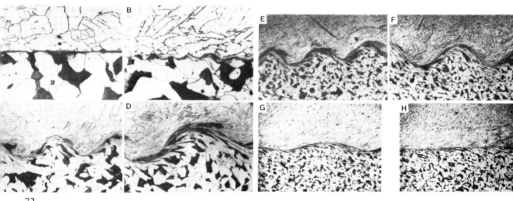

72

Plate 64   Plugging: top, the formed crack and white shear lines; below, the perforated plate.
Plate 65   A sectioned plate clearly showing the white shear line developed ahead of a projectile.
Plate 66   Lenticular-shaped shear zones, (a) slow and (b) fast blanking.[10.9]
Plate 67   High speed blanking[10.10] at various speeds (ft/sec.).
Plate 68   Photomicrographs of specimens partially blanked dynamically, where left and right the
stock hardness and penetration were 315 and 425 Vickers, and 0·036 and 0·012 in respectively.
The etching reagent used was 5 per cent Nital.[10.12]
Plate 69   Showing progression from cavity formation to perforation and spalling. Speed 7·4 km/sec.
Plate thicknesses[9.2] (A) 2·0 (B) 1·4 (C) 1·3 (D) 1·0 cm.
Plate 70   Hypervelocity impact with spalling. The diagram shows the stress wave propagation
through the plate, its reflection and spall formation.[10.8]
Plate 71   Showing a spallation cone or balloon.[9.2]
Plate 72   Photomicrographs[10.18] of mild steel welded to a semi-cylindrical mild steel parent plate

    (A) $\alpha = 0°$ ($\times 300$)   (B) $\alpha = 6°$ ($\times 300$)
    (C) $= 9°$ ($\times 110$)   (D) $= 12°$ ($\times 110$)
    (E) $= 12°$ ($\times 50$)   (F) $= 15°$ ($\times 50$)
    (G) $= 17°$ ($\times 37$)   (H) $= 21°$ ($\times 37$).

It is of course possible to make calculations allowing for elastic recovery or springback but the value of this is questionable in view of the many other assumptions made.

If $D_0 = 36$ in and $D = 42$ in, then for a ring of killed steel for which $B = 91\,000\ \varepsilon^{0.2}$ and $\rho g = 0.283$ lb/in^2, it is found that $v_0 \simeq 500$ ft/sec. The maximum engineering hoop strain rate occurs at the beginning of the process and is $\dot{e}_\theta = v_0/(D_0/2) = 500/1\frac{1}{2} \simeq 333$/sec; thus if the given equation for the stress-strain properties is based on *static* tests (say $\sim 10^{-3}$/sec) then very likely some adjustment would be needed to account for this, though this is only likely to be of the order of 15 % increase in stress for a given strain in aluminium. The ring would contract in length as well as thin, the strains in the radial and axial directions being equal to about one half the final hoop strain.

Yield criterion

The yielding, or the onset of plastic deformation, in *uniaxial* tension, compression or torsion is easily understood. It is less obvious to appreciate how a criterion for plastic flow may be arrived at in the case of *multi-axial* stress systems. Bearing in mind that in the plastic range we shall assume no change in volume, then whatever criterion is used, it is evident that (i) it must show itself to be independent of equal 'all-round' tension or compression (i.e. hydrostatic tension or compression), for a cube subject only to equal normal stresses on each of its faces is then clearly under no tendency to deform or change shape, and (ii) no work can be done in compressing the cube. Any test for yielding, assuming that it is only to be formulated in terms of stresses, must therefore be expressed as a function of principal stress differences, e.g. $(\sigma_1 - \sigma_2)$, for the addition or subtraction of equal 'all-round' pressures, p, then leaves this term unaltered, i.e. $[(\sigma_1 + p) - (\sigma_2 + p)] = (\sigma_1 - \sigma_2)$.

There are two criteria for the onset of plastic flow in *ductile* metals and in terms of principal stresses these appear as follows,

(i) *The Tresca yield criterion*

If each of the principal stresses is known, then when the greatest difference between any pair of them reaches a specific quantity, yield occurs. If, for instance, $\sigma_1 > \sigma_2 > \sigma_3$ then, when $(\sigma_1 - \sigma_3)$ attains a certain fixed magnitude, plastic flow is possible.

In simple tension, plastic flow starts when $\sigma_1 = Y$ and $\sigma_2 = \sigma_3 = 0$. Thus the fixed magnitude referred to, is just Y and we have

$$(\sigma_1 - \sigma_3) = Y \tag{4.50}$$

Hence, to use this criterion in any complex stress situation, the greatest principal stress difference is determined and if this set equal to Y, the condition for plastic flow is met.

(ii) *The Mises yield criterion*

This condition for plastic yield is,

$$(\sigma_1 - \sigma_2)^2 + (\sigma_2 - \sigma_3)^2 + (\sigma_3 - \sigma_1)^2 = \text{constant.} \tag{4.51}$$

This yield criterion is everywhere discussed below in terms of principal stress systems. But systems of normal stresses σ_x, σ_y and σ_z and shear stresses τ_{xy}, τ_{yz} and τ_{zx} could equally well be employed, since

$$(\sigma_1 - \sigma_2)^2 + (\sigma_2 - \sigma_3)^2 + (\sigma_3 - \sigma_1)^2$$
$$= (\sigma_x - \sigma_y)^2 + (\sigma_y - \sigma_z)^2 + (\sigma_z - \sigma_x)^2 + 6(\tau_{yz}^2 + \tau_{zx}^2 + \tau_{xy}^2),$$

see refs. 4.2, 4.4, 4.10 and 4.16.

By reference to the state of simple tension, as above, the constant is determined as $2Y^2$.

If a thin wall tube of mean radius a and thickness t, is loaded by an axial force P and a torque T, the mean axial stress $\sigma = P/2\pi at$ and the mean shear stress $\tau = T/2\pi a^2 t$, see Fig. 4.14. The principal stresses are, $2\sigma_1 = \sigma + (\sigma^2 + 4\tau^2)^{1/2}$, $2\sigma_3 = \sigma - (\sigma^2 + 4\tau^2)^{1/2}$ and $\sigma_2 = 0$, which when inserted into equation (4.50) gives,

$$\sigma^2 + 4\tau^2 = Y^2 \quad \text{or} \quad a^2 P^2 + 4T^2 = (2\pi a^2 t)^2 \cdot Y^2 \tag{4.52}$$

as the criterion for yielding following Tresca; and when inserted into (4.51) gives,

$$\sigma^2 + 3\tau^2 = Y^2 \quad \text{or} \quad a^2 P^2 + 3T^2 = (2\pi a^2 t)^2 \cdot Y^2 \tag{4.53}$$

as the criterion for yielding following Mises.

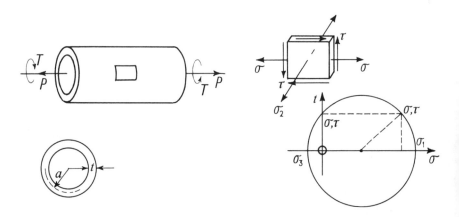

Fig. 4.14.

If in equations (4.52) and (4.53) we put $\sigma = 0$ then the yield shear stress according to the Tresca criterion is $Y/2$, whilst according to the Mises criterion it is $Y\frac{\sqrt{3}}{3}$. There is a 15% difference between the two predictions; this is the greatest difference that can be predicted by use of the two criteria.

In choosing the two yield criteria above we accepted that equal all-round normal stress does not incline an element to deform or change shape, and therefore undergo plastic deformation. We implied that shape changes depend on the degree to which a given stress system deviates from the state of equal 'all-round' normal stress. This is clearly brought out by plotting the equation for the Mises yield criterion in principal stress space. If $O\sigma_1$, $O\sigma_2$ and $O\sigma_3$ is a system of three orthogonal Cartesian axes, then the point σ_1, σ_2 and σ_3 represents a stress state. The space in this Cartesian system is called 'stress-space'[4.10]. The Mises criterion when plotted appears as a right circular cylinder whose axis, OM, see Fig. 4.15(a) is equally inclined to all three coordinate axes and whose radius is $Y\sqrt{\frac{2}{3}}$. A stress state which plots as a point inside the cylinder denotes an elastic state; a point which falls on the cylinder surface represents a state of plastic yield. Because the cylinder axis is equally inclined to all the coordinate axes, it is therefore a line of equal all-round pressure states. Nearness to the cylinder surface thus indicates 'nearness' to yield; the 'distance' of a stress point from the cylinder axis is a measure of the degree of 'deviation' from an equilibrium all-round uniform stress state. The Tresca yield criterion in principal stress space is a regular hexagonal cylinder coaxial with the Mises cylinder and having contact with it along six lines parallel to the axis.

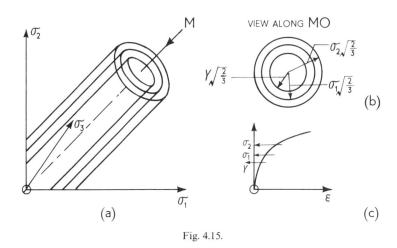

Fig. 4.15.

Since the uniaxial yield stress Y implies a cylinder whose initial radius is $Y\sqrt{\frac{2}{3}}$, therefore work-hardening is represented by a nest of cylinders of radius $\sigma_1\sqrt{\frac{2}{3}}$, $\sigma_2\sqrt{\frac{2}{3}}$, etc., see Fig. 4.15—indeed the radius of the cylinders can be thought of as being simply a function of plastic strain, ε. Each increment of tensile stress leads to an increase in the size of the yield cylinder.

Lévy–Mises equations

In elasticity, for a given stress distribution there corresponds just *one* distribution of elastic strain; there is a one-to-one correspondence of elastic stress and elastic strain. The strain system prevailing is simply a function of the stress system applying at an instant, no matter how that final stress (supposing it has always been elastic) has been arrived at. This is not the case in situations where there has been plastic deformation: whilst in elasticity the strain is only dependent on *state*, in plasticity it is dependent on stress *history*. For this reason in the plastic range, stress is related to strain increment; the final or total strain undergone by a body which has been plastic is found by summing the increments of strain in accordance with change, or history, of stress development. When circumstances are such that the elastic components of strain are negligible by comparison with plastic components, it is usual to employ the Lévy–Mises equation,

$$\frac{d\varepsilon_1}{\sigma'_1} = \frac{d\varepsilon_2}{\sigma'_2} = \frac{d\varepsilon_3}{\sigma'_3} = d\lambda \tag{4.54}$$

The symbols $d\varepsilon_1$, $d\varepsilon_2$ and $d\varepsilon_3$ are total principal strain increments. Symbols σ'_1, σ'_2 and σ'_3 are known as reduced principal stresses, or the principal stress deviators, and $\sigma'_1 = \sigma_1 - \bar{\sigma}$ etc with $3\bar{\sigma} = \sigma_1 + \sigma_2 + \sigma_3$. $d\lambda$ is just a constant of proportionality which may change as σ_1, σ_2 and σ_3 change.

Equation (4.54) only informs us about the *ratio* of the strain increments for a small increment in stress at the stress level $\sigma_1, \sigma_2, \sigma_3$; it is a 'flow' law, not a 'state' law.

Instead of (4.54), we may write, $d\varepsilon_1 : d\varepsilon_2 : d\varepsilon_3 = \sigma'_1 : \sigma'_2 : \sigma'_3$. This form is intimately[4.2] related to the Mises' yield criterion in conjunction with which it should be used. The corresponding form for the Tresca yield criterion is

$$d\varepsilon_1 : d\varepsilon_2 : d\varepsilon_3 = 1 : 0 : -1, \tag{4.55}$$

when yield is defined by $(\sigma_1 - \sigma_3) = Y$ and σ_2 is the intermediate stress.

Plane-strain bending

As an example of the direct use of the Lévy–Mises equations, we anticipate later sections and consider a plate bent by end couples which render it plastic through its entire thickness, see Fig. 4.16. Away from the plate edges *AB*, and in towards the middle of the plate, particles in a given vertical plane before bending will still be in the same plane after bending, i.e. strain in the O2-direction will be zero; this is a state of plane-strain. Suppose we wish to determine the tensile yield stress parallel to the plane of bending, i.e. σ_1 using the Mises' yield criterion; the stress through the thickness of the plate, σ_3, is clearly zero and we let the remaining principal stress be σ_2. As remarked, there is plane-strain bending, so that $d\varepsilon_2 = 0$ and since $d\varepsilon_1 + d\varepsilon_2 + d\varepsilon_3 = 0$, then

$$d\varepsilon_1 + d\varepsilon_3 = 0 \tag{4.56}$$

However, using the Lévy–Mises equation (4.54), we have $d\varepsilon_1 : d\varepsilon_3 = \sigma'_1 : \sigma'_3$ so that, with equation (4.56), $(\sigma'_1 + \sigma'_3) = 0$. Now, $\sigma'_1 = (\sigma_1 - \bar{\sigma})$, $\sigma'_3 = (\sigma_3 - \bar{\sigma})$ and $3\bar{\sigma} = (\sigma_1 + \sigma_2 + 0)$, and thus $\sigma'_1 = (2\sigma_1 - \sigma_2)/3$ and $\sigma'_3 = -(\sigma_1 + \sigma_2)/3$.

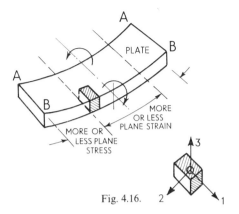

Fig. 4.16.

Hence $(\sigma_1' + \sigma_3') = 0$ gives $\sigma_2 = \sigma_1/2$. Substituting in the equation for the Mises yield criterion it is found that,

$$\sigma_1 = 2Y\sqrt{3}/3 \qquad (4.57)$$

Quasi-static compression of a short cylinder of perfectly plastic material

We consider a short circular cylinder of rigid-perfectly plastic material whose height to radius ratio, h/a is less than about 3, compressed between rigid parallel dies at a relatively constant slow speed—for most metals at room temperature this would be less than about 50 ft/sec, so that all inertia and wave effects may be neglected. Let the coefficient of friction between the flat end faces of the cylinder and the dies be μ; this interfacial friction is usually detected as a barrelling of the cylinder. Let the three normal stresses be σ_r, σ_θ and σ_z and assume that they may be considered to be independent of z and to be principal stresses also. Then the equation of equilibrium for an element of the cylinder, see Fig. 4.17, is

$$\frac{\sigma_r - \sigma_\theta}{r} + \frac{\partial \sigma_r}{\partial r} = -\frac{2\mu\sigma_z}{h} \qquad (4.58)$$

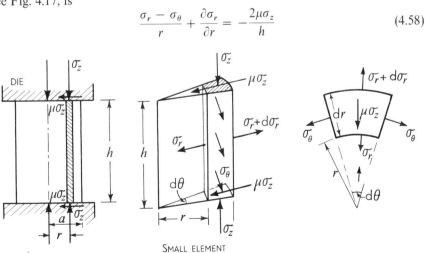

SMALL ELEMENT

Fig. 4.17.

Using equation (4.10iii) which can apply in this situation, in differential form as $d\varepsilon_\theta = d\varepsilon_r$, then through the Lévy–Mises equation therefore, $\sigma_\theta = \sigma_r$. This last equation depends on the assumption that σ_θ and σ_r are principal stresses. Thus, (4.58) becomes,

$$\frac{d\sigma_r}{dr} = -\frac{2\mu}{h} \cdot \sigma_z \tag{4.59}$$

Using Tresca's yield criterion, where $\sigma_r, \sigma_\theta > \sigma_z$, we have $(\sigma_r - \sigma_z) = Y$ or $d\sigma_r = d\sigma_z$, where Y is the uniaxial yield stress of the material. Substituting for $d\sigma_r$ in (4.59) and integrating,

$$\ln \sigma_z = -\frac{2\mu r}{h} + c \tag{4.60}$$

At $r = a$, $\sigma_r = 0$ and $\sigma_z = -Y$, so that equation (4.60) becomes, if we write p for $-\sigma_z$,

$$p = Y \exp\left(2\mu(a - r)/h\right) \tag{4.61}$$

and if μ is small,

$$p \simeq Y \left\{ 1 + \frac{2\mu(a - r)}{h} \right\} \tag{4.62}$$

The total force over a compression die is P, and

$$P \simeq \pi a^2 Y \left\{ 1 + \frac{2}{3}\mu \cdot \frac{a}{h} \right\} \tag{4.63}$$

Figure 4.18 shows how p varies with radius across the die; this pressure distribution is known as a *friction-hill*. If $a/h = 3$ and $\mu = 0.12$, then the load to effect compression of the cylinder following (4.63) is increased by 24% because of end interfacial friction.

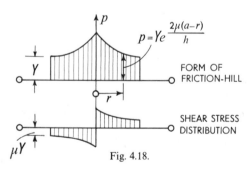

$$p = Y e^{\frac{2\mu(a-r)}{h}}$$

FORM OF FRICTION-HILL

SHEAR STRESS DISTRIBUTION

Fig. 4.18.

Fast compression of a short cylinder

When a short, uniform circular cylinder is *rapidly* compressed between rigid parallel plates or dies, inertia stresses and forces are generated which modify those ordinarily required to bring about plastic yield and compression in the quasi-static process. Rapid compression here refers to the regime in which the constant speed of compression for most metals is in the range of about 100 to 1000 ft/sec (30 to 300 m/s). For speeds in excess of about 1000 ft/sec (30 m/s), stress wave effects will assume importance. In the range of speeds quoted, it will be possible for any elastic or plastic stress waves initiated to travel up and down any cylindrical block many times during the course of compression.

It may be anticipated that the load-upper die travel diagram in a simple drop hammer forging operation will be modified as against that in a simple compression operation as follows.

First, the load 'felt' by each of the upper and lower dies will be different; the upper die is subject to a load in excess of the quasi-static load in the early part of the compressive process whilst it is accelerating material. And correspondingly, having enforced a high speed on the metal, the load will be reduced in the last stages of the compression since the inertia so acts as to assist the compression sought. The sequence of events and consequences will tend to be reversed in the case of the lower die.†

However, to assess the influence of speed in simple compression we confine attention to the simplest case of the frictionless compression of a short circular cylinder by an upper die moving at constant speed v, the lower die being at rest. This is the case when compression is carried out in a cam-plastometer, see ref. 4.25.

Figure 4.19 shows an upper die descending with speed v; u_r and f_r denote radial speed and acceleration, which are assumed to be independent of z at a given time. Then the equation for constancy of volume is,

$$v \cdot \pi r^2 = 2\pi r h \cdot u_r$$

or

$$u_r = \frac{r}{2h} \cdot v \tag{4.64}$$

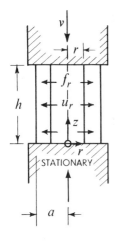
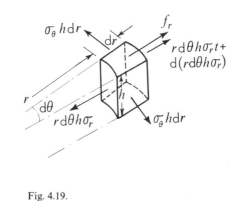

Fig. 4.19.

---

† See also, 'Influence of Billet Inertia and Die Friction in Forging Processes' by T. H. Dean, 11th Machine Tool Design and Research Conf., Pergamon Press, 1970.

Also,

$$f_r = \frac{du_r}{dt} = \frac{\partial r}{\partial t} \cdot \frac{v}{2h} + \frac{r}{2h} \frac{\partial v}{\partial t} - \frac{rv}{2h^2} \frac{\partial h}{\partial t}$$

$$= \frac{u_r v}{2h} + \frac{r}{2h} \cdot \dot{v} + \frac{rv^2}{2h^2},$$

and using (4.64),

$$f_r = \frac{rv^2}{4h^2} + \frac{r\dot{v}}{2h} + \frac{rv^2}{2h^2}$$

$$= \frac{3rv^2}{4h^2} + \frac{r\dot{v}}{2h} \tag{4.65}$$

Thus the radial acceleration f_r is just $3rv^2/4h^2$ for a constant speed upper die. The equation of radial motion of an element, see Fig. 4.19, is

$$d(r\,d\theta . h\sigma_r) - \sigma_\theta h\,dr\,d\theta = r\,d\theta . h\,dr\rho f_r \tag{4.66}$$

where ρ is the density of the cylinder.
   Equation (4.66) reduces to,

$$\frac{\sigma_r - \sigma_\theta}{r} + \frac{\partial \sigma_r}{\partial r} = \rho . f_r \tag{4.67}$$

Assuming $\sigma_r = \sigma_\theta$, as on p. 152, and recalling that $f_r = 3rv^2/4h^2$, equation (4.67) becomes

$$\frac{\partial \sigma_r}{\partial r} = \frac{3\rho v^2}{4h^2} r$$

or

$$\sigma_r = \frac{3\rho v^2}{4h^2} \cdot \frac{r^2}{2} + c \tag{4.68}$$

Noting that $\sigma_r = 0$ when $r = a$ it follows from equation (4.68) that,

$$\sigma_r = \frac{3\rho v^2}{8h^2} \cdot (r^2 - a^2)$$

In the absence of acceleration parallel to the axis of the cylinder (if $\dot{v} \neq 0$, then equation (4.68) should be modified) and using the Tresca yield criterion as

$$\sigma_r - \sigma_z = Y \tag{4.69}$$

we have, for the compressive stress on the dies p,

$$p = -\sigma_z = Y - \sigma_r = Y + \frac{3\rho v^2}{8h^2} \cdot (a^2 - r^2) \tag{4.70}$$

The load on the dies is P and

$$P = \pi a^2 Y \cdot \left[1 + \frac{3}{16} \cdot \frac{\rho v^2}{Y} \cdot \left(\frac{a}{h} \right)^2 \right], \tag{4.71}$$

where a and h are current dimensions of the cylinder. The second term on the right hand side of (4.71), for steel, and with $a/h = 1/2$ and using $Y \simeq 16$ ton/in^2 $(0.246 . 10^9$ N/m^2) would only contribute 1 % of the total load if the velocity was 100 ft/sec. This topic is discussed at much greater length in references 4.42 and 4.43 and the influence of friction at the die-material interfaces is also examined. In the latter two papers the circumstance in which $\dot{v} \neq 0$ is discussed and in the first paper the influence of viscosity is considered also.

Elastic-plastic stress distribution in thick-walled cylinders

It may be shown that for a thick-wall uniform cylinder of inner radius a and outer radius b, subjected to an internal pressure $-p_i$ and an external pressure $-p_0$, under conditions of plane strain, i.e. in Fig. 4.20, $e_z = 0$, the elastic hoop, radial and axial stresses set up are, respectively, σ_θ, σ_r and σ_z, and

$$\left. \begin{array}{l} \sigma_r = \dfrac{a^2 b^2 (p_0 - p_i)}{b^2 - a^2} \cdot \dfrac{1}{r^2} + \dfrac{p_i a^2 - p_0 b^2}{b^2 - a^2} \\[3mm] \sigma_\theta = -\dfrac{a^2 b^2 (p_0 - p_i)}{b^2 - a^2} \cdot \dfrac{1}{r^2} + \dfrac{p_i a^2 - p_0 b^2}{b^2 - a^2} \\[3mm] \sigma_z = \dfrac{p_i a^2 - p_0 b^2}{b^2 - a^2} \cdot 2v, \end{array} \right\} \tag{4.72}$$

and v is Poisson's ratio.

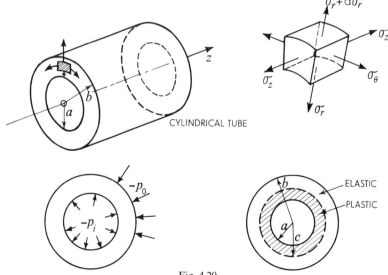

CYLINDRICAL TUBE

ELASTIC

PLASTIC

Fig. 4.20.

For $p_0 = 0$, the greatest principal stress difference is $(\sigma_\theta - \sigma_r)$ and this occurs at the inner surface of the cylinder, so that

$$\sigma_\theta - \sigma_r = \frac{p_i}{m^2 - 1} \cdot \frac{2b^2}{r^2} \qquad (4.73)$$

where $m = b/a$. Thus, plastic yield first occurs at the bore if we assume the Tresca yield criterion to apply, i.e. $(\sigma_\theta - \sigma_r) = Y$. Hence, substituting in equation (4.73),

$$\frac{p_i^*}{Y} = \frac{m^2 - 1}{2m^2} ; \qquad (4.74)$$

p_i^* is the pressure necessary for the onset of plastic yield. Evidently $0 < p_i^*/Y < \frac{1}{2}$ since $1 < m < \infty$.

If the Mises' criterion is used, plastic yield still occurs first at the bore but now,

$$\frac{p_i^*}{Y} = \frac{m^2 - 1}{2m^2} \cdot \frac{1}{\left(\dfrac{3}{4} + \dfrac{(1 - 2v)^2}{4m^4}\right)^{1/2}} \qquad (4.75)$$

When the applied pressure exceeds p_i^*, a cylindrically symmetric zone of plastically yielded material extends outwards from the bore, part way through the cylinder wall, see Fig. 4.20. Now the radial equilibrium equation for an element of the cylinder wall is,

$$\frac{d\sigma_r}{dr} + \frac{\sigma_r - \sigma_\theta}{r} = 0 \qquad (4.76)$$

and if the Tresca criterion applies, equation (4.76) becomes,

$$\frac{d\sigma_r}{dr} = \frac{Y}{r} \qquad (4.77)$$

Hence,

$$\sigma_r = Y \ln r + c \qquad (4.78)$$

At $r = a, \sigma_r = -p_i$ and if the zone of plastic yield extends out to radius c where the radial stress is σ_c, then after substitution,

$$\sigma_c = Y \ln (c/a) - p_i \qquad (4.79)$$

For $r > c$, the cylinder is elastic but at $r = c$, i.e. the elastic-plastic interface, it is just on the point of yield so that recalling (4.74)

$$-\frac{\sigma_c}{Y} = \frac{b^2 - c^2}{2b^2} \qquad (4.80)$$

and eliminating σ_c as between (4.79) and (4.80), we have

$$\frac{p_i}{Y} = \ln\frac{c}{a} + \frac{1}{2}\left(1 - \frac{c^2}{b^2}\right) \tag{4.81}$$

When $c = b$,

$$\frac{p_i^{**}}{Y} = \ln\frac{b}{a} \tag{4.82}$$

Thus the pressure to bring the whole cylinder up to a state of full plasticity is $Y \ln b/a$. Strictly, when equation (4.82) applies the radius ratio $m = b/a$, is that prevailing at total yield which is certainly different from what it is before the cylinder is loaded; the *current* ratio b/a is only significantly different from the unloaded ratio for large initial radius ratios.

Elastic-plastic stress distribution in thick spherical shells

It may be shown that for a spherical shell of inner radius a and outer radius b, subjected to an internal pressure $-p_i$ and an external pressure $-p_0$, see Fig. 4.21, that the hoop and radial stresses σ_θ and σ_r are given by,

$$\sigma_r = -\frac{(p_i - p_0)(b^3 - r^3)a^3}{r^3(a^3 - b^3)} \tag{4.83}$$

and

$$\sigma_\theta = -\frac{(p_i - p_0)(2r^3 + b^3)a^3}{2r^3(b^3 - a^3)} \tag{4.84}$$

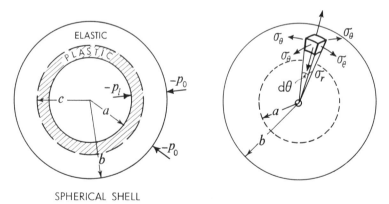

SPHERICAL SHELL

Fig. 4.21.

For $p_0 = 0$, the principal stress difference is everywhere

$$\sigma_\theta - \sigma_r = -\frac{3p_i a^3 b^3}{2r^3(b^3 - a^3)} \tag{4.85}$$

and this is greatest when $r = a$, i.e. at the inner surface of the spherical shell.

Thus, plastic yielding commences at the inner surface of a spherical shell at pressure p_i^*, and for either a Tresca or a Mises criterion, is given by

$$\sigma_\theta - \sigma_r = Y = -\frac{3p_i^* b^3}{2(b^3 - a^3)} \quad \text{or} \quad \frac{p_i^*}{Y} = \frac{2(m^3 - 1)}{3m^3} \tag{4.86}$$

where $m = b/a$. Since $p^*/Y = \frac{2}{3}(1 - 1/m^3)$ then for all values of $1 < m < \infty$, $0 < p^*/Y < \frac{2}{3}$; or, in particular, when $m \to \infty$, $p^*/Y \to \frac{2}{3}$.

When the applied pressure exceeds $-p_i^*$, a spherically symmetric zone of plastically-yielded material surrounds the inner surface out to radius c, which locates the elastic-plastic interface, see Fig. 4.21. Now, for the plastic spherical shell, the equation of radial equilibrium is

$$\frac{d\sigma_r}{dr} + \frac{2(\sigma_r - \sigma_\theta)}{r} = 0 \tag{4.87}$$

and putting $(\sigma_\theta - \sigma_r) = Y$, equation (4.87) becomes

$$d\sigma_r = 2Y \cdot \frac{dr}{r}$$

or

$$\sigma_r = 2Y \ln r + c \tag{4.88}$$

At $r = a$, $\sigma_r = -p_i$ and equation (4.88) becomes

$$\sigma_r = -p_i + 2Y \ln r/a \tag{4.89}$$

At $r = c$, the outer elastic shell is on the point of yielding and hence the radial pressure, σ_c, is, using equation (4.86)

$$Y = \frac{-3\sigma_c \cdot b^3}{2(b^3 - c^3)} \tag{4.90}$$

But using equation (4.89)

$$\sigma_c = -p_i + 2Y \ln c/a \tag{4.91}$$

and hence eliminating σ_c from equations (4.90) and (4.91) it is found that,

$$\frac{p_i}{Y} = \ln\left(\frac{c}{a}\right) + \frac{1}{3} \cdot \left(1 - \frac{c^3}{b^3}\right) \tag{4.92}$$

When $c = b$, the shell is wholly plastic and the internal pressure is given by,

$$\frac{p_i^{**}}{2Y} = \ln\frac{b}{a} \tag{4.93i}$$

The radial expansion Δb^{**} when pressure p_i^{**} is reached is obtained by realising that the outermost element of the shell is stressed just to the point of yielding. We have at $r = b$, $Ee_\theta = \sigma_\theta - v(\sigma_\theta + \sigma_r)$, but $\sigma_r = 0$ and since $e_\theta = \Delta b^{**}/b$, then

$$\Delta b^{**} = \frac{b\sigma_\theta(1 - v)}{E} = \frac{bY(1 - v)}{E} \tag{4.94}$$

Similarly, the radial expansion Δa^* at the inner surface for pressure p_i^* is

$$E \cdot \frac{\Delta a^*}{a} = \sigma_\theta - v(\sigma_\theta - p_i^*)$$

or

$$\Delta a^* = \frac{aY}{3E}\left[(1 + v) + \frac{2}{m^3}(1 - 2v)\right] \qquad (4.95)$$

If the material of the sphere is incompressible, i.e. $v = \frac{1}{2}$, it follows from equations (4.94) and (4.95) that,

$$\Delta a^* = \frac{aY}{2E} \quad \text{and} \quad \Delta b^{**} = \frac{bY}{2E} \qquad (4.96)$$

Also for the incompressible material, since

$$b^3 - a^3 = b^{*3} - a^{*3}$$

then

$$b^* = b\frac{\left[m^3 - 1 + \left(1 + \frac{Y}{2E}\right)^3\right]^{1/3}}{m} \simeq b\left(1 + \frac{1}{m^3} \cdot \frac{Y}{2E}\right) \qquad (4.97)$$

because Y/E is small. Further, with

$$b^{**3} - a^{**3} = b^3 - a^3$$

then,

$$a^{**} = a\left[m^3\left(1 + \frac{Y}{2E}\right)^3 - m^3 + 1\right]^{1/3} \qquad (4.98\text{i})$$

$$\simeq a\left(1 + \frac{3Y}{2E}m^3\right)^{1/3}, \qquad (4.98\text{ii})$$

when m is large.

Qualifications concerning spherical shell plastic expansion calculations

The analyses above, especially of the spherical shell, are not accurate for large radius ratios. The calculations took no account of geometry changes or the expansion of the shell during the application of the pressure; it was assumed for instance that at the moment the whole shell became plastic that the internal and external radii had exactly the same values as they did when there was no pressure at all applied. The results from equations (4.98ii) and (4.96) indicate that when the pressure p^{**} is reached,

$$a^{**} \doteqdot a\left(1 + \frac{3Y}{2E}m^3\right)^{1/3} \quad \text{and} \quad b^{**} \doteqdot b\left(1 + \frac{Y}{2E}\right)$$

Typically, $Y/E = \frac{1}{1000}$ so that for say $m = 10$, $m^{**} = b^{**}/a^{**} \doteq 7.37$ which is very significantly different from the initial ratio.

Thus if account is taken of the radial displacements undergone by the spherical shell wall in the act of straining and becoming fully plastic, then for the elastic-perfectly plastic incompressible material

$$b^{**}/a^{**} = b\left(1 + \frac{Y}{2E}\right) \Big/ a\left(1 + m^3 \cdot \frac{3Y}{2E}\right)^{1/3} \simeq \left[m^3 \Big/ \left(1 + m^3 \cdot \frac{3Y}{2E}\right)\right]^{1/3}$$

and hence

$$\frac{p^{**}}{Y} = 2\ln\frac{b^{**}}{a^{**}} = \frac{2}{3}\ln\frac{m^3}{\left(1 + \dfrac{3m^3 Y}{2E}\right)} \qquad (4.93\text{ii})$$

where $m = b/a$. Clearly, for large values of m, $p^{**}/Y \to \frac{2}{3}\ln(2E/3Y)$. Table 4.1 shows values calculated following equation (4.93i) and that for p^{**}/Y above.

TABLE 4.1   ASSUMING, $Y/E = \frac{1}{1000}$

$m = b/a$	1·5	2	4	6	10	∞
b^{**}/a^{**}	1·5	1·99	3·87	5·45	7·37	—
$p^{**}/2Y$ (using equation (4.93ii))	0·40	0·69	1·35	1·70	1·99	2·17
$p^{**}/2Y$ (using equation (4.93i))	0·41	0·69	1·39	1·79	2·30	—

Pressure to expand a spherical shell of work-hardening material of infinite radius ratio

The analysis[4.2] of the infinite radius ratio spherical shell allowing for geometry changes of the shell and possessing a linear strain-hardening, stress-strain law of the form, $\sigma = Y + P.\varepsilon$, leads to a pressure for p^{**} to bring the whole shell to a plastic state, of

$$p^{**} = \frac{2}{3}Y\ln\frac{2E}{3Y} + \frac{2\pi^2}{27}.P$$

If $E/Y = \frac{1}{1000}$ and $P/Y = \frac{1}{3}$, $p^{**}/Y = 4.58$.

Work to expand a spherical shell

The work required to plastically expand a spherical shell of incompressible non-hardening material from internal initial radius a_0 to some current radius a by quasi-static internal pressure, is given by

$$W = \int_{a_0}^{a} 4\pi a^2 \cdot p_i \cdot da$$

Neglecting the work required to be done in order to bring the shell up to full plastic yield and using only equation (4.93i),

$$W = \int_{a_0}^{a} 4\pi a^2 \cdot \frac{2Y}{3} \ln \frac{b^3}{a^3} \cdot da$$

$$= \frac{8\pi Y}{3} \int_{a_0}^{a} a^2 \ln \left(1 + \frac{b_0^3 - a_0^3}{a^3} \right) da \qquad (4.99)$$

since $(b_0^3 - a_0^3) = (b^3 - a^3)$, where b_0 in the initial external radius.

Radial speed of inner surface to achieve a given expansion in a thick spherical shell

A spherical shell when packed with explosive and detonated, causes the shell to rapidly expand, the inner surface acquiring some initial radial speed v_0. If this speed is acquired in a much shorter time than it takes the shell to expand, then the kinetic energy of the shell may be taken to be dissipated as the plastic work of expansion. If all stress wave effects are neglected, then the speed to achieve a specified expansion to radius a, or b which is considerably in excess of b^{**}, may be estimated for the incompressible material as follows.

The speed of an element of the shell at radius r is $a_0^2 v_0 / r^2$ and hence, the total kinetic energy of the shell wall is,

$$\int_{a_0}^{b_0} \frac{1}{2} \cdot 4\pi r^2 \rho \cdot \left(\frac{a_0^2 v_0}{r^2} \right)^2 \cdot dr = 2\pi \rho a_0^3 (b_0 - a_0) v_0^2 / b_0 \qquad (4.100)$$

By equating (4.99) and (4.100), v_0 may be found.

In ref. 4.49 these equations were used with moderate success to calculate the form assumed by the surface of a semi-infinite mass due to a slightly sub-surface explosive charge.

Expanding an infinitely small cavity by internal pressure, in an infinite elastic-perfectly plastic spherical shell when the external pressure is zero

In Fig. 4.22 application of internal pressure, p^{***}, over the inner surface of radius a creates (i) a spherically symmetric, fully plastic shell of radius a^{**}, out to radius c^{**}, and (ii) from c^{**} to the outer radius b^*, an outer shell which is entirely elastic apart from being in a state of plastic yield on its inner surface of radius c^{**}. If symbols a, b and c denote the *original* values of the internal and

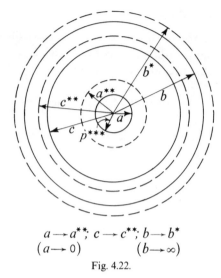

$$a \longrightarrow a^{**}; \quad c \longrightarrow c^{**}; \quad b \longrightarrow b^*$$
$$(a \longrightarrow 0) \qquad\qquad (b \longrightarrow \infty)$$

Fig. 4.22.

external radius and the elastic-plastic interface, then a^{**}, b^* and c^{**} denote the values to which the latter are increased when the pressure to be found is attained.

The spherical shell in its expanded state may thus be considered as consisting of *two* concentric spherical shells and hence for the incompressible, elastic-perfectly plastic shell we can use equations (4.91) and (4.86), thus

(i)
$$\frac{p^{***}}{Y} = \frac{2}{3} \ln \left(\frac{c^{**}}{a^{**}}\right)^3 + \frac{\sigma_{c^{**}}}{Y}. \qquad (4.101)$$

$\sigma_{c^{**}}$ denotes the radial *pressure* at radius c^{**},

(ii)
$$\frac{\sigma_{c^{**}}}{Y} = \frac{2}{3} Y, \quad \text{since} \quad b^*/c^{**} \to \infty \qquad (4.102)$$

Hence,

$$\frac{p^{***}}{Y} = \frac{2}{3}\left(1 + \ln \frac{2E}{3Y}\right)$$

The elastic-plastic interface extends to c^{**} and $c^{**}/a^{**} \to (2E/3Y)^{1/3}$ using equation (4.96). If $Y/E = \frac{1}{300}, c^{**} \simeq (200)^{1/3} a^{**} \simeq 5.8 \cdot a^{**}$. (And if $Y/E = \frac{1}{1000}$, $c^{**} \simeq 8.7 a^{**}$.)

Dynamic expansion of a small cavity in an infinite elastic-perfectly plastic solid using a quasi-static approach

Let a pressure p', which is a function of time and radius be applied to the inside surface of a cavity such that initially, i.e. at $t = 0$, the cavity radius is infinitely small. If $p' > p^{***}$ then each element of the expanding infinitely-extensive spherical shell will accelerate radially. When the current cavity radius is a and its radial speed $\dot{a}$, the kinetic energy E of the whole shell is given by,

$$E = \int_a^\infty \tfrac{1}{2}(4\pi r^2 \, dr\rho) \, . \, \dot{r}^2 \tag{4.103}$$

where r is the current radius and $\dot{r}$ the radial speed of an element, and ρ is the density. The incompressibility condition gives $4\pi a^2 \, . \, \dot{a} = 4\pi r^2 \, . \, \dot{r}$ so that, substituting in (4.103), we have

$$E = \int_a^\infty 2\pi\rho r^2 \left(\frac{a^2 \, . \, \dot{a}}{r^2}\right)^2 dr$$

$$= 2\pi\rho a^4 \, . \, \dot{a}^2 \left[-\frac{1}{r}\right]_a^\infty = 2\pi\rho a^3 \, . \, \dot{a}^2$$

At time t, pressure p' is doing work at a rate $p' \, . \, 4\pi a^2 \, . \, \dot{a}$ so that

$$p' \, . \, 4\pi a^2 \, . \, \dot{a} = p^{***} \, . \, 4\pi a^2 \, . \, \dot{a} + \dot{E} \tag{4.104}$$

Now, $\dot{E} = 2\pi\rho(3a^2 \, . \, \dot{a}^3 + 2a^3 \, . \, \dot{a} \, . \, \ddot{a})$, and hence substituting in (4.104),

$$p' = p^{***} + \rho(\tfrac{3}{2}\dot{a}^2 + a \, . \, \ddot{a}) \tag{4.105}$$

If when $\ddot{a} = 0$, $\dot{a} = V_0$, then

$$p'(t) = \frac{2}{3}Y\left[1 + \ln\frac{2E}{3Y}\right] + \frac{3}{2}\rho V_0^2 \tag{4.106}$$

There are serious shortcomings pertaining to the analysis just described; these are,
(i) that, following p. 162, for $E/Y = 300$, supersonic values of $\dot{c}^{**}$ are implied for $\dot{a}^{**}$ in excess of $1/5 \cdot 8$ or $0 \cdot 17$ of the velocity of small amplitude plastic waves,
(ii) the incompressible model implies the unrealistic instantaneous transmission of energy to the most remote regions of the body.

Bombs: the very high speed expansion of cylinders and spherical shells

Bombs are usually constructed from suitably corrugated iron or steel casings packed with high explosive. At detonation the high pressure of the explosion products drives the wall of the bomb outwards at high speed such that multi-fractures are initiated, and as expansion proceeds further, complete fragmentation occurs. The onset of the latter is detected from the appearance of smoke when high speed cine-films are taken of bomb explosions. The most frequently used shape of bomb casing is tubular which is usually detonated axially from one end. Plate 21 shows such a casing in process of expansion; see also Fig. 4.23. Such tubes are known to expand to more than twice their original radius before fragmentation takes place.

The prediction of the radius at which fragmentation starts has long been the subject of empirical intensive examination, but Taylor[4.45] in a paper in

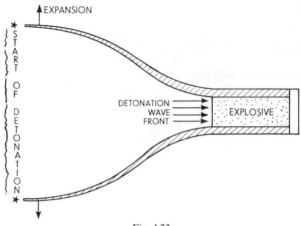

Fig. 4.23.

1948 presented a simple and elegant analysis that, with the help of a few assumptions, accounted for the radius of fracture at complete fragmentation in the explosion of a thin tubular bomb. This analysis makes use of the fact that when very high pressure acts on the inside of the casing, compressive hoop stresses exist over an inner region of the casing, and the depth of this region is governed predominantly by the magnitude of this applied pressure. Taylor's assumption is that radial cracks are initiated only in the region of tensile stress and cannot propagate through and into the compressive zone. Taylor concluded that complete fragmentation takes place only when the compressive region completely disappears, hence allowing cracks to propagate right up to the inside surface, see Fig. 4.24. His analysis predicts that the depth, y, to which the tensile hoop stress region extends at any time during the expansion process, measured from the outside surface is approximately Yh/p_a, where h is the current cylinder wall thickness, Y is the uniaxial yield stress of the material and p_a is the current

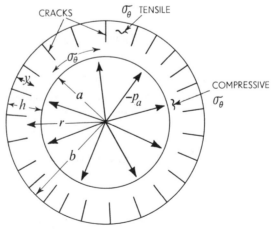

Fig. 4.24.

internal radial pressure. Thus, if the condition for complete fragmentation is given by $y = h$, this occurs when $p_a = Y$. Hence if p_a can be calculated as a function of radius a, the fracture radius may be deduced.

The approach below[4.46] is essentially the same as that of Taylor; it is however more complete and pertains more generally to thick-walled cylinders.

The idealised equation of radial motion of an element, see Fig. 4.25, is

$$\frac{\sigma_r - \sigma_\theta}{r} + \frac{\partial \sigma_r}{\partial r} = \rho \frac{d^2 r}{dt^2} \qquad (4.107)$$

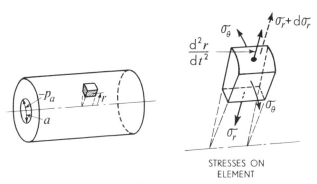

STRESSES ON ELEMENT

Fig. 4.25.

where $d^2 r/dt^2$ is the *total* acceleration of the element. Now for there to be no change in volume,

$$r^2 - a^2 = r_0^2 - a_0^2 \qquad (4.108)$$

The symbol r denotes the current radial distance of the element from the centre line of the bomb, r_0 is its original location and a_0 and a are its original and the current internal radius; b_0 is the original external radius of the bomb.

Hence, from (4.108),

$$r \frac{\partial r}{\partial t} - a \frac{\partial a}{\partial t} = 0$$

Differentiating again, but writing $\partial a/\partial t = v_a$

$$\frac{d^2 r}{dt^2} = \frac{v_a^2}{r} + \frac{a}{r} \cdot \frac{\partial v_a}{\partial t} - \frac{a^2}{r^3} \cdot v_a^2 \qquad (4.109)$$

Using the Tresca yield criterion as,

$$\sigma_\theta - \sigma_r = Y, \qquad (4.110)$$

and substituting (4.109) and (4.110) into (4.107),

$$\frac{\partial \sigma_r}{\partial r} = \frac{Y}{r} + \rho \left(\frac{v_a^2}{r} + \frac{a}{r} \cdot \frac{\partial v_a}{\partial t} - \frac{a^2 v_a^2}{r^3} \right)$$

which after integration gives,

$$\sigma_r = \left[Y + \rho \left(v_a^2 + a \frac{\partial v_a}{\partial t} \right) \right] \ln r + \frac{1}{2} \rho \frac{a^2 v_a^2}{r^2} + C \qquad (4.111)$$

Now $\sigma_r = -p_a$ at $r = a$, so that from (4.111),

$$-p_a = \left[Y + \rho \left(v_a^2 + a \frac{\partial v_a}{\partial t} \right) \right] \ln a + \tfrac{1}{2} \rho v_a^2 + C \qquad (4.112)$$

and hence eliminating C from (4.111) and (4.112),

$$\sigma_r + p_a = \left[Y + \rho \left(v_a^2 + a \frac{\partial v_a}{\partial t} \right) \right] \ln \frac{r}{a} + \frac{1}{2} \rho v_a^2 \left(\frac{a^2}{r^2} - 1 \right) \qquad (4.113)$$

Now using (4.110) and (4.113)

$$\sigma_\theta = Y - p_a + \left[Y + \rho \left(v_a^2 + a \frac{\partial v_a}{\partial t} \right) \right] \ln \frac{r}{a} + \frac{1}{2} \rho v_a^2 \left(\frac{a^2}{r^2} - 1 \right) \qquad (4.114)$$

Two different regions of stress distribution may be distinguished within the tube wall as indicated in Figs. 4.24 and 4.26, the boundary between them being defined by $\sigma_\theta = 0$, i.e. at the depth $y = b - r$. Using this definition in equation (4.114), the value of y is given by,

$$p_a - Y = \left[Y + \rho \left(v_a^2 + a \frac{\partial v_a}{\partial t} \right) \right] \ln \left(\frac{b - y}{a} \right) + \frac{1}{2} \rho v_a^2 \left[\frac{a^2}{(b - y)^2} - 1 \right] \qquad (4.115)$$

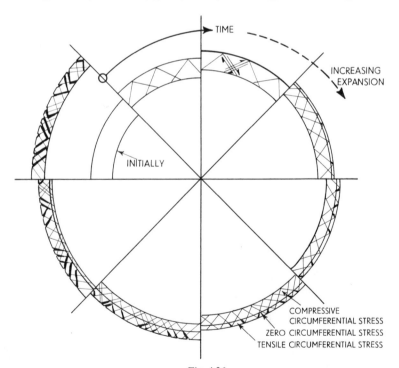

Fig. 4.26.

The region of compressive stress i.e. $\sigma_\theta < 0$ and $\sigma_r < 0$, will just disappear when $y = b - a = h$ and equation (4.115) then shows that

$$p_a = Y \qquad (4.116)$$

This is the same condition as that originally obtained by Taylor and completes the Strength of Materials aspect of this situation.

However, to determine when complete fracture takes place, an expression for the pressure exerted by the gaseous explosion products on the inner wall of the casing as a function of internal wall radius is required. This expression can be approximated reasonably well by assuming an isentropic expansion of the explosion products. Thus,

$$p_a = p_0 \left(\frac{a}{a_0}\right)^{-2\gamma} \qquad (4.117)$$

where p_0 is the effective detonation pressure acting on the inside surface when $a = a_0$ and γ is the adiabatic exponent. Aside from the assumption of a homogeneous thermodynamic state throughout the fully detonated explosive within the bomb, the isentropic equation of state of the gaseous explosion products is very complex for a number of chemical and physical reasons, and in particular γ is not constant during the expansion. Typically, however, for TNT, γ has an initial value of about 3·4 when the pressure p_0 is about $2·3 . 10^6$ lb/in² ($15·8 . 10^9$ N/m²) and, when the density is reduced to about one quarter of its initial value, γ is about 1·9. For a moderate expansion to fracture, the fixed value $\gamma = 3$ is a satisfactory approximation.

The criterion for complete fracture of the casing i.e. equation (4.116) i.e. when $p_a = Y$, inserted into equation (4.117) gives

$$\frac{a}{a_0} = \left(\frac{p_0}{Y}\right)^{1/2\gamma}$$

$$\simeq \left(\frac{p_0}{Y}\right)^{1/6}$$

If then we put $p_0 = 2·3 . 10^6$ lb/in² and assume a representative figure for Y of say $6·9 . 10^4$ lb/in (about 30 ton/in²), then $a/a_0 \simeq (10^2/3)^{1/6} \simeq 1·8$. Note that the higher the yield stress, Y, of the casing material, the smaller the resistance to crack propagation as measured by the expansion radius at complete fracture.

Hoggatt and Recht[4.47] have proposed a model of fracturing, similar to that of Taylor but based on the assumption that the fractures take place along planes of maximum shear stress; their idea is indicated in Fig. 4.26.

The procedure for analysing the fragmentation of spherical bombs may be carried out in a similar manner to that used above for cylindrical shells, to arrive at the same result, i.e. complete fracture occurs when the internal radial pressure has fallen to the uniaxial yield stress (or strength) of the casing. The casing radius of fracture is now given by,

$$\frac{a}{a_0} = \left(\frac{p_0}{Y}\right)^{1/3\gamma} \qquad (4.118)$$

For the same values of p_0, Y, and γ as earlier, we find $a/a_0 \simeq 1.5$. The speed of casings at fracture, 5000 to 15 000 ft/sec (1520 to 4550 m/s), may be calculated using the approach above, and the increase in radius with time. The subject is dealt with at length in ref. 4.48.

Indentation and hardness

Static hardness testing or the study of the static indentation of surfaces by rigid indenters has been the subject of many books[4,5] and papers and we shall only summarise some of the principal features here. The usual concern is to be able to estimate how indentation load or pressure varies with penetration depth and to describe the flow of material beneath and in the vicinity of the indenter. The mechanical properties of the indented material which are used to predict or interpret results are E, Y and its strain hardening exponent; friction between the indenter and the material also affects the flow of metal.

Two categories of indentation should be distinguished: those in which there is *geometric similarity* and those in which there is not. Wedges and cones give rise to a pattern of material displacement which is constant and depth of penetration affects only the *scale* of the pattern. The pressure to indent is constant and the load varies as the first or second power of the depth of penetration according to whether the indenter is a straight sided wedge or a cone. When the indenter is, say, a ball, the ratio of the contacting spherical surface to penetration depth alters with depth of penetration so that the pressure and flow change continuously. Constant indentation pressure and flow pattern are consequences of an indentation process in which there is geometrical similarity whilst varying pressure and changing flow pattern are associated with the circumstances of the lack of geometric similarity.

It is usual to distinguish two kinds of indenter—blunt and sharp. The rigid flat (blunt) indenter, when applying a pressure of approximately $1.1Y$ where Y is the yield stress of the indented material, causes yielding to start at about one half the indenter width below its mid-point in the material. As the indentation pressure increases, the extent of the zone of plastic deformation increases but is entirely contained by surrounding elastic material; when the pressure attains a value of about $3Y$, the material is plastic across the whole of the indenter and may flow grossly, or unconstrainedly, along the sides of the indenter thus causing the original surface to be raised. When a cone indents a surface the severity of surface displacement depends heavily on the work hardening characteristic of the material. If it is a work-hardened material a more-or-less clear 'coronet' or 'elevated ridge' will be developed, Fig. 4.27(a), but in the case of annealed material a 'sinking-in' type of impression is found, Fig. 4.27(b). Experiment shows that indentation pressure increases with cone angle and lies between about $2.3Y$ and $3Y$. With sharp angle indenters cones, wedges and pyramidal indenters, interfacial friction can increase the indentation pressure significantly but its other effect is to promote the possibility of a 'false' cap of 'dead' metal, see Fig. 4.27(c), being formed over the apex of a large angle indenter; a new 'natural' cone angle may thus be acquired by the indenter so

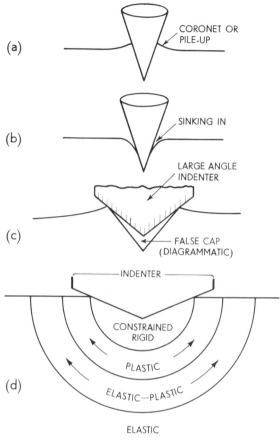

Fig. 4.27.

that as indentation proceeds a region of strong internal shearing is likely; the value of the indentation pressure is then about $3Y$.

With a rounded indenter—a ball for instance—where there is no geometrical similarity and a false cap over the indenter is created, the zone of plastic deformation extends as the load increases; initially, material is displaced approximately radially from the point where contact is first made but when the pressure is about $3Y$ it is able to flow in order to pile-up at the sides of the intenter.

A sharp indenter acts so as to 'cut' material and to compel upwards flow.

Blunt indenters tend to give rise to predominantly radial compression and to a general stress and strain distribution which in some ways is not unlike that created by high internal pressure in a very thick cylinder or sphere; the similarity between the latter, see Fig. 4.27(d), and the blunt indentation situation see Fig. 4.27(c) will be obvious.

The value of Y for calculating pressure can be found from a simple compression test and is the value of the compressive flow stress after about 8 % engineering compressive strain. The hardness of a material is thus just a property of the stress-strain curve of the material indented, the geometry of the indenter and of the interfacial friction which prevails.

Dynamic indentation may be wholly elastic or elastic-plastic. For say, a non-plastically deforming ball impinging against a typical flat metal surface at a speed of order 1 cm/sec, elastic stresses are set up and may be calculated using Hertz theory. The kinetic energy at impact will first be wholly converted into elastic strain energy in the ball and the indented material, and elastic stress waves will be radiated into the latter. Elastic recovery occurs especially in the region between and near the interface, so that the ball rebounds; some small percentage of the initial energy is 'lost' as elastic waves. If the mean maximum stress at impact exceeds 1·1 Y, due to higher impact speeds, plastic deformation occurs and thus some of the initial kinetic energy will be irrecoverable. Elastic recovery and rebound occurs, but to a proportionately lesser degree than for purely elastic impact. The higher the impact speed the greater is the energy loss due to plastic deformation and the greater the difference between rebound and initial impact speed. This subject has been discussed at length by Tabor[4,5] and we shall therefore not pursue it except to note Martel's equation which can be of use in some situations.

If the penetration at an instant is h then the increment in work to enforce a further penetration dh is $\simeq 3Y.A.dh$ where A is the contact area. The total plastic work done in achieving a penetration H is then $\simeq 3\,Y\int_0^H A\,dh = 3Y$ times the volume of the 'plastic' cavity created. The final cavity as seen is, however, the 'plastic' cavity after elastic rebound has occurred and this may be significantly different from the 'plastic' cavity before rebound starts. In any energy balance performed then, the three major factors are plastic work dissipation, elastic recovery near the surface of the material and the rebound kinetic energy in the indenter.

Representative stress and representative strain

A single magnitude chosen to characterise the stress state of a plastically deforming element in the strain-hardened state when subject to three principal stresses, σ_1, σ_2 and σ_3 is

$$\bar{\sigma} = \left[\frac{(\sigma_1 - \sigma_2)^2 + (\sigma_2 - \sigma_3)^2 + (\sigma_3 - \sigma_1)^2}{2}\right]^{1/2}. \qquad (4.119)$$

$\bar{\sigma}$ is called a representative or generalised stress. In general form, $\bar{\sigma}$ is evidently similar to the Mises' yield criterion expression. The constant $\frac{1}{2}$ is inserted in order that $\bar{\sigma}$ shall be equal to a uniaxial flow stress, i.e. $\bar{\sigma} = \sigma_1$.

By analogy with $\bar{\sigma}$, a representative or generalised strain increment is defined such that,

$$\overline{d\varepsilon} = [\tfrac{2}{9}\{(d\varepsilon_1 - d\varepsilon_2)^2 + (d\varepsilon_2 - d\varepsilon_3)^2 + (d\varepsilon_3 - d\varepsilon_1)^2\}]^{1/2} \qquad (4.120)$$

The constant $\frac{2}{9}$ is introduced so that $\overline{d\varepsilon}$ shall be equal to the strain increment in the direction of the applied stress in uniaxial loading say $d\varepsilon_1$. Clearly in this case $d\varepsilon_2 = d\varepsilon_3$ and since $d\varepsilon_1 + d\varepsilon_2 + d\varepsilon_3 = 0$ then $d\varepsilon_2 = -d\varepsilon_1/2$ and hence

$d\varepsilon = d\varepsilon_1$. In all the analyses in which we are interested below, $d\varepsilon_1$, $d\varepsilon_2$ and $d\varepsilon_3$ are principal plastic strain increments and all elastic components of the strain are neglected.

If a plastic straining process proceeds such that the proportionality between the three operative principal stresses remains fixed, then the total strains, e.g. ε_1, may be used in place of strain increments, i.e. $d\varepsilon_1$, in equation (4.120); this is clearly the case for simple tension and compression. It is also usual to work with total strains when considering a process where it is believed that there is little deviation of proportionality as between the principal stresses at all stages, especially if rigorous calculations appear likely to be difficult. For many engineering situations the use of total strain is often justified when regard is had to the imprecision attaching to data available, e.g. nebulous coefficients of friction and strain rate effects, etc.

Representative stress and strain are empirically connected by equations of the kind given by (4.32) and (4.33) for many metals. The most frequently used form is,

$$\bar{\sigma} = B\bar{\varepsilon}^n \tag{4.121}$$

Since $\bar{\sigma}$ and $\bar{\varepsilon}$ were so defined in equations (4.119) and (4.120) as to coincide with the uniaxial stress and strain measures, it follows that the empirical constants B and n of equation (4.121) could be determined from a simple tensile test. For much sheet metal work, it is better to use a test method in which a circular specimen is clamped at its periphery and then subjected to a lateral hydrostatic pressure, causing it to bulge. Near the pole of the bulge the form is spherical and the material thickness nearly constant, so that by measuring simple total extension and curvature over the pole, the equal biaxial stresses in the sheet and the total strains there may be found. Compounding these quantities according to equations (4.119) and (4.120), a graph of $\bar{\sigma}$ versus $\bar{\varepsilon}$ may be arrived at and thence constants B and n deduced empirically. Details of this and other methods for determining $\bar{\sigma}/\bar{\varepsilon}$ curves may be found in ref. 4.10.

Equation (4.121) may be thought of in terms of a Mises cylinder, see Fig. 4.15, of radius $\bar{\sigma}\sqrt{\frac{2}{3}}$; the cylinder radius is then a function of $\bar{\varepsilon}$.

Initial speed required to expand a thin spherical shell or a thin cylindrical shell to a given radius: speeds required to attain static instability strains

The permanent plastic straining of a spherical or cylindrical shell of initial radius r_0 of strain-hardening material by imparting a radially outward initial velocity, v_0, simultaneously to all parts of it, to give a radius of r, is considered in order to find the radius to which the sphere or cylinder is expanded. For both kinds of shell all elastic strains are neglected as being small in comparison with the plastic strain. For an element of the spherical shell the equation of radial motion is, assuming the stress distribution through the shell wall is uniform,

$$2\sigma_\theta hr\,d\theta\,.\,d\phi + \rho hr^2\,d\theta\,.\,d\phi\,.\,\frac{d^2r}{dt^2} = 0$$

or

$$\frac{d^2r}{dt^2} + \frac{2\sigma_\theta}{\rho r} = 0;\qquad(4.122)$$

the meaning of the symbols will be clear from Fig. 4.28 and r and h denote current values of radius and thickness.

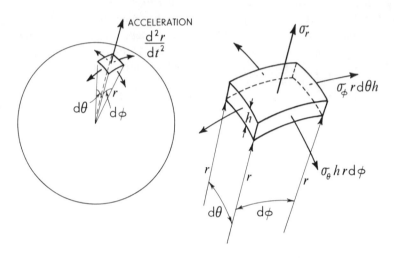

Fig. 4.28.

Now throughout the expansion process $\sigma_\theta = \sigma_\phi$ and $\sigma_r = 0$ so that substituting in equation (4.119), $\bar\sigma = \sigma_\theta$; and since in this circumstance of uniform expansion it is permissible to use total strains, for which $\varepsilon_\theta = \varepsilon_\phi = -\varepsilon_t/2$ then $\bar\varepsilon = 2\varepsilon_\theta$, using equation (4.120).

Adapting equation (4.34) and writing it in terms of $\bar\sigma$ and $\bar\varepsilon$, we have $\bar\sigma = B(C + \bar\varepsilon)^n$, so that $\sigma_\theta = B(C + 2\varepsilon_\theta)^n$. Hence from (4.122) and putting $d^2r/dt^2 = v \cdot dv/dr$,

$$\int_{v_0}^0 v \cdot dv = -\frac{2B}{\rho}\int_{r_0}^r \frac{(C + 2\varepsilon_\theta)^n}{r}\,.\,dr$$

and thus

$$v_0^2 = \frac{2BC^{n+1}}{\rho(n+1)}\left[\left(1 + \frac{2}{C}\ln\frac{r}{r_0}\right)^{n+1} - 1\right],\qquad(4.123)$$

where $\varepsilon_\theta = \ln r/r_0$

For the element of the cylindrical shell shown in Fig. 4.29 the equation of radial motion is

$$\frac{d^2r}{dt^2} + \frac{\sigma_\theta}{\rho r} = 0\qquad(4.124)$$

Proceeding as previously, it is easily shown then that for plane strain expansion,

$$v_0^2 = \frac{2BC^{n+1}}{\rho(n+1)}\left[\left(1 + \frac{1}{C}\ln\frac{r}{r_0}\right)^{n+1} - 1\right] \tag{4.125}$$

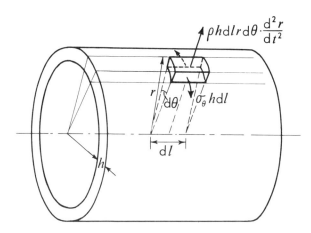

Fig. 4.29.

Expressions for v_0 to cause the shells to reach the tensile instability strain may now easily be arrived at; these strains are those prevailing when some internal, slowly applied hydrostatic pressure reaches its greatest value, see ref. 4.10. Values of v_0 for real materials, on this basis, can be taken to indicate the speeds that could reasonably be tolerated in any high speed expansion (or explosive) situation, in order to obtain significant amounts of straining, before difficulties due to local thinning and fracture arise. For the spherical shell at instability, the hoop strain, $\ln r/r_0$ is equal to $(2n - 3C)/6$. The initial velocity v_0^* required to produce strain equal to the instability strain is therefore

$$v_0^{*2} = \frac{2BC^{n+1}}{\rho(n+1)}\left[\left(\frac{2n}{3C}\right)^{n+1} - 1\right] \tag{4.126}$$

The initial velocity v_0^{**} required to produce strains equal to the static instability strain in a long cylindrical shell is found to be given by

$$v_0^{**2} = \frac{2BC^{n+1}}{\rho(n+1)}\left[\left(\frac{n}{C\sqrt{3}}\right)^{n+1} - 1\right] \tag{4.127}$$

Some representative values of v_0^* and v_0^{**}, given in Table 4.2, can be arrived at for stainless steel, half-hard copper and half-hard brass by selecting suitable values of B, C and n. The values chosen were statically determined and are taken from ref. 4.10; they are likely to be sufficiently accurate for exploratory purposes.

TABLE 4.2

Material	Density (Slugs/ft³)	$B \div 10^6$ (lb/ft²)	C	n	ft/sec v_0^* sphere	ft/sec v_0^{**} cylinder	Instability hoop strain, ε_θ sphere	Instability hoop strain, ε_θ cylinder
Copper ($\frac{1}{2}$-hard)	17·1	0·895	0·114	0·3	227	186	0·043	0·051
Brass ($\frac{1}{2}$-hard)	16·6	1·58	0·127	0·48	414	357	0·177	0·130
Stainless steel	15·1	3·20	0·016	0·50	734	658	0·240	0·236

Elastic response of a thin spherical shell to symmetric internal blast loading

For contrast with the previous section, consider a thin spherical shell of radius a subjected to an internal blast load which evokes only an *elastic* response, or vibration of the shell. If $p(t)$ denotes the variation of pulse pressure with time, t, and u_r is the (small) radial displacement of the shell of thickness h it is straightforward to adapt equation (4.122) to this situation, as

$$\frac{d^2 u_r}{dt^2} + \frac{2\sigma_\theta}{\rho a} = \frac{p(t)}{\rho h} \tag{4.128}$$

Using the elastic stress-strain equation $\sigma_\theta = Ee_\theta/(1 - v)$, where $e_\theta = u_r/a$, and substituting in (4.128), we find

$$\rho \frac{d^2 u_r}{dt^2} + \frac{2E}{(1 - v)} \cdot \frac{u_r}{a^2} = \frac{p(t)}{h} \tag{4.129}$$

The simple fundamental radial mode of vibration found by letting $p(t) = 0$ shows the shell to have a period of vibration of $\pi a[2\rho(1 - v)/E]^{1/2}$.

Suppose the blast pulse is defined by $p(t) = P(1 - t/T)$ for $0 < t < T$ and that $p(t) = 0$ for $t > T$, see Fig. 4.30. Then substituting in (4.129) and solving we have

$$u_r = \frac{P}{\omega^2 \rho h_0}\left[1 - \frac{t}{T} - \cos \omega t + \frac{\sin \omega t}{\omega T}\right], \quad 0 < t \le T$$

and

$$u_r = A \cos \omega(t - T) + B \sin \omega(t - T), \quad t \ge T \tag{4.130}$$

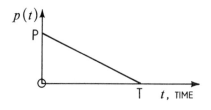

Fig. 4.30.

where

$$\omega^2 = \frac{2E}{\rho a^2 (1 - v)}$$

$$A = \frac{P}{\omega^2 \rho h_0} \cdot \left[\frac{\sin \omega T}{\omega T} - \cos \omega T \right]$$

and

$$B = \frac{P}{\omega^2 \rho h_0} \left[\sin \omega T + \frac{\cos \omega T}{\omega T} - \frac{1}{\omega T} \right]$$

This theory is approximate and according to it the shell possesses only a single radial mode of vibration. Together with the exact theory for thin vessels, it was given by Baker and Allen.[4.50]

These authors described experiments carried out on a hollow cast aluminium bronze sphere for which $h = \frac{1}{2}$ in and $a = 11\frac{1}{2}$ in, which was blast loaded by detonating 10 gm of Tetryl pellets at the sphere centre. A piezo-electric air blast gauge flush with the inner surface of the sphere measured the blast pressure–time history and wire strain gauges the sphere strain–time history, see the diagram in Fig. 4.31. Single frequency, quickly damped oscillations were recorded.

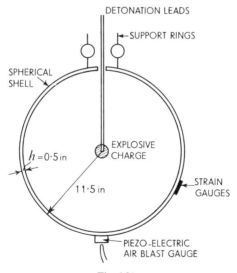

DETONATION LEADS

←SUPPORT RINGS

SPHERICAL
SHELL

EXPLOSIVE
CHARGE

$h = 0.5$ in

11.5 in

STRAIN
GAUGES

PIEZO-ELECTRIC
AIR BLAST GAUGE

Fig. 4.31.

With the constants $v = 0.3$, $\rho g = 0.321$ lbf/in^2 ($2.21 . 10^3$ N/m^2), $E = 12 . 10^6$ lbf/in^2 ($82.5 . 10^9$ N/m^2) and $h/a = 0.0435$, the computed value of the frequency ω is 2680 cycles/second; the maximum displacement $(A^2 + B^2)^{1/2}$ is $1.475 . 10^{-3}$ in, and $e_{\theta_{max}} = 1.23 . 10^{-4}$. The experimental results were as given in Table 4.3.

TABLE 4.3 EXPERIMENTAL RESULTS

Loading			Response	
P lbf/in^2	Impulse lbf/in^2 ms	T ms	Vibration frequency, cycles/sec	Strain amplitude $e_\theta \cdot 10^4$
528	10·5	0·040	2190	1·68
467	7·9	0·034	2260	1·87

Technological calculations to determine a typical initial speed of movement in the underwater explosive forming of thin circular sheet metal blanks

A common explosive sheet metal forming operation is that in which a thin air-backed circular blank is clamped around its circumference, immersed in water and subject to the shock wave generated by a detonated underwater explosive charge made up in the shape of a sphere and stood-off from the blank at a distance about equal to the blank radius, see Fig. 4.32(a). The action of the shock wave on the blank is to give the blank a certain initial speed, and thus kinetic energy, which is then dissipated in doing plastic work; the simple circular sheet may become a part-spherical shell, see Fig. 4.32(b). The work below is carried out to demonstrate the use of some of the equations introduced above and to show how an approximate technological calculation can be made which predicts speeds of about the same magnitude as those actually measured in experiment[4.51]; it assumes stretching of the blank and neglects bending.

Plastic work done on the blank

The plastic work done, ΔW_p, on an annulus of volume dV in increasing its representative strain from $\bar\varepsilon$ to $(\bar\varepsilon + d\bar\varepsilon)$ is

$$\Delta W_p = (\bar\sigma \cdot d\bar\varepsilon) \cdot dV \qquad (4.131)$$

Using equation (4.121), which may be presumed to be known from a biaxial bulge test[4.10] (all strain rate effects are neglected), equation (4.131) becomes

$$W_p = \left(\int_0^{\bar\varepsilon} B\bar\varepsilon^n \cdot d\bar\varepsilon \right) \cdot dV = \frac{B\bar\varepsilon^{n+1}}{n+1} \cdot dV \qquad (4.132)$$

Thus the total plastic work done on the blank $\mathscr{W}_p$ is, assuming that the principal stress ratios have remained constant throughout the deformation and thus that the stress–total strain form for the representative strain may be used, see Fig. 4.32(c),

$$\mathscr{W}_p = \int_0^a \frac{B\bar\varepsilon^{n+1}}{n+1} \cdot 2\pi x_0 h_0 \, dx_0. \qquad (4.133)$$

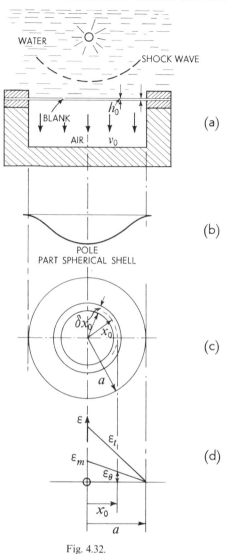

Fig. 4.32.

a is the radius of the blank at the periphery where it is clamped, x_0 is the original radial position of a particle in the blank measured from its centre and h_0 is its original thickness.

Experiments on explosively loaded blanks show the final hoop strain ε_θ and the radial strain ε_r to be nearly equal, see Fig. 4.32(d), so that the thickness strain ε_t is twice ε_θ in magnitude. Hence,

$$\bar{\varepsilon}^2 = \tfrac{2}{9}[(\varepsilon_\theta - \varepsilon_r)^2 + (\varepsilon_r - \varepsilon_t)^2 + (\varepsilon_t - \varepsilon_\theta)^2] = 4\varepsilon_\theta^2 \quad \text{or} \quad \bar{\varepsilon} = 2\varepsilon_\theta \quad (4.134)$$

Experiment also shows that blanks which are clamped around their circumference deform under 'point' explosive attack so that approximately the hoop strain (or the thickness strain) varies linearly with the radius, and hence that

$$\varepsilon_\theta = \varepsilon_m(1 - x_0/a); \tag{4.135}$$

ε_m is the hoop strain at the pole of the blank.

Thus equation (4.133) becomes, using (4.134) and (4.135),

$$\mathscr{W}_p = \int_0^a \frac{B}{n+1} \cdot \left[2\varepsilon_m\left(1 - \frac{x_0}{a}\right) \right]^{n+1} \cdot 2\pi x_0 h_0 \, dx_0$$

$$= \frac{B}{n+1} \cdot 2\pi h_0 \cdot a^2 \cdot \frac{(2\varepsilon_m)^{n+1}}{(n+2)(n+3)} \tag{4.136}$$

If the blank is subject to one impulsive loading (this is only partly true in underwater forming) and acquires an initial speed, v_0, which is such that its kinetic energy $E = \pi a^2 h_0 \rho v_0^2/2$, to accomplish the necessary work of plastic deformation, $\mathscr{W}_p$, where ρ denotes the density of the blank material, then

$$v_0^2 = \frac{2^{n+3} \cdot B\varepsilon_m^{n+1}}{\rho(n+1)(n+2)(n+3)} \tag{4.137}$$

If the blank was of killed steel[4.10] for which $\bar{\sigma} = 91\,000 \cdot \bar{\varepsilon}^{0.2}$ where $\bar{\sigma}$ is given in lb/in², then to attain a hoop strain of, say, 0·2 or a thickness strain of 0·4, equation (4.137) predicts that an initial velocity of 244 ft/sec is required.

Elementary theory of plastic bending

A straight beam of rectangular cross-section $b \times h$, Fig. 4.33(a), of elastic–perfectly plastic material, when subjected to an elastic bending moment M, is bent into the arc of a circle of radius R, see Fig. 4.33(b); it also acquires an anti-clastic curvature of v/R, see Fig. 4.33(c). On the assumption that sections which are plane before bending are plane afterwards, the stress distribution across the section is linear and elastic for $M \le M_E = bh^2Y/6$; when $M = M_E$ *the normal stress on a section in the extreme fibres is just the yield stress*, Fig. 4.33(d), the two principal stresses in the transverse direction being either zero or negligibly small. For $M_E < M \le M_p = bh^2Y/4$, the stress distribution is elastic–plastic, see Fig. 4.33(e); the central portion of the beam on either side of the neutral axis is elastically stressed, the whole of the remaining two outer portions being plastic. In the limit, the whole section becomes plastic, see Fig. 4.33(f), and then $M = M_p = [bh/2 \cdot Y] \cdot h/2 = bh^2Y/4$; M_p *is called the full plastic bending moment for the section.*

The ratio M_p/M_E is called the *shape factor* for the section and for the rectangle it is 1·5. For a circular section it is $16/3\pi$ and for an isosceles triangle it is $4(2 - \sqrt{2})$, if the two equal sides of the triangle are equally inclined to the neutral plane of the triangle. In this latter case the neutral axis, which in elastic bending is at $h/3$ above the base, moves in to $(\sqrt{2} - 1)h/\sqrt{2}$ for the fully plastic case; h is the height of the triangle.

If $b \gg h$ the rectangular bar or beam of Fig. 4.33(a) is better described as a plate, see Fig. 4.16, and then at the edges of the plate bending is predominantly

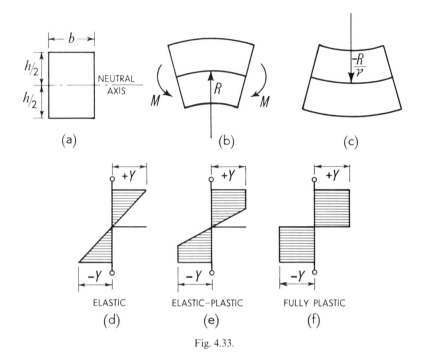

Fig. 4.33.

plane stress bending, i.e. the principal stress in the breadth direction is zero, and plane strain bending prevails over the mid portion of the plate. Anti-clastic curvature tends to be suppressed in this mid region and because there is no strain in the breadth direction, a transverse bending moment arises. For a wide plate the plane strain region greatly exceeds in extent the plane stress region so that for material following the Tresca yield criterion the normal stress on a section at yield may be taken to be Y, but for the Mises' criterion it is $2Y\sqrt{3}/3$ following (4.57). In the latter case, then, $M_p = (bh^2 Y/4)(2\sqrt{3}/3)$.

If the beam considered has an initial curvature then, provided this is not substantially altered during loading, M_p is the same as it is for a straight beam of the same section.

For the purpose of some analyses it is usual to think of the beam as being made of rigid-perfectly plastic material. In this case it undergoes no deflection at all until it is fully plastic, when it is said to reach its *collapse load*; as long as there is a rigid core to the beam, its behaviour is entirely rigid. More generally and in reality, the collapse load (elastic buckling neglected) is simply that load for which a metal structure starts to undergo large deflection; modest increments in load after the collapse load is reached, cause relatively large increments in deformation.

After a load causing plastic collapse is removed, a real beam or structure usually recovers or springs back elastically by a small amount and develops residual stresses; ref. 4.10 gives detailed calculations concerning elastic spring-back and residual stresses.

The stress distribution across the section of a fully plastic rectangular beam which is subject to an axial force, F, and a bending moment, M, appears as in Fig. 4.34. The force, F, obviously affects the distribution of normal stress in a section and it may easily be verified that, if $F_p = bhY$, then

$$\left(\frac{M}{M_p}\right) + \left(\frac{F}{F_p}\right)^2 = 1 \tag{4.138}$$

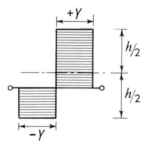

Fig. 4.34.

Equation (4.138) is useful for considering the transverse load necessary to cause plastic collapse in a bar carrying an in-plane tension, as on p. 283.

Plastic hinges in beams

Figure 4.35 shows a rectangular beam of length L of rigid-perfectly plastic material built-in at one end—called the root—and loaded at the other end by a concentrated transverse force P. The maximum bending moment occurs at the built-in end and when plastic collapse occurs, the tendency is for the beam to rotate about its root as a rigid body. The whole section at the root is plastic and the moment prevailing is M_p. At the instant collapse occurs, work will be done by load P moving downwards with speed $L\omega$, where ω is the angular speed of the beam about the root; all this work is dissipated plastically at the root at a rate of $M_p\omega$. Hence, the collapse load is given by,

$$PL\omega = M_p\omega \quad \text{or} \quad P = M_p/L$$

The fully plastic section at the root of the beam is called a *plastic hinge*.

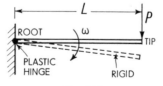

Fig. 4.35.

For a simply supported beam, see Fig. 4.36, $P = 2M_p/L$. For a beam built-in at both ends, see Fig. 4.37, four hinges arise, and $P = 4M_p/L$.

Fig. 4.36.

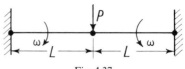

Fig. 4.37.

If a mass M moving with speed v_0 impinges on the end of a rigid-perfectly plastic cantilever of mass m, then it may be supposed that the end deflection Δ may simply be estimated by equating the plastic work done in the hinge at the root, to the initial kinetic energy of M, all inertia effects being neglected, and it being supposed that the cantilever rotates about the root as a rigid body. We have, neglecting losses due to impact and losses in potential energy of both beam and mass,

$$\tfrac{1}{2}Mv_0^2 = M_p \cdot \frac{\Delta}{L}$$

i.e.

$$\Delta = \frac{Mv_0^2 L}{2M_p} \tag{4.139}$$

A much more thorough investigation of this situation which allows for beam inertia is given in Chapter 6; the case just referred to emerges as being reliable only for the condition, $M \gg m$, the mass of the cantilever.

If a cantilever rotates as a rigid bar about its root, the tip having a downward speed of u_0, its total kinetic energy is $\tfrac{1}{2}I\omega^2$ where I is the moment of inertia of the cantilever about the root, i.e. $bL^3h\rho/3$ and angular velocity $\omega = u_0/L$. The end deflection Δ for deflections which are not too large is given by,

$$\tfrac{1}{2}I\omega^2 = M_p \cdot \frac{\Delta}{L}$$

or

$$\Delta = bL^2h\rho u_0^2/6M_p \tag{4.140}$$

Plastic hinges in circular rings

A circular ring which is neither too thin nor too flexible, of mean radius R when subjected to diametral loads P can only collapse plastically when four hinges have been formed to permit it to behave as a mechanism, see Fig. 4.38. The plastic hinges are assumed to arise at the locations where maximum elastic bending moments occur. It is easy to see that, if the centre of the ring, O, remains stationary, then at collapse the four rigid portions of the ring between the hinges rotate with angular speed, Ω, about instantaneous centre, I, and the forces P, move towards the centre of the ring with speed $R \cdot \Omega$. The work input rate is therefore $2P.R.\Omega$ and the plastic work dissipation rate is $8M_p.\Omega$. Thus,

$$2P \cdot R\Omega = 8M_p \cdot \Omega \quad \text{and hence} \quad P = 4M_p/R \tag{4.141}$$

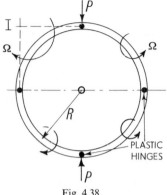

Fig. 4.38.

Plate 22 shows a thin and a thick ring after diametral compression; by use of an etching technique the four plastic hinges, evident at the four quarter points of each ring, can be made to stand out dark against a light background.[4.52]

When a large mass, M, impinges with low speed, v_0, on a supported, circular ring of diameter D and small mass, see Fig. 4.39, then if all inertia effects in the ring can be neglected, and all the kinetic energy in the mass is used up in enforcing plastic deformation on the ring, the diametral compression ΔD, provided $\Delta D/D$ is small, is very approximately given by,

$$\frac{4M_p}{D/2} \cdot \Delta D = \tfrac{1}{2} M v_0^2 \quad \text{or} \quad \Delta D = \frac{M v_0^2 D}{16 M_p}, \tag{4.142}$$

using (4.141) and assuming that the force resisting M is constant.

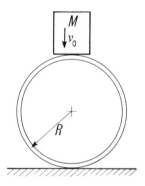

Fig. 4.39.

Plate 35 shows a lead ring after impact in this situation. The retardation of M is just P/M so that the time for plastic impact is $M v_0/P = M v_0 R/4 M_p$ and the variation of amount of ring compression with time will be quadratic.

Experiments show that in order to allow for stress wave transmission and other forms of energy loss it is useful to assume that about 85% of the kinetic energy available is used in doing plastic work.

When continued quasi-static crushing of a ring occurs between rigid, parallel surfaces[4.53], it is evident that the crushing force increases with reduction in vertical diameter of the ring. An indication of the force—vertical deflection characteristic to be expected is to be had by conceiving the deformation to proceed as indicated in Fig. 4.40. The original four plastic hinges are maintained but the point(s) of application of the compressing force(s) moves away the centre line, splitting into two equal components, $P/2$. Each quadrant of the ring may be supposed to rotate though remaining rigid. Applying the same work approach as above, for one quadrant, we have,

$$\frac{P}{2} . NI . \Omega = 2M_p . \Omega$$

or

$$P = 4M_p/NI \tag{4.143}$$

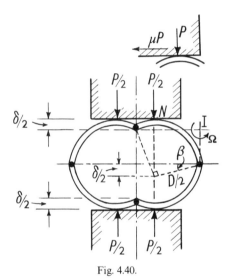

Fig. 4.40.

If δ denotes the *total* ring deflection $NI^2 = (D^2 - \delta^2)/4$ and thus

$$\frac{P}{4M_p/R} = \frac{1}{[1 - (\delta/D)^2]^{1/2}} \tag{4.144}$$

The form of this $P/(\delta/D)$ curve is shown in Fig. 4.41; this solution holds for $0 \le \beta \le \pi/4$. A frictional force of $\mu P/2$ would modify (4.143) and (4.144) to read

$$\frac{P}{2} . NI . \Omega + \mu\frac{P}{2} . MI . \Omega = 2M_p . \Omega$$

and

$$\frac{P}{4M_p/R} = \frac{1}{[1 - (\delta/D)^2]^{1/2} + \mu(1 - \cos \beta)} ; \tag{4.145}$$

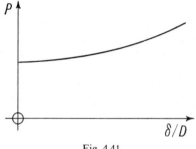

Fig. 4.41.

in general the effect of friction will be small and for any real material, strain hardening in the hinges will be much more significant. The solution outlined above presumes that two kinks will be formed in the ring, one at the top and the other at the bottom near the crushing platens; this is observed experimentally.

Ziz-zag structure

As an example of the value of quasi-static analyses using the idea of plastic hinges, we refer to the simple zig-zag structure shown in Fig. 4.42 which was used by Rawlings[4.54] to evaluate its capacity to dissipate energy for use in crash barriers.

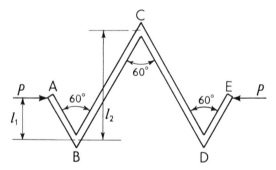

Fig. 4.42   Static test results.

If the member carries end loads applied along the line AE, it will first deform elastically. The bending moment distribution, ignoring inertia loading due to the mass of the material itself, is as shown in Fig. 4.43. Provided the ductility of the material is sufficiently high, specimens of the form shown should fold up, concertina fashion, to a locking configuration, with a considerable absorption and dissipation of energy, see Plate 23.

Records of a test on a specimen of $\frac{1}{4}$ in square mild steel due to an impinging body gave a dynamic force-deflection curve substantially the same as the static force-deflection curve shown in Fig. 4.44 which was obtained on an identical specimen.

The specimen deforms elastically at first and after considerable deformation a plastic hinge forms at C, Fig. 4.42. As this joint closes, the lever arm increases

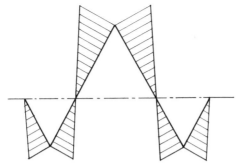

Fig. 4.43   Bending moment diagram.

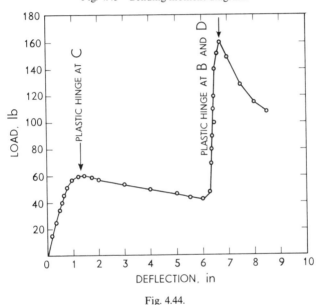

Fig. 4.44.

and the load decreases correspondingly. When points B and D come into contact, the load suddenly increases to the value associated with plastic hinge development at these latter points, after which the load falls off again as before.

Portal frames

Figure 4.45 shows a portal frame subject to a vertical load P and a horizontal load Q, all members of the frame being of the same material and cross-sectional area and shape. If the mode of deformation shown in Fig. 4.45 is assumed to occur with plastic hinges at A, C, D and E, it is easily confirmed that,

$$Q \cdot a\omega + P.AC.\omega \cdot \cos\theta = \underset{(A)}{\omega M_p} + \underset{(C)}{2\omega M_p} + \underset{(D)}{2\omega M_p} + \underset{(E)}{\omega M_p}$$

or

$$Q \cdot a + P \cdot b = 6M_p \tag{4.146}$$

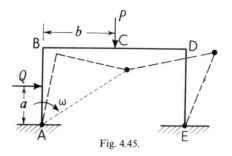

Fig. 4.45.

Many different deformation modes may be postulated but the simple example above is sufficient to illustrate an approach in respect of frames. The reader should consult reference 4.19 for a detailed discussion of this kind of problem.

Rawlings[4.55] has studied how the mode of plastic deformation alters in portal frames when concentrated masses are attached to the structural elements and whose inertia predominates over that of the members of the frame. Impulses are applied to one element of the structure, but not at a corner. Typical frames after testing are shown in Plate 24; the impulse was applied at the middle of the right hand vertical strut. Rawlings analysed the behaviour of the frames using a rigid-plastic analysis which is usually found to be reliable if the energy dissipated is an order of magnitude greater than the possible elastic resilience of the frame. Plastic hinges at corners or near the attached masses only were considered but some allowance for rate effects has to be made in mild steel frames.

Thin wall pressure vessel subjected to internal pressure

When a long, square section pressure vessel of side length $2a$ and uniform thickness $2h$ is subject to an internal pressure p, h/a being small, see Fig. 4.46, the magnitude of p to cause plastic collapse may be estimated using the idea of plastic hinges, see Fig. 4.47, assuming that membrane stresses are negligible.

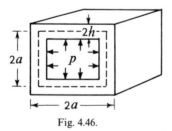

Fig. 4.46.

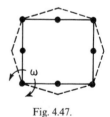

Fig. 4.47.

Equating the work done by the internal pressure to the plastic work dissipated in the sixteen plastic hinges indicated in Fig. 4.47, in tending to move to the configuration shown, we have, if the angular speed of each portion of the vessel is ω,

$$pa \cdot \frac{a\omega}{2} = 2M_p \cdot \omega$$

or

$$p = 4M_p/a^2$$

$$= 4\left(\frac{h}{a}\right)^2 . Y \qquad (4.147)$$

using the Tresca yield criterion.

Experiment reveals hinges as shown in Plate 25(a), see ref. 4.56. If plastic failure had been assumed to be due purely to tension in the vessel walls, then $p = 2Y(h/a)$; this is an order of magnitude larger than $4(h/a)^2 Y$.

The detailed shape of plastic hinges in the situation described above can often be determined using the theory of slip lines, see refs. 4.22 and 4.56.

Plastic hinges in non-circular rings

Plates 24(b) and (c) show an elliptical ring and an elliptical shackle plastically[4.57] compressed between parallel rigid plates. Substantial plastic deformation at each of the four hinges has occurred in the case of the elliptical ring; in the case of the shackle the etch pattern indicates that at least seven plastic hinges have formed—sufficient for an asymmetrical plastic deformation mechanism. In ref. 4.10 a simple analysis of the shackle is made which assumes eight symmetrically disposed hinges.

Crushing a thin cylinder by axial loading

The following simple analysis has been given by Alexander[4.58] for establishing the basis of an empirical relationship, concerning design against the accidental dropping of components in nuclear reactor fuel channels. It is arranged that the dropped component falls on to a thin, uniform cylinder that will buckle lengthwise; it is necessary to be able to estimate the energy absorbing capacity of the cylinder. On the assumption that a 'concertina' type mode of collapse ensues when an axial load is applied, see Fig. 4.48, the energy absorption may be calculated after summing that due to (i) the energy dissipated due to plastic bending, W_B, in the four circular hinges and (ii) the energy dissipated in stretching, W_S, under substantially uniform tensile yield hoop stress in the metal between the hinges.

Assuming the material of the cylinder is rigid-perfectly plastic, then using the notation obvious from Fig. 4.48, to attain complete collapse of one hinge system (i.e. θ increasing from zero to $\pi/2$),

(i), $$W_B = 2M_p . \pi D . \frac{\pi}{2} + 2M_p \int_0^{\pi/2} \pi(D + 2h \sin \theta) \, d\theta$$

$$= M_p \pi^2 D + 2M_p \pi\{D\pi/2 + 2h\}$$

$$= 2M_p \pi(\pi D + 2h) \qquad (4.148)$$

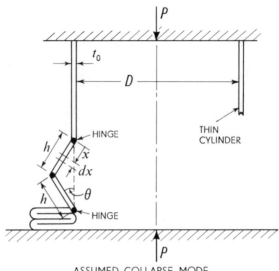

ASSUMED COLLAPSE MODE

Fig. 4.48.

where, using the Mises criterion, $M_p = 2Yt_0^2/4\sqrt{3}$ and

(ii),
$$W_S = 2 \int_0^x Y \cdot \pi D t_0 \, dx \cdot \ln(D + 2x \sin\theta)/D$$

$$\simeq 2Y \int_0^h \pi D t_0 \frac{2x}{D} \cdot dx, \quad \text{when } \theta \text{ is } 90°,$$

$$= 2Y\pi t_0 h^2 \tag{4.149}$$

Expressions (4.148) and (4.149) assume no interaction between the bending and hoop stresses, and that in collapsing the length h† and the distance of its elements from a hinge remain fixed. The energy for plastic dissipation is supplied by the axial compressive force, P, and is $P \cdot 2h$. Thus,

$$P \cdot 2h = 2\left(\frac{2}{\sqrt{3}} \cdot \frac{Yt_0^2}{4}\right)\pi(\pi D + 2h) + 2Y\pi t_0 h^2$$

or
$$\frac{P}{Y} = \frac{\pi t_0^2}{\sqrt{3}}\left(\frac{\pi D}{2h} + 1\right) + \pi h t_0 \tag{4.150}$$

The value of h is now determined by minimising (P/Y) with respect to h and thus

$$\frac{d}{dh}\left(\frac{P}{Y}\right) = \frac{\pi t_0^2}{\sqrt{3}}\left(-\frac{\pi D}{2h^2}\right) + \pi t_0 = 0$$

† Following the method on p. 139, the initial, h_0, to final length, h_f, is related by $D(D + 3h_0)^2 = (D + 2h_f)^3$.

or

$$h = \left(\frac{\pi}{2\sqrt{3}}\right)^{1/2} (Dt_0)^{1/2} \simeq 0 \cdot 95 . (Dt_0)^{1/2} \tag{4.151}$$

Substituting h from (4.151) in (4.150), we find

$$P/Y \simeq 6t_0(Dt_0)^{1/2} + 1 \cdot 8 . t_0^2 \tag{4.152i}$$

If the buckling convolutions had been entirely internal, rather than wholly external as treated above, it would be found that

$$P/Y \simeq 6t_0(Dt_0)^{1/2} - 1 \cdot 8 . t_0^2 \tag{4.152ii}$$

Since the 'concertina-ing' which actually occurs is likely to fall between the extremes discussed, a mean value for P/Y can reasonably be taken to be $6t_0(Dt_0)^{1/2}$.

As noted on p. 96, in dynamic axial impact situations involving plastic deformation, only the front part of a structure near to the area of impact will be subject to damage or be crushed. For a simple tubular shell structure† this may be estimated as follows. Denoting the crushed length by x, then if a steady force P applies during the process and assuming all the initial kinetic energy is dissipated in plastic deformation, we have

$$Px = \tfrac{1}{2}Mv^2 \quad \text{or} \quad x = \frac{Mv^2}{12Yt_0\sqrt{Dt_0}}$$

where M is the mass of the structure. Putting $M = \rho\pi Dt_0 L$ where L is the structure length

$$\frac{x}{L} = \frac{\pi}{12} . \sqrt{\frac{D}{t_0}} . \left(\frac{\rho v^2}{Y}\right) \tag{4.153}$$

Equation (4.153) could be useful in connection with vehicle design.

The reader interested in motor car safety design is referred to Vol. 183, Part 3A of the Proceedings of the Symposium on this subject held by the Institution of Mechanical Engineers in London, 1968–69. On p. 25 the following experimental facts are noted,

(i) that front and rear ends, in the case of frontal or rear collision respectively, "collapse and absorb energy before the centre portion deforms permanently",

(ii) "approximately 90 per cent of the energy goes into permanent and 10 per cent into elastic deformation".

These simple facts are implicit in many topics discussed above and below.

Model motor coaches have been tested, see ref. 4.59, and Plate 25(a) shows one such before testing. Plate 25(b) shows a distributed crumpling when such a coach is axially loaded by a steadily increasing static load, whilst Plate 25(c) shows a coach after being impact loaded on the left hand end, the more concentrated deformation at that end being clearly evident.

---

† See, 'Use of collapsible structural elements as impact isolators with special reference to automotive applications', by H. E. Postlethwaite and B. Mills, *J. Strain Analysis*, **5**, 58, 1970.

Inversion tubes

A simple expendable energy absorber which possesses a rectangular force-displacement characteristic and a high energy absorption capacity is the 'Inver' tube device. Basically this is a process which allows a thin-walled ductile metal tube to be turned inside-out or outside-in. If the tube shown in Fig. 4.49(a) is pushed against the supporting anvil which contains an appropriate fillet radius, it may then of its own accord be inverted as shown in Fig. 4.49(b). Figure 4.49(c) and (d) shows the arrangement for turning a tube outside-in. Plate 26(a) and (b) shows partially inverted tubes and their dies.

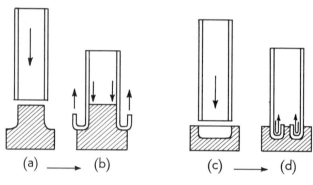

(a) ⟶ (b)   (c) ⟶ (d)

Fig. 4.49.

Of course inversion is not the only mode of deformation possible for an inver-tube device; alternative modes are
  (i) column or Euler buckling
 (ii) concertina-ing or axisymmetric buckling, see Plate 26(c)
(iii) diamond buckling, see Plate 26(d)
 (iv) tearing of the tube, see Plate 26(e)
  (v) brittle fracture, or shattering, and
 (vi) uniform compression.
The mode of failure which prevails depends on the tube dimensions and the material characteristics. The mean load for (i), (ii), (iii) and sometimes (iv) above may be less than the constant inverting load but their initiating buckling loads tend, in most cases, to be much higher. The examples shown are taken from ref. 4.60.

Figure 4.50 shows diagrammatically,[4.61] more positive arrangements made up by General Motors Corporation for effecting the inversion of aluminium tubes. Capsules are preformed by first flaring one end of a tube and then clamping the periphery; the intention will be clear from the figure. Note that the displacement of the top of a tube is about twice its original length.

Inversion tubes have been considered in relation to the design of force attenuating collapsible steering wheels, for facilitating lunar and planetary soft landings of spacecraft, for cushioning air drop cargo, as overload protectors for railway rolling stock, as a safety device for elevators, as buffer elements for

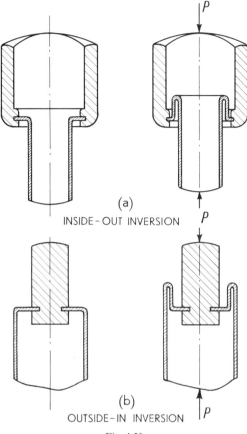

(a)

INSIDE - OUT INVERSION

(b)

OUTSIDE - IN INVERSION

Fig. 4.50.

nuclear reactor control rods and as yieldable aircraft seat anchors. The rectangular force-displacement characteristic ensures substantially uniform retardation.

The process of outside-in tube inversion is somewhat similar to that of the re-drawing of a cup (see ref. 4.10, p. 220) and involves, therefore, the plastic bending and unbending of the tube with concurrent circumferential contraction (or extension). Typical experimental slow-speed force-displacement diagrams show a build-up to a steady or constant force of resistance to inversion after end-effects and inversion initiating forces have been applied. The final tube diameter has an equilibrium value depending upon its initial diameter and thickness.

An approximate analytical expression[4.62] for the steady compressive load necessary to maintain an inside-out inversion is easily arrived at by assuming that the tube material is perfectly plastic, that no tube length or thickness changes occur during bending, that the energy dissipation consists solely in (i) bending and unbending the tube and (ii) in increasing its radius; any inter-action between bending and other imposed stresses is neglected and buckling or instability is not envisaged. If the radius of inversion is c and the tube thickness is t_0, see Fig. 4.51, the work done per unit time in bending a straight element of tube W_B (neglecting interaction with hoop extension and Bauschinger effects) at the entrance to the bending zone is

$$W_B \simeq 2 \int_0^{t_0/2} (\pi D \, dyu) Y . \left(\frac{y\theta}{c\theta}\right) = \frac{\pi D t_0^2 u}{4c} . Y \tag{4.154}$$

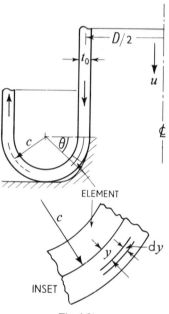

Fig. 4.51.

The amount of work done per unit time in extending tube elements W_E is, compare (4.43),

$$W_E = \pi D t_0 u Y \ln\left(1 + \frac{2c}{D/2}\right) \simeq 4\pi t_0 c Y u \tag{4.155}$$

when $2c/D$ is small. The rate at which work is done by the compressing force P is thus found as

$$P . u = 2W_B + W_E = \pi t_0 Y \left\{\frac{Dt_0}{2c} + 4c\right\} u \tag{4.156}$$

The work done in unbending at exit from the curved zone is assumed equal to that done in bending at the entrance to it. c is found by supposing it to acquire a value which makes P a minimum. Hence, for $dP/dc = 0$, we have

$$\frac{Dt_0}{2c^2} = 4 \quad \text{or} \quad c = \sqrt{\frac{Dt_0}{8}}$$

(The same result for c may be shown[4.60] to hold for a strain-hardening material described by equation (4.32).)

Putting this value of c into (4.156)

$$P = \pi t_0 Y (8Dt_0)^{1/2} \qquad (4.157)$$

If the system shown in Fig. 4.50 is considered, then the compressive force is just $P/2$. Experiment shows calculated loads to be underestimated by about 25%.

The energy, E, dissipated by plastically inverting the tube, per unit weight, w, of the tube, is

$$E = \frac{PL}{\pi Dt_0 Lw} = \frac{Y}{w} \sqrt{\frac{8t_0}{D}}$$

The mean strain ε_m imparted to each element of the tube following equation (4.157) is the work done on the tube per unit time, divided by the volume deformed times Y. Hence,

$$\varepsilon_m = \frac{P \cdot L}{Y \cdot \pi Dt_0 L} = \sqrt{\frac{8t_0}{D}}$$

Thus, for a strain hardening material the appropriate value to use for Y in (4.157), is the mean value of σ over the range of strain 0 to ε_m, say $\overline{Y}$, as taken from, say, a tensile stress, σ-natural strain, ε, curve of the tube material obtained at a rate of strain which corresponds to that at which the inversion test is carried out.

For a material described by $\sigma = B\varepsilon^n$, i.e. equation (4.32),

$$\overline{Y} \cdot \varepsilon_m = \int_0^{\varepsilon_m} \sigma \, d\varepsilon = \frac{B\varepsilon_m^{n+1}}{n+1} \quad \text{and} \quad \overline{Y} = \frac{B\varepsilon_m^n}{n+1}$$

A tube pushed at a speed u, has an approximate mean strain rate of $\dot{\varepsilon}_m \simeq \varepsilon_m u/\pi c = v/\pi D$. For a 3 in dia tube, if $u = 30$ mph (44 ft/sec), $\dot{\varepsilon}_m \simeq 600$ sec, and at this rate of strain for aluminium the mean yield stress is likely to be between about 20 and 80% greater than the quasi-static yield stress (i.e. at 10^{-3}/sec).

Tubes with low strain hardening rates buckle rather than invert. It may be shown from ref. 4.63 that the axisymmetric buckling load P_B for a tube whose reduced modulus is E_k is approximately $P_B = 4\pi t_0^2 E_k/3$. Thus, calling on equation (4.157), inversion would occur only if $P < P_B$ or $E_k/Y > 3(D/2t_0)^{1/2}$.

Plastic bending of thin flat plates

The method used above for calculating the plastic collapse load for a rigid-perfectly plastic beam and generally of structures, by using the idea of a plastic hinge in conjunction with the choice of a satisfactory mechanism, is now extended to analyse thin, flat, circular plates and rectangular plates when subjected to a transverse load. Strictly, it may be shown that any calculated load will be in excess of the actual load required to cause plastic deformation when we assume that a certain mechanism obtains at the instant collapse occurs; but for many engineering purposes the load magnitude calculated is not likely to be greatly overestimated. (In any case with any real material differential strain-hardening will occur and increase the load carrying capacity).

In all the cases examined the applied loads are perpendicular to the plane of a plate. Usually, bending action in a plate only is considered and all membrane stresses and local shear stress distributions are neglected. Deflections undergone by a plate for the loads calculated below are thought of as being large by comparison with possible elastic deflections.

Recall that for a plate, the magnitude of the *fully plastic bending moment per unit width*, is $M_p = \sigma_0 h_0^2/4$. If Y is the uniaxial yield stress of the material then, for a Tresca material, $\sigma_0 = Y$ and for a Mises' material $\sigma_0 = 2Y\sqrt{3}/3$ and h_0 is the plate thickness.

The early plastic collapse cases investigated below are treated as ones of incipient deformation: the deformation which starts to occur is related to the rate at which the initial configuration is changing so that no difficulties about the amount of deflection need arise.

Annular plate clamped at its outer boundary

An annulus of uniform thickness h_0, of outer radius a and inner radius b, is supposed firmly clamped at its outside and free along the inner circumference where, say, a uniformly distributed line load is applied of intensity P per unit length.

Because of symmetry, assume the plate to be divided into a very large number of identical sectors 1, 2, 3, 4, 5, . . . , each of which subtends a very small angle $\delta\theta$ at the centre of the plate, see Fig. 4.52(a). Let the inner circumference $A, B, C, D, . . .$, descend with speed u_0, the outer circumference $\alpha, \beta, \gamma, \delta . . .$ being stationary, and let each sectional element of the annulus 1, 2, 3, 4, . . . , rotate as a rigid body with angular speed $u_0/(a - b)$ about $\alpha\beta$, $\beta\gamma$, $\gamma\delta$ etc., Fig. 4.52(b).

At the boundary $\alpha\beta$ there is full plastic bending—a plastic hinge—whilst additional plastic hinges are conceived to exist where the separate sectors are joined along radii. The rotation of each sector may be represented by a vector ω of magnitude $u_0/(a - b)$, drawn in a clockwise direction parallel to its boundary, in accordance with the conventional right hand screw rule, see Fig. 4.52(b). In a separate diagram concerned only with representing the angular velocity of all parts of the plate, the vector for sector 1 is represented by **01** and that for section 2 by **02** etc. The diagram which shows the angular velocity of all parts of the annulus is called a *hodograph* and Fig. 4.52(c) shows the hodograph for the sectorially divided annulus. Note, in the hodograph, that **12, 23, 34**, etc., represent the rate of rotation between one sector and the next. To see this, in Fig. 4.52(c), first joint **12** and then resolve **02** into **0n** and **n2**, and **01** into **0n** and **n1**. Since **0n** is the same for sectors 1 and 2, therefore both of them rotate at the same rate and in the same direction about an axis perpendicular to the common radial hinge $B\beta$. The total rate of change of angle, between sector 1 and sector 2, in radial hinge $B\beta$, is the difference between **n1** and **n2**, i.e. is of magnitude [12]. Thus the work done in the plastic bending of the sector 1 is the sum of (i) the length $\alpha\beta . \omega . M_p$ and (ii) length $B\beta . [12] . M_p$. The fully plastic bending moment per unit length is M_p. Hence the total work dissipated in the annulus is the sum of (i) and (ii), multiplied by the number of sectors.

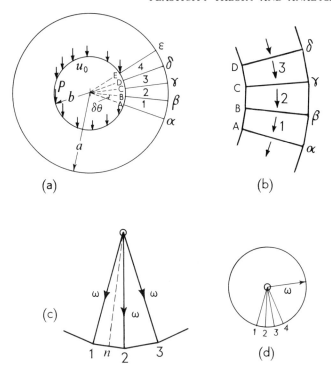

Fig. 4.52.

Now, in the limit $\delta\theta \to 0$, each sector becomes infinitely small and the hodograph becomes a circle of radius ω, Fig. 4.52(d).

The rate of dissipation of energy in the outer circumferential plastic hinge, i.e. the sum of (i) for each sector, is $(2\pi a) . \omega . M_p$ and in the radial hinges, i.e. the sum of (ii) for each sector, is $(a - b) . (2\pi\omega) . M_p$.

The rate at which work is done by the externally applied load is $2\pi b . P . u_0$ and hence,

$$2\pi b . P . u_0 = 2\pi a\omega M_p + (a - b)2\pi\omega M_p \tag{4.158}$$

or

$$P = \frac{2a - b}{a - b} . \frac{M_p}{b} \tag{4.159}$$

The total applied load, P_0, is

$$P_0 = 2\pi b . P = 2\pi . \frac{2a - b}{a - b} . M_p \tag{4.160}$$

For a solid circular plate for which $b = 0$, the concentrated load required to cause collapse is

$$P_0 = 4\pi . M_p \tag{4.161}$$

If the same frustum type mode of deformation was assumed when the annulus was carrying a uniform transverse pressure, p, then, by the same approach as above, the rate at which work is done by the pressure, $\dot{W}$, is

$$\dot{W} = \int_b^a p \cdot 2\pi r \cdot dr \cdot u_0 \cdot \frac{a - r}{a - b}$$

$$= \frac{\pi p u_0}{3}(a - b)(a + 2b) \tag{4.162}$$

and thus using the right hand side of (4.160),

$$\frac{\pi p u_0}{3}(a - b)(a + 2b) = \frac{2\pi M p \cdot u_0}{a - b}(2a - b)$$

or

$$p = \frac{6M_p(2a - b)}{(a - b)^2 \cdot (a + 2b)} \tag{4.163}$$

For the solid circular disc, $b = 0$ and thus,

$$p = \frac{12M_p}{a^2} \tag{4.164}$$

Annular plate position fixed (zero fixing moment) at its outer periphery and free at its inner boundary

The condition investigated is shown in Fig. 4.53. The approach, the method of analysis and the angular velocity field assumed are identical with those investigated for the clamped plate above. We may easily arrive at an expression similar to equation (4.160); the first term on the right hand side would be omitted since the outer edge of the plate is free. Thus,

$$2\pi b \cdot P \cdot u_0 = (a - b) \cdot 2\pi \omega \cdot M_p \tag{4.165}$$

or

$$P = \frac{M_p}{b} \tag{4.166}$$

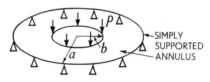

Fig. 4.53.

The total applied load is,

$$P_0 = 2\pi b \cdot P = 2\pi \cdot M_p \tag{4.167}$$

If the annulus was subjected to a uniformly distributed pressure, p, it is easily verified, with the help of equations (4.162) and (4.165) that

$$p = \frac{6M_p}{(a - b)(a + 2b)} \qquad (4.168)$$

For the circular disc, $b = 0$, and

$$p = \frac{6M_p}{a^2} \qquad (4.169)$$

Obviously, this situation is basically similar to that in which the initial condition prescribed for the plate is, that it is position-fixed at its *inner radius*, b. If it carries a uniform load P' at its outer edge, then $P' = P . (b/a)$.

Annulus clamped along its inner boundary

In principle, the analysis of this case is the same as that on p. 195. It may be verified, see Fig. 4.54, that if the annulus is line-loaded along its outer boundary,

$$P = \frac{M_p}{a - b} \qquad (4.170)$$

and

$$P_0 = 2\pi . \frac{a}{a - b} . M_p \qquad (4.171)$$

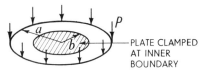

PLATE CLAMPED AT INNER BOUNDARY

Fig. 4.54.

If the annulus is loaded with a uniform transverse pressure, p, then the plastic collapse pressure is,

$$p = \frac{6M_p . a}{(a - b)^2 . (2a + b)} \qquad (4.172)$$

Dynamic loading of an annular plate perfectly clamped along its inner boundary

The previous case may be re-considered in the following form which is a useful approximate approach for certain situations which arise in dynamic plasticity. We investigate here the homologue of the case of the dynamically loaded cantilever of p. 181.

A flat, uniformly thick annular plate, clamped at its inner edge, is subjected to an impulsive vertical load which causes the outer boundary to start to move downward with speed u_0 and the speed to decrease linearly with radius and to zero, where the plate is clamped. This initial kinetic energy is dissipated by enforcing full plastic bending throughout the annulus—the possibility of buckling is neglected—and we require to estimate the plate deflection, presuming that the deflections are not too large for the approximations used. We may approach it in the same way as before.

The initial kinetic energy of the plate, E, is

$$E = \frac{1}{2} \int_b^a 2\pi r \, dr \cdot \rho \cdot h_0 \cdot u^2 \tag{4.173}$$

where u is the plate speed at radius r, h_0 is the plate thickness and ρ the plate density. Now $u/u_0 = (r - b)/(a - b)$, and after substituting in equation (4.173), integrating and simplifying,

$$E = \frac{\rho h_0 u_0^2}{12} \cdot \pi(3a^2 - 2ab - b^2) \tag{4.174}$$

Instead of referring to ω, the angular velocity of sectors, refer to ϕ, the angular rotation of an annular radial element about the inner plate boundary. Then $\phi = \omega t/2$ where t denotes time; sectors will be retarded at a uniform rate since the opposing bending moments are nearly constant in magnitude for the small deflections envisaged.

Following (4.158) the total plastic work done on the plate, W, is given by

$$W = 2\pi b M_p \phi + (a - b)M_p \cdot 2\pi\phi \tag{4.175}$$

(This neglects the increase in plate stiffness as deflection increases, such as is indicated through pp. 201 to 204.)

Equating (4.174) and (4.175), we find

$$\phi = u_0^2 \cdot \frac{\rho h_0(3a^2 - 2ab - b^2)}{24M_p a} \tag{4.176}$$

Thus the peripheral deflection $\varDelta$ is simply

$$\varDelta = (a - b)\phi = \frac{\rho u_0^2 h_0(a - b)^2(3a + b)}{24aM_p} \tag{4.177}$$

The deflection, equation (4.177), may be re-written as

$$\varDelta = \left(\frac{\rho u_0^2 h_0 l^2}{6M_p}\right) \cdot \left(\frac{(b/a) + 3}{4}\right) \tag{4.178}$$

where $l = (a - b)$. As $b/a \to 1$, then $\varDelta \to \rho u_0^2 h_0 l^2/6M_p$, as given by equation (4.140) for the simple cantilever. Obviously this should be so, since the closer $b/a \to 1$, the less influence do radial hinges possess and the more important is the root circumferential hinge.

Expression (4.177) for $\varDelta$ also applies for a uniformly thick annulus which is a regular polygon, when its outer edge is projected downwards with speed u_0, the inner circumference being securely clamped, see Fig. 4.55. (Compare the treatment of this problem with that on p. 204.)

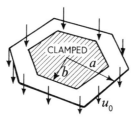

Fig. 4.55.

We may consider in the same way a square plate of side $2a$, clamped around its outside but caused to move downwards at its centre with speed u_0 in the first place, see Fig. 4.56(a). Incipient deformation may be imagined, the plate diagonals being conceived as hinge lines; the hodograph is shown in Fig. 4.56(b). The plastic work done in causing a body rotation ϕ of each quarter of the plate of moment of inertia, I, about the side where it is clamped, is $16aM_p\phi$.

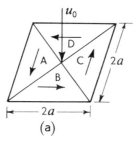

(a)

a (b)

Fig. 4.56.

The kinetic energy of the whole plate is $4 \times \frac{1}{2}I(u_0/a)^2$, so that equating the latter two quantities, we have

$$\phi = \frac{I(u_0/a)^2}{8aM_p}$$

and hence the deflection Δ is given by

$$\Delta = a\phi = \frac{Iu_0^2}{8a^2M_p} = \frac{\rho u_0^2 h_0 a^2}{48M_p} \qquad (4.179)$$

noting that $I = \rho h_0 a^4/6$.

Note that the assumed modes of deformation in the plate problems just discussed strictly apply only at the instant deflection starts. In the case of the annular square plate, clamped over the inner periphery, there must be a kind of buckling near the corners of the plate after a significant amount of deformation—in effect there is 'too much' material at the corners. By introducing two more hinge lines at each corner a mode of deformation that will allow for corner 'folds' or finite deflection is as shown in Fig. 4.57(a); this mode accounts for bringing about the square box shape of Fig. 4.57(b). Assuming this mode persists during the whole deformation, i.e. from flat plate to box, it is easily shown that

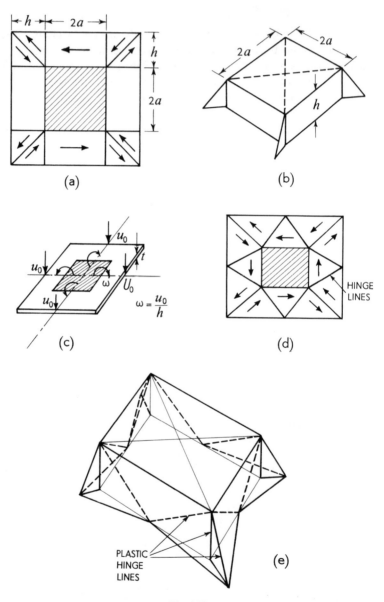

Fig. 4.57.

the work done to achieve a box of depth h and base $2a$ is,

$$4\pi a M_p\left[1 + \frac{h}{a}\left(\frac{1 + 2\sqrt{2}}{2}\right)\right]$$ (4.180)

Thus if the plate periphery had a downward speed of u_0 to begin with, see Fig. 4.57(c), then the annulus has a kinetic energy equal to that dissipated plastically and as given by (4.180) if,

$$\frac{u_0^2 h \rho t (4a + 3h)}{3} = 4\pi a M_p\left[1 + \frac{h}{a}\left(\frac{1 + 2\sqrt{2}}{2}\right)\right]$$

or

$$u_0^2 = \frac{3\pi M_p}{h\rho t} \cdot \frac{1 + \dfrac{h}{a} \cdot \dfrac{1 + 2\sqrt{2}}{2}}{1 + \dfrac{h}{a} \cdot \dfrac{3}{4}},$$ (4.181)

where t is the plate thickness.

An alternative system of plastic hinge lines for bringing about a box-like form but with more 'open' corner folds is shown in Fig. 4.57(d) and (e).

Plastic collapse load at large deflection

(i) *Simply-supported plate*

Experiment shows that even for circular plates of rigid perfectly plastic material, when once the initial collapse load P_0 is reached, then to cause further plastic deformation or to continue increasing the central deflection, increasing loads $P > P_0$, must be applied. If we consider a simply supported thin flat plate carrying a concentrated load at its centre, then when $P > P_0$, it will have developed into a shallow conical shell. The plate is shown supported on rollers in Fig. 4.58(a) at A, so that as the deflection develops these are able to move horizontally. In the deflected position, for small plastic deflections there will be a thin horizontal elemental disc of the plate at some height, z, above A, which is not strained in bending.

For a mode of deformation in which a developing conical shell is assumed, rotation of elements in the horizontal plane through I shows them not to be extending or contracting but for an element distant y above II', if y is positive the element will be subject to compressive hoop yield stress σ_0, and if it is negative to tensile hoop yield stress. By considering the stress distribution on a diametral plane, see Fig. 4.58(b) it is evident that for equilibrium the compressive force above II' must equal the tensile force below it and hence that II' must divide the plate section into equal trapezoidal areas. If δ denotes the current central deflection and h_0 the plate thickness, see Fig. 4.58(c), then clearly $(h_0 - z) = (z + \delta)$ and $z = (h_0 - \delta)/2$. The plastic hoop moment M_R

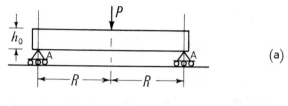

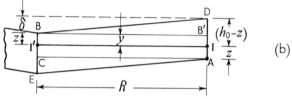

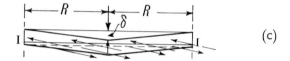

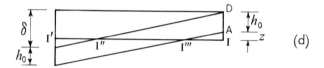

Fig. 4.58.

for a whole radial section created by the yield stresses acting above II' is,

M_R = moment of stresses over rectangles $II'BB'$ and $II'CA$ about II'

+ moment of stresses in triangles $BB'D$ and CAE about II'

$$= \left[\sigma_0 Rz \cdot \frac{z}{2} + \frac{1}{2}R\sigma_0(h_0 - 2z)\left(z + \frac{h_0 - 2z}{3}\right) \right]$$

$$= \frac{R\sigma_0}{3}[3z^2 + (h_0 - 2z)(h_0 + z)]$$

Substituting for z,

$$M_R = \frac{R\sigma_0 h_0^2}{4}\left[1 + \frac{1}{3} \cdot \left(\frac{\delta}{h_0}\right)^2\right] \tag{4.182}$$

Thus the collapse load after deflection δ following the method on p. 196, is

$$P \cdot R\omega = M_R \cdot 2\pi\omega \quad \text{or} \quad P = 2\pi M_R / R$$

and hence substituting for M_R from (4.182),

$$\frac{P}{P_0} = 1 + \frac{1}{3} \cdot \left(\frac{\delta}{h_0}\right)^2 \tag{4.183}$$

where P_0 is the initial collapse load when $\delta = 0$. Equation (4.183) holds for $\delta \le h_0$. When $\delta > h_0$, the same approach as above may still be used, Fig. 4.58(d) applying instead of Fig. 4.58(b). Considering the moment of the stresses about II′

$$M_R/2 = \text{Moment of stresses in triangle II″D about II′}$$

$$- \text{moment of stresses in triangle II‴A about II′}$$

$$M_R = \frac{R\sigma_0}{24\delta}[(\delta + h_0)^2 - (\delta - h_0)^2]$$

$$= \frac{R\sigma_0 h_0^2}{4}\left[\frac{\delta}{h_0} + \frac{1}{3} \cdot \left(\frac{h_0}{\delta}\right)\right] \tag{4.184i}$$

Now from (4.182), $P_0 = R\sigma_0 h_0^2 / 4$ and thus for $\delta/h_0 > 1$

$$\frac{P}{P_0} = \frac{\delta}{h_0} + \frac{1}{3}\left(\frac{h_0}{\delta}\right) \tag{4.185}$$

(ii) *Peripherally clamped circular plate*

When the plate is built-in at its circumference, the horizontal circle in which there is zero rate of extension or contraction is not obvious; on a radial section, see Fig. 4.59, the area above the line where the circle cuts the section is not necessarily equal to that below it. We therefore follow the previous procedure but add a term—moment $2\pi R M_c\omega$—for the rate at which work in plastic bending is done at the periphery of the ring, and then minimise the rate at which the external load does work in order to find the optimum value of z. We have,

$$P \cdot R\omega = M_R \cdot 2\pi\omega + 2\pi R \cdot M_c\omega$$

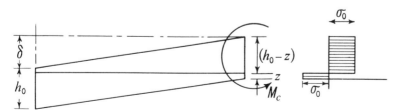

Fig. 4.59.

where

$$M_R/R\sigma_0 = \frac{\delta}{2}\left(h_0 - z - \delta + \frac{\delta}{3}\right) + \frac{(h_0 - z - \delta)^2}{2} + \frac{z^2}{2} + \frac{\delta}{2}\left(z + \frac{\delta}{3}\right)$$

$$= \frac{3h_0^2 - 6h_0z + 6z^2 + 6z\delta + 2\delta^2 - 3\delta h_0}{6} \qquad (4.184\text{ii})$$

and

$$M_c/\sigma_0 = [(h_0 - z)^2 + z^2]/2 = (h_0^2 - 2h_0 z + 2z^2)/2 \qquad (4.186)$$

Thus,

$$\frac{P}{\sigma_0} = M_R \cdot \frac{2\pi}{R\sigma_0} + \frac{M_c}{\sigma_0} \cdot 2\pi$$

or

$$\frac{P}{\pi\sigma_0/3} = [6h_0^2 - 12h_0z + 12z^2 + 2\delta^2 + 6z\delta - 3\delta h_0] \qquad (4.187)$$

Then,

$$\frac{d}{dz}\left(\frac{P}{\pi\sigma_0/3}\right) = -12h_0 + 24z + 6\delta = 0$$

whence

$$z = (2h_0 - \delta)/4 \qquad (4.188)$$

Substituting (4.188) in (4.187), we find

$$P = \pi\sigma_0 h_0^2\left\{1 + \frac{5}{12}\cdot\left(\frac{\delta}{h_0}\right)^2\right\}$$

$$= P_0\left\{1 + \frac{5}{12}\cdot\left(\frac{\delta}{h_0}\right)^2\right\} \qquad (4.189)$$

(iii) *Peripherally clamped polygonal plate*

A uniformly thick clamped plate which is a regular polygon of n sides becomes a shallow conical shell when deflected by amount δ. When a concentrated load, P, is applied along the axis of the cone, see Fig. 4.60, it is easy to show, following the methods outlined above, that for small values of δ/h_0,

$$P \cdot R \cdot \omega \cos \pi/n = nM_R \cdot 2\omega \sin \pi/n + n\omega M_c 2R \sin \pi/n$$

or

$$P = \frac{2n \tan \pi/n}{R}[M_R + RM_c] \qquad (4.190)$$

M_R is given by (4.184ii), M_c by (4.186) and R is the radius of the circumcircle of the polygon. Clearly when $n \to \infty$, expression (4.190) becomes (4.189). The

SHALLOW POLYGONAL
CONICAL SHELL

Fig. 4.60.

procedure, i.e. of minimising P with respect to z, in order to determine the least value for P follows as before.

The approach used in this section is prompted by that of Calladine in ref. 4.64.

Elastic-plastic bending of circular plates by transverse pressure in experiment

In a number of papers, Ohashi and Murakami[4.65] presented the results of theoretical calculations for the elastic-plastic deflections undergone by solid and annular plates when transversely loaded by a uniform hydrostatic pressure. They investigated simply supported and clamped mild steel plates and compared their results with those found by experiments. These authors found that at a circumferential strain of about 0·1 at the plate centre, the simple limit load was attained. Generally, however, it transpired that as distance from the plate centre increased it became increasingly difficult to identify a collapse load by reference to a deflection or a strain which increases rapidly with pressure, see Fig. 4.61.

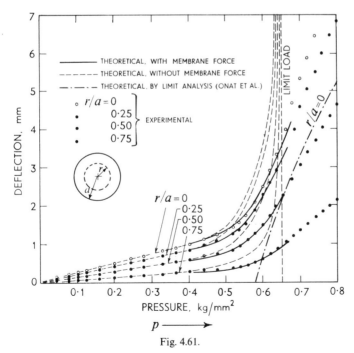

Fig. 4.61.

Plastic collapse loads, such as those given by Onat and Haythornthwaite,[4.66] and e.g. (4.183) which take deflection into account give greatly improved correlation with experiment. A general conclusion is, that after about 85% of the limit load is reached, membrane forces become significant or, alternatively, when the central plane deflection is equal to about one half the plate thickness. The regions and the extent in plates in which material has become plastic due to transverse load, were calculated by Ohashi *et al.* and then observed by sectioning and etching; the general shape of the yielded zones are sketched in Fig. 4.62. Note that the extent of the region of plasticity is unsymmetrical due to the membrane tension imposed on the bending stresses; the theory and experiment reported by these workers were in good agreement. The theoretical results of most of this work were numerically evaluated.

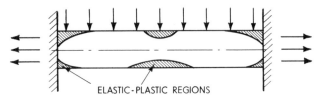

ELASTIC-PLASTIC REGIONS

Fig. 4.62.

Recent experimental work has been carried out by Hooke[4.67] to determine the applicability of rigid-perfectly plastic bending theory for predicting collapse loads for circular mild steel plates of diameter-thickness ratio between 124 and 213, by more or less concentrated loads applied through a central boss or uniform transverse pressure, for a variety of edge conditions. He found that consideration of membrane action was vital for predicting load–deflexion relationships where the deflexion extends to more than ten times the plate thickness. Hooke notes that simple collapse loads, of the kind derived above, satisfactorily predict experimental "first yield pressure" and are a guide to permanent set behaviour.

Plastic collapse of a circular pressure vessel

In Fig. 4.63(a) a thin wall cylindrical vessel is shown subject to an internal pressure p; plastic collapse may be assumed to occur by the formation of 'ring' plastic hinges at the top, the bottom and in the centre and by hoop stretching everywhere between the top and the bottom. An estimate of the value of p may be found by proceeding as in the previous sections. If the sides of the vessel at the instant of collapse rotate with angular speed ω and h is the vessel thickness, then,

(i) the rate of energy dissipation in all the hinges is $4\pi D\omega M_p$, and   (4.191)

(ii) the rate of energy dissipation in hoop stretching is

$$2\int_0^{L/2} \pi Dh\, dx\sigma_0 \ln\left(1 + \frac{x\omega}{D/2}\right) \simeq 4\pi h\sigma_0\omega \int_0^{L/2} x\, dx$$

$$= 4\pi h\sigma_0\omega L^2/8 \qquad (4.192)$$

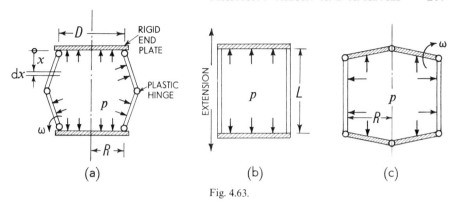

Fig. 4.63.

The rate at which work is done by the pressure is

$$2 \int_0^{L/2} p\pi D \, dx \, . \, x\omega = p\pi D\omega L^2/4 \qquad (4.193)$$

Thus, after adding (4.191) and (4.192) and equating it to (4.193),

$$p \, . \, \pi D\omega \frac{L^2}{4} = 4\pi D\omega M_p + 4\pi h\sigma_0 \omega L^2/8$$

$$= 4\pi\omega \left[D \frac{\sigma_0 h^2}{4} + \frac{h\sigma_0 L^2}{8} \right]$$

and

$$\frac{p}{\sigma_0} = \frac{L^2}{16R^2} \left[\left(8\frac{Rh}{L^2} + 1 \right)^2 - 1 \right], \qquad (4.194)$$

when $\sigma_0 = 2Y/\sqrt{3}$ or Y according to how closely the shell material follows a Mises or Tresca yield criterion.

If the wall of the shell was to collapse by extending, see Fig. 4.63(b), we should have,

$$\pi R^2 p = 2\pi Rh\sigma_0$$

or

$$\frac{p}{\sigma_0} = 2 \, . \, \frac{h}{R} \qquad (4.195)$$

Yet a third mode of collapse is that in which the end plates only collapse, see Fig. 4.63(c). In this case, adapting and using (4.163),

$$p \, . \, \frac{R\omega \, . \, \pi R^2}{3} = 2\pi R\omega M_p + R \, . \, 2\pi\omega \, . \, M_p$$

and thus,

$$p = \frac{12M_p}{R^2} \quad \text{or} \quad \frac{p}{\sigma_0} = 3\left(\frac{h}{R} \right)^2 \qquad (4.196)$$

Besides the three distinct modes of plastic deformation described, some of them may obtain simultaneously, see for instance Fig. 4.64.

The most appropriate mode to choose is clearly that for which p is least, so that for specified values of L/R and h/R, the least value of p/σ_0 is sought as between (4.194), (4.195) and (4.196) or some combination of them.

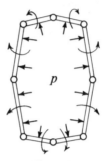

Fig. 4.64.

Heat lines

When a block of metal is rapidly compressed under conditions of plane-strain between parallel rigid platens, the plastic work done is dissipated as heat in a particular manner. However, for the geometry indicated in Fig. 4.65, the plastic work done is concentrated in a fairly well-defined cross; the work, and hence the heat production, is *not* generated more-or-less uniformly throughout the block between the platens. Experiment gives evidence of the concentration of energy dissipation in the cross, especially if the forging is carried out in mild steel at the dull red heat of about $700\,^\circ\text{C}$; the plastic energy appears as concentrated thermal energy and a thermal cross, or a pair of 'heat lines', becomes visible having a temperature of about $800\,^\circ\text{C}$. The existence of heat lines in this and in other circumstances of plastic deformation is important because the temperature that may be reached in the body of the metal is much greater than may otherwise be expected. The consequences of this temperature jump are that unlooked for metallurgical phase changes may occur.

In Fig. 4.65, if $\Delta\theta$ is the adiabatic temperature rise, then the rate at which the platens do plastic work, i.e. $Y.2a.u_0$, is equal to the gain in thermal energy, i.e. $J\rho c.2au_0.\Delta\theta$, by the material which traverses the cross, i.e., in passing from region 1 to region 2. Thus

$$\Delta\theta = \frac{Y}{J\rho c} \tag{4.197}$$

More complex examples of lines of thermal discontinuity are discussed in ref. 4.10; see also ref. 10.13.

This subject is especially important in relation to high speed plate penetration by projectiles and in metal working impact operations, see Chapter 10.

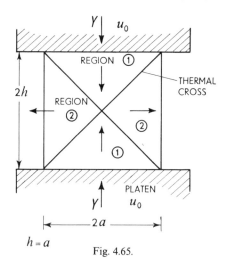

Fig. 4.65.

$h = a$

REFERENCES

4.1 FREUDENTHAL, A. M. *The Inelastic Behaviour of Engineering Materials and Structures.* J. Wiley, New York; Chapman & Hall, London, pp. 587 (1950).

4.2 HILL, R. *The Mathematical Theory of Plasticity.* Clarendon Press, Oxford, pp. 356 (1950).

4.3 NADAI, A. *Theory of Flow and Fracture of Solids.* Vol. I. McGraw-Hill, New York, pp. 572 (1950).

4.4 PRAGER, W. and HODGE, P. G. JR. *Theory of Perfectly Plastic Solids.* Chapman & Hall, London, pp. 264 (1951).

4.5 TABOR, D. *The Hardness of Metals.* Clarendon Press, Oxford, pp. 175 (1951).

4.6 HOFFMAN, O. and SACHS, G. *Introduction to the Theory of Plasticity for Engineers.* McGraw-Hill, New York, pp. 276 (1953).

4.7 JAEGER, J. G. *Elasticity, Fracture and Flow.* Methuen, London, pp. 152 (1956).

4.8 PRAGER, W. *Introduction to Plasticity.* Addison-Wesley, Massachusetts, pp. 148 (1959).

4.9 UNKSOV, E. P. *An Engineering Theory of Plasticity.* Butterworths, London, pp. 275 (1961).

4.10 JOHNSON, W. and MELLOR, P. B. *Plasticity for Mechanical Engineers.* Van Nostrand, London, pp. 412 (1962).

4.11 NADAI, A. *Theory of Flow and Fracture of Solids.* Vol. II. McGraw-Hill, New York, pp. 705 (1963).

4.12 FORD, H. and ALEXANDER, J. M. *Advanced Mechanics of Materials.* Longmans Green, London, pp. 672 (1963).

4.13 ALEXANDER, J. M. and BREWER, R. C. *Manufacturing Properties of Materials.* Van Nostrand, London, pp. 489 (1963).

4.14 THOMSEN, E. G., YANG, C. T. and KOBAYASHI, S. *Mechanics of Plastic Deformation in Metal Processing.* Macmillan Co., New York; Collier-Macmillan, London, pp. 486 (1965).

4.15 ROWE, G. W. *An Introduction to the Principles of Metalworking.* Edward Arnold. London, pp. 306 (1965).

4.16 MENDELSON, A. *Plasticity: Theory and Application.* Collier-Macmillan, London, pp. 353 (1968).

4.17 PARKINS, R. N. *Mechanical Treatment of Metals.* Allen and Unwin, London, pp. 352 (1968).

4.18 ILYUSHIN, A. A. and LENSKY, V. S. *Strength of Materials* (in English). Pergamon Press, pp. 442 (1967).

4.19 BAKER, SIR J. and HEYMAN, J. *Plastic Design of Frames. Vol. 1,* Cambridge Univ. Press, pp. 228 (1969).

4.20 HODGE, P. G. *Plastic Analysis of Structures.* McGraw-Hill, New York, pp. 364 (1959).

4.21 CALLADINE, C. R. *Engineering Plasticity.* Pergamon Press, pp. 318 (1969).

4.22 JOHNSON, W., SOWERBY, R. and HADDOW, J. B. *Plane-Strain Slip Line Fields: Theory and Bibliography*. Edward Arnold, London, pp. 176 (1970).

4.23 MAHTAB, F. U., JOHNSON, W. and SLATER, R. A. C. Dynamic indentation of copper at elevated temperature. *Proc. int. mech. Engrs*, **180**, 285 (1965).

4.24 SLATER, R. A. C. and JOHNSON, W. Effects of temperature, speed and strain rate on the force and energy required in blanking. *I.J.M.S.*, **9**, 271 (1966).

4.25 COOK, P. M. True stress-strain curves for steel compression at high temperatures and strain rates. *Proc. Conf. Prop. at high rates of strain, Instn Mech Engnrs*, Paper 2 (1957).

4.26 CONRAD, H. *The Cryogenic Properties of Metals in High Strength Materials*. J. Wiley, New York, pp. 436 (1965).

4.27 HAWKYARD, J. B., EATON, D. and JOHNSON, W. Dynamic yield strength of copper and low carbon steel at elevated temperatures. *I.J.M.S.* **10**, 929 (1968).

4.28 LUDWIK, P. *Elemente der Technologischen Mechanik*. Springer, Berlin (1909).

4.29 MANJOINE, M. J. and NADAI, A. High speed tension tests at elevated temperatures. *Proc. Am. Soc. Test. Mater.* **40**, 822 (1940).

4.30 ALDER, J. F. and PHILLIPS, K. A. The effect of strain rate and temperature on the resistance of aluminium, copper and steel to compression. *J. Inst. Metals*, **83**, 80 (1954).

4.31 MACGREGOR, C. W. and FISHER, J. C. A velocity-modified temperature for plastic flow of metals. *Trans. Am. Soc. mech. Engrs. J. appl. Mech.*, **13**, 1, A11–A16 (1946).

4.32 PUGH, H. LL. (editor). *The Mechanical Behaviour of Metals under Pressure*. Elsevier Publishing Co., pp. 785 (1970).

4.33 MALVERN, L. E. Experimental studies of strain rate effects and plastic wave propagation in annealed aluminium. *Proc. Soc. mech. Engrs, Coll. Behaviour of Materials under Dynamic Loading*, 81 (1965).

4.34 RIPPERBERGER, E. A. Experimental studies of strain rate effects and plastic wave propagation in annealed aluminium. *Proc. Am. Soc. mech. Engrs Coll. Behaviour of Materials under Dynamic Loading*, Chicago, pp. 62 (1965).

4.35 BELL, J. F. *The Physics of Large Deformation of Crystalline Solids*. Springer-Verlag, New York Inc., pp. 253 (1968).

4.36 TAYLOR, G. I. Formation and enlargement of circular hole in thin plastic sheet. *Q. Jl. Mech. appl. Math.*, **1**, 1,103–24 (1948).

4.37 DUNCAN, J. L. and JOHNSON, W. Unpublished work (1968).

4.38 HOGATT, C. R. and RECHT, R. F. Dynamic stress-strain relationship determined from expanding ring experiments. *Second Intl. Conf.*, Center for High Energy Forming, Univ. Denver, Colorado, vol. I, 2.2.1 (1969).

4.39 MOTT, N. F. Fragmentation of shell cases. *Proc. R. Soc.*, **189**, 300 (1947).

4.40 CRISTESCU, N. *Dynamic Plasticity*. North Holland Publishing Co., pp. 624 (1967).

4.41 CHING, L. K. W. and WEESE, J. A. The explosive forming of rings. *Proc. Second Int. Conf.*, Center for High Energy Forming, Univ. Denver, Colorado, vol. 1, 3.31 (1969).

4.42 HADDOW, J. B. On the compression of a thin disc. *I.J.M.S.*, **7**, 657 (1965).

4.43 LIPPMANN, H. *On the Dynamics of Forging, 7th Int. Conf. M.T.D.R.*, Pergamon Press (1966).

4.44 Advertising literature of Barr and Stroud. No. E-1624.

4.45 TAYLOR, SIR G. I. *Fragmentation of Tubular Bombs, Sci. Pap. of Sir G. I. Taylor, Vol. III*, No. 44, Cambridge Univ. Press, pp. 559 (1963).

4.46 AL-HASSANI, S. T. S., HOPKINS, H. G. and JOHNSON, W. A note on the fragmentation of tubular bombs, *I.J.M.S.*, **11**, 6, 545–549 (1969).

4.47 HOGGATT, C. R. and RECHT, R. F. Fracture behaviour of tubular bombs, *J. appl. Phys.*, **39**, 3, 1856 (1968).

4.48 AL-HASSANI, S. T. S. and JOHNSON, W. The dynamics of the fragmentation process for spherical bombs, *I.J.M.S.*, **11**, 811 (1969).

4.49 LYNCH, J., HAWKYARD, J. B. and JOHNSON, W. Laboratory scale experiments into cavity and crater formation by high explosive charges, *J. mech. Enging Sci.* **12**, 339 (1970).

4.50 BAKER, W. E. and ALLEN, F. J. The response of elastic spherical shells to spherically symmetric internal blast loading. *3rd U.S. Cong. appl. Mech.*, Am. Soc. mech. Engrs, 79 (1958).

4.51 JOHNSON, W. Extrusion . . . and high rate sheet metal forming, *Int. Res. Prod. Eng.*, Am. Soc. mech. Engrs, 342 (1963).

4.52 SOWERBY, R., JOHNSON, W. and SAMANTA, S. K., The diametral compression of circular rings by 'point' loads, *I.J.M.S.*, **10**, 369 (1968).

4.53 DE RUNTZ, J. A. and HODGE, P. G. Crushing of a tube between rigid plates, *J. appl. Mech.*, 391 (1963).

4.54 RAWLINGS, B. Experimental equipment for impulsive testing of structures, *J. Instr. Engrs Aust.*, 59, (April 1967).

4.55 RAWLINGS, B. Mode changes in frames deforming under impulsive loads. *J. mech. Engng Sci.*, **6**, 327 (1964).

4.56 SOWERBY, R. and JOHNSON, W. Use of slip line field theory for the plastic design of pressure vessels. *Experimental Stress Analysis Conf., Proc. Instn mech. Engrs*, 74 (1970).

4.57 CHEUNG, E. C. O. *Yield Hinges Occurring in Diametrically Loaded Rings.* M.Sc. dissertation, Univ. Manchester Inst. Sci. Technol. (1970).

4.58 ALEXANDER, J. M. An approximate analysis of the collapse of thin cylindrical shells under axial loading. *Q.J. Mech. Appl. Math.*, **13**, 10 (1960).

4.59 AL-HASSANI, S. T. S., JOHNSON, W. and LOWE, W. T. Impact of model vehicles. *Proc. Inst. Mech. Engrs* (1972) (at Press).

4.60 AL-HASSANI, S. T. S., JOHNSON, W. and LOWE, W. T. Mechanical characteristics of inversion tubes. *Proc. Inst. Mech. Engrs* (1972) (at Press).

4.61 KROELL, C. K. A simple, efficient, one shot energy absorber. *G. M. Bulletin*, **30**, Part III (Feb. 1962).

4.62 GUIST, L. R. and MARBLE, D. P. Prediction of the inversion load of a circular tube. *NASA TN D-3622* (1966).

4.63 TIMOSHENKO, S. *Theory of Elastic Stability*, McGraw-Hill, New York, pp. 442 (1936).

4.64 CALLADINE, C. R. *Large-Deflection Plastic Theory of Plates. Engineering Plasticity*, Cambridge Univ. Press, 93 (1968).

4.65 OHASHI, Y. and MURAKAMI, S. Elasto-plastic bending of a clamped thin circular plate. *Proc. 11th Int. Cong. appl. Mech.* (1964).

4.66 ONAT, E. T. and HAYTHORNTHWAITE, R. M. Load-carrying capacity of circular plates at large deflection. *Trans. J. appl. Mech.*, **23**, 49 (1956).

4.67 HOOKE, R. An experimental evaluation of the rigid-perfectly plastic theory of bending of plates. *Civ. Engng Trans. Instr Engrs Aust.*, 141 (1968).

5: One-dimensional elastic-plastic stress waves in bars

Elastic-plastic waves in a long uniform bar

The first portion of this chapter can be considered essentially as an extension of Chapter 1 in which we dealt with elastic pulse propagation for small strain, linear, elastic materials; many of the same notions are used but developed to take account of the elastic-plastic behaviour of materials. This is currently an area in which much research work is proceeding and in some respects one in which there are still major disagreements between workers. The aim below is, however, to introduce a sufficiency of working notions for the engineer to be able to engage in intelligent discussions on this subject and to facilitate his understanding and appreciation of the phenomena he may encounter when impulsive, elastic-plastic loadings are possible. The book by Cristescu[4.40] is essential reading for comprehensive studies in this area.

We consider the dynamic loading in tension of a long thin bar, the loaded end of which moves in some prescribed way so as to initiate elastic and plastic longitudinal waves; the bar is said to be long so that there are no wave reflection effects. We assume throughout that the tensile stress-tensile strain relation for monotonic loading is at all times independent of the rate of strain and as with previous cases that radial inertia effects are negligible.

(i) *The bilinear $\sigma_0 - e$ curve: Donnell's approach*

Donnell[5.1] apparently first investigated longitudinal plastic wave propagation in a paper published in 1930 though major contributions to the theory of plastic wave propagation in long bars were made known[4.40] after the Second World War in the papers of Taylor in 1946, Rakhmatulin in 1945 and Karman and Duwez in 1950. The approach taken below, though not rigorous, is presented because of its attractive simplicity and because it provides insight and understanding of the situation and makes no call on mathematical expertise.

Consider a bar of idealised material possessing a bilinear *nominal* stress-engineering strain curve, see Fig. 5.1, such that the two gradients of the curve are E and P where E is the elastic Young's modulus, P the plastic modulus and Y is the yield stress. If the nominal stress suddenly reached at the end of the bar is $\sigma_0 \leq Y$, it will be propagated through the unstrained bar at a speed of $\sqrt{E/\rho_0}$. Further, if a stress σ_0 is applied where $\sigma_0 > Y$ so that the nominal stress increment $(\sigma_0 - Y)$ and strain increment $(e_0 - e_Y)$ are related through the modulus P, then intuitively it seems obvious that this excess stress should be propagated with a speed of $\sqrt{P/\rho_0}$ through the bar in its unstrained configuration.

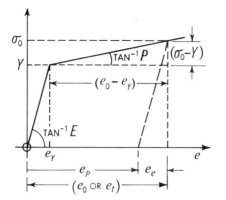

Fig. 5.1.

If the speed at which the free end of the bar is moved at an instant results in a tensile stress $\sigma_0 > Y$, this stress may be expected to be transmitted by two waves, which start at the same instant from the loaded end of the bar but move at the different speeds $c_0 = \sqrt{E/\rho_0}$ and $c_p = \sqrt{P/\rho_0}$. These speeds refer to an origin of coordinates in a fixed space which coincides with the impact end of the bar at time $t = 0$. The stress and strain distribution at time t after loading will, by reference to these fixed laboratory coordinates or to the unstressed material coordinates, be as shown in Fig. 5.2. As t increases the distance between the head of each of the two waves increases. Thus elastic stress Y and corresponding elastic strain e_Y are propagated at speed c_0 whilst the plastic wave following up at speed c_p increases Y to σ_0 and e_Y to e_0.

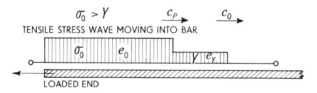

Fig. 5.2.

(ii) General nominal stress-engineering strain curve

A slight generalisation may now be arrived at for the speed of propagation of a longitudinal stress wave through a bar of material which has a continuously turning $\sigma_0 - e$ curve, concave to the strain axis. The equation of motion for an element whose unstressed length is dx at time $t = 0$, see Fig. 5.3, is,

$$d(A\sigma) = \rho_0 A_0 \, dx \cdot \partial^2 u/\partial t^2 \qquad (5.1i)$$

where u is the displacement undergone by an element originally distant x from the origin fixed in space, at time $t = 0$. σ is the *true* longitudinal stress across the element whose current cross-sectional area is A. However, as $A_0\sigma_0 = A\sigma$ where A_0 is the initial cross-sectional area of the bar, then equation (5.1i) is equally well written as

$$d(A_0\sigma_0) = \rho_0 A_0 \, dx \cdot \partial^2 u/\partial t^2$$

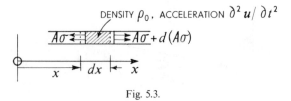

DENSITY ρ_0, ACCELERATION $\partial^2 u / \partial t^2$

Fig. 5.3.

and hence,

$$\frac{d\sigma_0}{de} = \rho_0 \frac{dx}{de} \cdot \frac{\partial^2 u}{\partial t^2}; \qquad (5.1\text{ii})$$

ρ_0 is the density of the unstressed bar, assumed constant throughout. Since $e = \partial u/\partial x$ then $de/dx = \partial^2 u/\partial x^2$ so that equation (5.1ii) becomes

$$\frac{\partial^2 u}{\partial t^2} = \frac{d\sigma_0/de}{\rho_0} \cdot \frac{\partial^2 u}{\partial x^2}; \qquad (5.2)$$

thus the speed of wave propagation along the x-axis is, by comparison with (1.2i),

$$c_p = \sqrt{(d\sigma_0/de)/\rho_0} \qquad (5.3)$$

Note that $d\sigma_0/de$ is just the slope of the nominal stress-engineering strain curve at σ_0. For elastic wave propagation, i.e. $\sigma_0 < Y$, see Fig. 5.4, $d\sigma_0/de = E$ and (5.3) gives $c_0 = \sqrt{E/\rho_0}$; for the bilinear stress-strain curve of the previous section, Fig. 5.1, $d\sigma_0/de = P$ for $\sigma_0 > Y$ and thus $c_P = \sqrt{P/\rho_0}$.

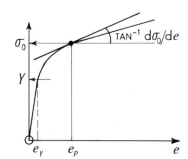

Fig. 5.4.

To utilise the equation (5.3), there should be available a nominal stress-engineering strain curve, or a load extension curve for the material concerned, precisely appropriate to the physical conditions of the wave propagation, and in particular to the local strain rate. This is never known *ab initio* and it is usual to employ the 'static' load-extension curve; however see p. 136 concerning the work of J. F. Bell and reference 4.35.

(iii) *Strain distribution in a bar propagating an elastic-plastic stress wave*

If the long bar is loaded to a nominal stress level of σ_0 instantaneously, with which is associated a strain e_p, then over the elastic range of stress the wave speed is constant at $c_0 = \sqrt{E/\rho_0}$, whilst for every stress level $\sigma_0 > Y$, the wave speed is less, at $\sqrt{(d\sigma_0/de)/\rho_0}$, being the smaller, the greater is σ_0.

Three distinct regions at given time t may be identified by reference to the position of the unstressed bar, see Fig. 5.5.

(i) Between $x = 0$ and $x = c_p t$, the strain is constant at e_p; $c_p = \sqrt{(d\sigma_0/de)/\rho_0}$ where σ_0 is the greatest nominal stress imposed.

(ii) Between $x = c_p t$ and $x = c_0 t$, there is a variable distribution of strain between e_p and e_Y.

(iii) For $x > c_0 t$ i.e. ahead of the elastic wave, the bar is physically unstressed.

It is not difficult to see that the curve in Fig. 5.5 is concave upwards for a typical stress-strain curve which is concave downwards; the particular case of a trilinear stress-strain curve needs only to be considered.

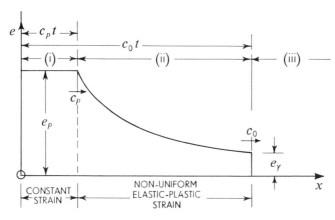

Fig. 5.5.

(iv) *Particle speed required to attain a given stress level*

A simple and direct derivation of the speed of movement at the end of a bar in order to produce a strain of e_p, is obtained after considering a small element of the bar in its unstretched state of length dx, and noting that the time, dt, taken for it to propagate a force increment $d(A_0\sigma_0)$ at stress level σ_0 is dx/c_p; we emphasise that the speed here has reference to the unstretched length of the element or the space occupied by it.

$$dt = \frac{dx}{\sqrt{(d\sigma_0/de)/\rho_0}} \tag{5.4}$$

However, applying the momentum equation to the element of the bar

$$(\rho_0 A_0 \, dx) \cdot dv = d(A_0\sigma_0) \, dt \tag{5.5}$$

where dv is the increment in speed of the element due to excess force $d(A_0\sigma_0)$ or $d(A\sigma)$. Hence, eliminating dt between (5.4) and (5.5)

$$dv = \frac{d\sigma_0}{\rho_0\sqrt{\dfrac{d\sigma_0/de}{\rho_0}}} ; \qquad (5.6)$$

thus the *total* speed acquired by the element—relative to a fixed background of coordinates specified at time $t = 0$—is, in order to attain nominal stress level σ_0,

$$v = \int_0^{e_P} \sqrt{\frac{d\sigma_0/de}{\rho_0}} . de = \int_0^{e_P} c_0\sqrt{\frac{d\sigma_0/de}{E}} . de \qquad (5.7)$$

For the bilinear nominal stress-engineering curve of Fig. 5.1, equation (5.7) gives,

$$v = e_Y\sqrt{E/\rho_0} + (e_P - e_Y)\sqrt{P/\rho_0}$$

or

$$v = e_Y c_0 + (e_P - e_Y)c_1$$

$$\left.\begin{array}{c}\\[2.5em]\end{array}\right\} \qquad (5.8)$$

where $e_Y = Y/E$.

(v) *Critical impact speed*

The statical ultimate strength of a stressed bar occurs when $d\sigma_0/de = 0$; it marks the end of the ability of the bar to carry a uniform strain and stresses (or strains) in excess of the ultimate stress will cause necking and subsequently fracture. Now under dynamic loading we may assume that fracture occurs at the ultimate strength; this is easily seen from (5.5) above, because at the ultimate strength, i.e. *where $d\sigma_0/de = 0$, the speed of plastic wave propagation is zero*. The speed of the loaded end of the bar is given by (5.7), where the limits of integration for strain will be zero and the tensile instability strain e_u. At this critical speed of movement, the end of the bar will be moving as fast as the bar can pass on, or propagate, information about its own particle movements, i.e. from the loaded end to further up the bar. The critical impact speed for a bar, v_c, is then the speed of the loaded end which will cause fracture in the bar under tension. Generally, the strength of the bar will be reached at a critical section where the plastic wave therefrom is zero.

We have,

$$v_c = \int_0^{e_u} \sqrt{\frac{d\sigma_0/de}{\rho_0}} . de \qquad (5.9)$$

Figures 5.6 and 5.7 are taken from the papers by Karman and Duwez and White and Griffis, see ref. 1.2. In the case of Fig. 5.6 from the stress-strain curve given, the computed value of v_c was 150 ft/sec and rupture of the specimen actually occurred at an impact speed of 171 ft/sec.

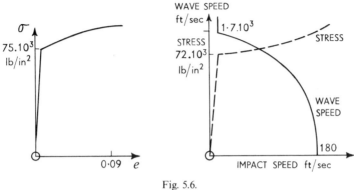

Fig. 5.6.

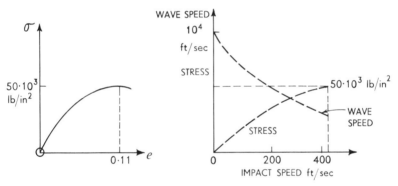

Fig. 5.7.

(vi) *Shock waves and the locking medium*

In all the cases so far considered the stress-strain curve has been concave towards the strain axis, but in a few cases (e.g. nickel-chrome steel and polycrystalline ~~material behaviour is shown in Fig. 5.9 and this is a locking medium; using~~ relatively large strains are concerned. In this case because the slope of the $\sigma_0 - e$ curves increases with strain, the speed of propagation of a stress wave in a long rod increases with increase in stress intensity. Curves of the form shown in Fig. 5.8 are representative of some soils and rubbers. One form of idealised material behaviour is shown in Fig. 5.9 and this is a locking medium; using equation (5.3), clearly there are only two wave speeds associated with this curve, i.e. $\sqrt{E/\rho_0}$ and an infinite speed. Equation (5.3) shows that, when the end of a bar is loaded, the latest and therefore largest stress or strain imposed is propagated at a faster rate than the early or lower stresses and strains so that, if the bar is sufficiently long, following waves will overtake early waves and eventually all should coalesce to give one strong wave front, a *shock wave*,

magnesium) the curve's convex towards the strain axes, see Fig 5.8, at least show

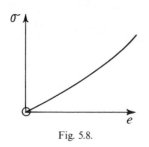

Fig. 5.8.

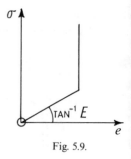

Fig. 5.9.

probably first predicted by White and Griffis in 1942.[1,2] In any case, the distance between any last-to-be-propagated and most intense stress wave, and the first and least intense stress wave, will be steadily reduced. Further discussion of this topic will be found in refs. 1.2 and 4.40.

(vii) *Stress waves in bars preloaded into the plastic range: the elastic precursor*

It would be expected that if a bar or rod is preloaded and carries a static load of amount P or stress σ_0', see Fig. 5.10, which is sufficient to induce some degree of plastic deformation, then the sudden addition of a small load, the stress increment $(d\sigma_0')$ or the increment of strain, would be propagated at a speed of $[(d\sigma_0'/de_e)/\rho_0]^{1/2}$; the common expectation is that information about a small additional load having been added would be conveyed along the bar at the plastic wave speed appropriate to the point σ_0' on the stress-strain curve. Experiment shows however that both elastic and plastic waves are propagated by the extra load. The elastic wave is commonly referred to as the 'precursor'; it is of course the precursor of the plastic waves of stress and strain. In fact, as Fig. 5.10 shows, imposing stress increment $d\sigma_0'$ causes a total strain increment de_t which is made up of elastic de_e, and plastic de_P, strain increments; the elastic strain increment must be propagated at the elastic wave speed.

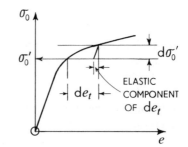

Fig. 5.10.

(viii) *Unloading waves*

Reverting to a consideration of the bilinear σ_0/e curve, it is easy to see how the elastic and plastic waves generated in loading such a bar of material to level σ_0 for interval $0 \le t \le t_0$, may be represented in a location diagram, see Fig. 5.11. If the load is now completely and instantaneously removed, this will take place as an *unloading* elastic wave, see p. 123 -effectively as an elastic compressive

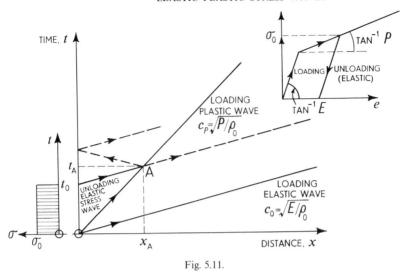

Fig. 5.11.

wave; it will be propagated into the bar and at time t_A will have overtaken the slower moving loading plastic wave at distance x_A from the original loaded end. When the two waves meet, depending upon the original intensity of the applied stress σ_0, the plastic wave may propagate further into the bar or it may be arrested and an elastic wave only, continue. Also, an elastic wave is reflected from a section distance x_A into the bar, back towards the now free end, there to be reflected yet again up the bar. Details of this case are fully discussed in ref. 4.40. But after practising in the use of the location diagram for the loading of an elastic-plastic material on p. 228 below, the nature of the calculations and 'book-keeping' regarding stress and particle speed, which has to be carried out in unloading problems, will be well appreciated.

Impact of a finite length uniform bar of elastic-linear strain-hardening material with a rigid flat anvil: the use of the location diagram

The work below is mainly attributable to Lensky deriving from his work published in the U.S.S.R. in 1949. It is presented here as an introduction to the treatment of one dimensional elastic and plastic waves in finite length bars (and therefore so that reflections are treated) as an example of how elastic and plastic waves may be simultaneously generated at a section *inside* a bar, and of how elastic unloading waves arise and are treated. Let a uniform bar of elastic-linear strain-hardening material, see Fig. 5.1, impinge normally on a rigid flat anvil and the nominal stress rise to $\sigma_0 > Y$, the yield stress. Only two wave speeds are possible, i.e. the elastic wave speed $c_0 = \sqrt{E/\rho_0}$ and the plastic wave speed $c_P = c_1 = \sqrt{P/\rho_0}$.

When impact with plastic deformation occurs, the two waves are simultaneously propagated from the interface between the impinging bar and the anvil; they travel outwards along the bar at speeds c_0 and c_1, see Fig. 5.12(a) and (b). There are, for $0 < t < l/c_0$, three distinct regions in the bar; region I which is that traversed by both the elastic and the plastic waves, region II which is traversed thus far only by elastic waves, and region III which is undisturbed. The material in region I will have been brought to rest; clearly, for it to exist and to have been plastically strained, the strain there must have exceeded e_Y, the simple compressive yield strain. The minimum velocity necessary to initiate plastic strains is just $Y/\rho c_0 = c_0 e_Y$. The speed of particles in region II is,

$$v = V - c_0 e_Y \tag{5.10}$$

and since this speed is reduced to zero when the plastic 'shock' front passes, the compressive stress jump, $(\sigma_0 - Y)$, is

$$\sigma_0 - Y = \rho_0 c_1 (V - c_0 e_Y)$$

so that, the compressive stress in region I is

$$\sigma_0 = Y + \rho_0 c_1 (V - c_0 e_Y) \tag{5.11}$$

Also the total compressive strain is,

$$e_t = e_Y + \frac{\sigma_0 - Y}{P} = e_Y + \frac{V - c_0 e_Y}{c_1} \tag{5.12}$$

If there is no further plastic strain in this region, then the residual plastic strain e_P, see Fig. 5.1, is given by,

$$e_t = e_e + e_P$$

where e_e is the elastic strain component. Hence,

$$e_P = \left(e_Y + \frac{V - c_0 e_Y}{c_1} \right) - \frac{\sigma_0}{E}$$

$$= e_Y + \frac{V - c_0 e_Y}{c_1} - \left(\frac{Y + \rho_0 c_1 (V - c_0 e_Y)}{E} \right)$$

$$= (V - c_0 e_Y) \left(\frac{1}{c_1} - \frac{c_1}{c_0^2} \right)$$

$$= \frac{c_0^2 - c_1^2}{c_0^2 c_1} \cdot (V - c_0 e_Y) \tag{5.13}$$

Just after time $t = l/c_0$, the elastic wave will be reflected from the free end of the bar and the slower moving plastic wave front will have advanced further to the right; the situation is shown as Fig. 5.12(c). The effect of reflecting the elastic stress wave will be to progressively and completely *unload* the right hand end of the bar or much of region III; the velocity of region III will be decreased to $(V - 2c_0 e_Y)$. The approaching reflected elastic wave and the advancing plastic stress wave eventually meet at time T_1 after it has advanced x_1 from the end of the bar at which impact first took place, see Fig. 5.12(d). We have,

$$T_1 = \frac{x_1}{c_1} = \frac{2l - x_1}{c_0}$$

so that,

$$\frac{x_1}{l} = \frac{2c_1/c_0}{1 + c_1/c_0} \quad \text{and} \quad T_1 = \frac{2l}{c_0 + c_1} \tag{5.14}$$

Since c_1/c_0 is often about $\frac{1}{10}$ for many materials, $x_1/l \simeq 0.18$. The actual length of the plastically deformed region is $x_1(1 - e_P)$. When the reflected unloading wave and the outward going plastic wave meet, at some section S_1S_1 at time T_1, it will be as if the length of bar $(l - x_1)$ having a speed $(V - 2c_0e_Y)$ or $(2c_0e_Y - V)$, suddenly impinges on a stationary bar of length x_1, which is already subjected to a compressive stress σ_0. The result of this impact is that just after time T_1, waves will be reflected back into each part of the bar, see Fig. 5.12(e). If it is assumed that both the reflected waves are elastic, then immediately after impact the particle speed must be the same on both sides of S_1S_1. Let this speed be v to the right. The *change* in speed of that part of region I embraced by the reflected elastic wave from S_1 i.e. region V, is then just v; since this particle speed is oppositely directed to that of the wave it implies the propagation of a tensile stress wave and the imposition of tensile strain. And because region V is already loaded in compression and has zero speed, therefore the tensile wave *elastically* unloads region V by amount ρ_0c_0v, to $[P(e_t - e_Y) + Ee_Y - \rho_0c_0v]$.

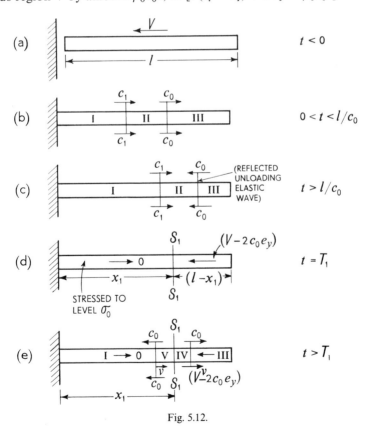

Fig. 5.12.

At the same time, the stress in that part of region III which is traversed by the rightward moving reflected elastic stress wave, i.e. region IV of Fig. 5.12(e), becomes $[\rho_0 c_0(V - 2c_0 e_Y + v)]$; the change in particle speed in this region is the term in brackets above. However, the forces at the interface $S_1 S_1$ must be the same for both region V and IV, so that

$$P(e_t - e_Y) + Ee_Y - \rho_0 c_0 v = \rho_0 c_0(V - 2c_0 e_Y + v) \tag{5.15}$$

Substituting for e_t from (5.12) in (5.15),

$$P\left[\frac{V - c_0 e_Y}{c_1} + e_Y - e_Y\right] + Ee_Y = 2\rho_0 c_0 v + \rho_0 c_0(V - 2c_0 e_Y)$$

This equation may be reduced to,

$$v = \frac{(c_1 - 3c_0)(V - c_0 e_Y)}{2c_0} + V \tag{5.16}$$

The elastic strain e_1 engendered in region IV is, using (5.16),

$$e_1 = \frac{\rho_0 c_0}{E}\left[\frac{(c_1 - 3c_0)(V - c_0 e_Y)}{2c_0} + 2V - 2c_0 e_Y\right]$$

$$= \frac{(c_1 + c_0)(V - c_0 e_Y)}{2c_0^2}$$

Now the greatest value which e_1 can take and region IV still remain elastic, is e_Y, so that if $e_1 = e_Y$, then

$$V = c_0 e_Y\left(1 + \frac{2c_0}{c_0 + c_1}\right) \tag{5.17}$$

The compressive strain e' remaining in regions I and V, after traversal by the elastic wave reflected from $S_1 S_1$ results from a change in compressive strain $e_Y + (V - c_0 e_Y)/c_1$, by an amount of tensile strain $\rho c_0 v/E$ and is just

$$e' = \left(e_Y + \frac{V - c_0 e_Y}{c_1}\right) - \frac{\rho_0 c_0 v}{E}$$

$$= \left(e^Y + \frac{V - c_0 e_Y}{c_1}\right) - \frac{\rho_0 c_0}{E}\left[\frac{(c_1 - 3c_0)(V - c_0 e_Y)}{2c_0} + V\right]$$

$$= (V - c_0 e_Y)\left[\frac{-c_1^2 + c_1 c_0 + 2c_0^2}{2c_0^2 c_1}\right] \tag{5.18}$$

Provided that only elastic waves leave section $S_1 S_1$, elastic waves will travel up and down the bar after contact with the anvil ceases and the *total* strain at any section will vary; but the plastic strains—particularly in region I—will remain constant. Thus provided that,

$$c_0 e_Y < V < c_0 e_Y\left(1 + \frac{2c_0}{c_0 + c_1}\right)$$

or

$$1 < \frac{V}{c_0 e_Y} < 3 - \frac{2c_1/c_0}{1 + c_1/c_0} \qquad (5.19)$$

there will only be one region embracing an original length of bar of extent x_1 in which plastic deformation occurs.

$S_1 S_1$ is known as a *stationary front of second order discontinuity in strain*; usually on either side of an elastic or plastic wave front, there is a first order discontinuity in strain—which is not of course stationary.

For say, steel, $c_0 \simeq 2 . 10^5$ in/sec or 17 000 ft/sec $(5 . 10^3$ m/s) and $e_Y \simeq 10^{-3}$, i.e. $Y \simeq 13$ ton/in^2 $(0.2 . 10^9$ N/m^2), so that the inequality (5.19) becomes,

$$1 < \frac{V}{200} < 3 - \frac{2c_1/c_0}{1 + c_1/c_0} \qquad (5.20)$$

where V is given in in/sec.

Since c_1/c_0 is usually small, say $\simeq \frac{1}{10}$, the range for V is between 17 and 50 ft/sec.

When V is just sufficient to initiate further plastic deformation, i.e. beyond SS_1, using (5.17), we find

$$\left.\begin{array}{c} e_t = e_Y \left[1 + \dfrac{2(c_0/c_1)^2}{1 + c_0/c_1} \right], \\[2mm] e' = e_Y \left[2\dfrac{c_0}{c_1} - 1 \right], \\[2mm] \text{and} \quad e_P = e_Y \left[\dfrac{c_0}{c_1} - 1 \right]. \end{array}\right\} \qquad (5.21)$$

If $V > c_0 e_Y(1 + 2c_0/(c_0 + c_1))$, then a further plastic wave propagates to the right from $S_1 S_1$ as well as elastic waves in both directions. Either of these latter elastic waves after reflection from the ends of the bar, may later intercept the plastic wave and cause a second stationary front of second order strain discontinuity $S_2 S_2$.

The bar, if only one stationary front arises, will appear, when exaggerated, as in Fig. 5.13(a) and if two are created as in Fig. 5.13(b).

The sequence of events and the interaction of the wave motions may be well represented in the characteristic (x, t) plane as shown in Fig. 5.14. Fig. 5.14 is drawn for a case in which a second stationary front of second order in strain discontinuity arises at $S_2 S_2$.

Which of the two elastic waves from $S_1 S_1$ first meets the plastic wave depends on the ratio c_0/c_1. The critical case arises when both elastic waves meet the plastic wave simultaneously. Let this happen after further time T_2 at a further distance along the unstrained bar from $S_1 S_1$ of x_2, i.e. at section $S_2 S_2$. For the elastic wave which travels to the left of the plastic wave, i.e. that

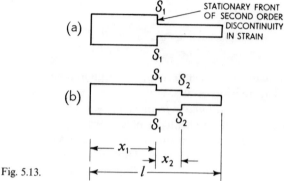

Fig. 5.13.

passes through region V, i.e. S_1AS_2 in Fig. 5.14,

$$T_2 = \frac{x_1}{c_0} + \frac{x_1 + x_2}{c_0} \,. \tag{5.22}$$

For the other elastic wave, i.e. S_1BS_2

$$T_2 = \frac{2(l - x_1) - x_2}{c_0} \tag{5.23}$$

and for the plastic wave,

$$T_2 = \frac{x_2}{c_1} \,. \tag{5.24}$$

From (5.23) and (5.24) and using (5.14),

$$\frac{x_2}{l} = \frac{2c_1(c_0 - c_1)}{(c_0 + c_1)^2} = \frac{2(1 - c_1/c_0)(c_1/c_0)}{(1 + c_1/c_0)^2} \tag{5.25}$$

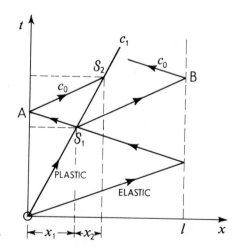

Fig. 5.14.

and

$$\frac{x_1 + x_2}{l} = \frac{4c_0c_1}{(c_0 + c_1)^2} = 4 \cdot \frac{\dfrac{c_1}{c_0}}{\left[1 + \dfrac{c_1}{c_0}\right]^2} ; \qquad (5.26)$$

and using (5.22) and (5.24) or (5.25) with (5.14),

$$\frac{l}{c_1} \cdot \frac{2\left(1 - \dfrac{c_1}{c_0}\right)\left(\dfrac{c_1}{c_0}\right)}{\left[1 + \dfrac{c_1}{c_0}\right]^2} = \frac{l}{c_0} \cdot \frac{2\left(\dfrac{c_1}{c_0}\right)}{1 + \dfrac{c_1}{c_0}} + \frac{l}{c_0} \cdot \frac{4\left(\dfrac{c_1}{c_0}\right)}{\left[1 + \left(\dfrac{c_1}{c_0}\right)^2\right]}$$

which reduces to,

$$c_0^2 - 4c_0c_1 - c_1^2 = 0,$$

so that,

$$c_0/c_1 = 2 + \sqrt{5} \simeq 4\cdot24 \qquad (5.27)$$

Thus if $c_0/c_1 > 4\cdot24$, then the leftward moving elastic wave from section S_1 first intercepts the plastic wave.

Analysis of the dynamic compression of a short cylinder between a constant speed flat rigid die and a stationary die using the characteristic diagram

We consider a short cylindrical block of elastic-linear strain-hardening material, situated on a frictionless flat rigid bottom die, which is compressed by an identical upper die moving with a speed V which remains constant for a period of time $6l_0/c_1$, where $c_1 = (P/\rho_0)^{1/2}$ is the plastic wave speed and l_0 is the original height of the cylinder, see Fig. 5.15(a).

To examine the distribution of strain and speed throughout the cylinder during this period we again use the characteristic or location plane diagram; this will also show the progress of the elastic and the plastic waves through the cylinder. At a time $0 < t < l_0/c_0$, where $c_0 = (E/\rho_0)^{1/2}$, the situation is as shown in Fig. 5.15(b) and when $t = l_0/c_0$ as in Fig. 5.15(c) and (d). All material engulfed by the plastic wave will be moving at speed V, i.e. the die speed, and that through which the elastic wave only has passed will have a speed u where

$$Y = \rho_0c_0u \quad \text{or} \quad u = \frac{Y}{\rho_0c_0} = \frac{Y}{E} \cdot \frac{E}{\rho_0} \cdot \frac{1}{c_0}$$

i.e.

$$u = c_0e_Y \qquad (5.28)$$

denoting Y/E by e_Y.

Since the particles in contact with the lower die are at rest, then the wave reflected from it must be such as to change the incident elastic wave particle speed from c_0e_Y to zero. Further, since the material is already stressed to the compressive yield stress, the reflected wave must be a plastic wave. The situation is now as shown in Fig. 5.15(e) and the material encompassed by the reflected plastic wave is under, say, a stress of intensity σ. We have

$$\sigma - Y = \rho_0 c_1 . \Delta V \qquad (5.29)$$

where ΔV is the change in particle speed that the plastic wave brings about. Now $\Delta V = c_0 e_Y$ and thus

$$\sigma = Y + \rho_0 c_1 . c_0 e_Y = Y\left(1 + c_1 c_0 \frac{\rho_0}{E}\right)$$

$$= Y\left(1 + \frac{c_1}{c_0}\right) \qquad (5.30)$$

The plastic wave from the lower die and the initiated plastic wave meet at A, distant X, from the bottom die. From this meeting of the two plastic waves, only two identical (or continuing) plastic waves can be produced; no elastic effects intervene since the cylinder is still being compressively loaded by the top die moving with speed V.

At time $t = l_0/c_1$, the location diagram appears as shown in Fig. 5.15(f). The stress level in zone [2] is,

$$Y + (V - c_0 e_Y)\rho_0 c_1 = Y\left(1 - \frac{c_1}{c_0}\right) + \rho_0 c_1 V \qquad (5.31)$$

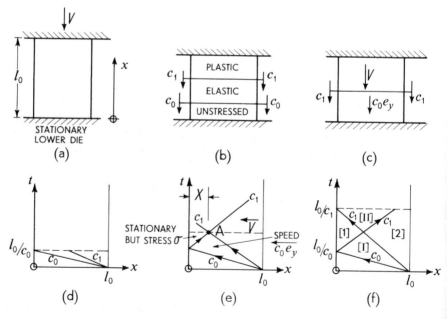

Fig. 5.15.

Let the particle speed in zone [II] be w, then from a consideration of zones [1] and [II], the stress in zone [II] is

$$Y\left(1 + \frac{c_1}{c_0}\right) + \rho_0 c_1 w$$

From a consideration of zones [2] and [II], the stress in zone [II] is

$$Y\left(1 - \frac{c_1}{c_0}\right) + \rho_0 c_1 V + \rho_0 c_1 (V - w)$$

However,

$$Y\left(1 + \frac{c_1}{c_0}\right) + \rho_0 c_1 w = Y\left(1 - \frac{c_1}{c_0}\right) + \rho_0 c_1 V + \rho_0 c_1 (V - w)$$

so that

$$w = V - c_0 e_Y \tag{5.32}$$

Thus the stress in zone [II] is,

$$\sigma = Y\left(1 + \frac{c_1}{c_0}\right) + \rho_0 c_1 (V - c_0 e_Y)$$

$$= Y + \rho_0 c_1 V \tag{5.33}$$

It is straightforward to arrive at the strain and stress levels in each region from observations about the particle speed; the completed location diagram which is Fig. 5.16, should be checked. Note that when the upper die is arrested at $t = 6l_0/c_1$, an unloading wave of intensity $(Y + 6\rho_0 c_1 V)$ is propagated into the cylinder and results in it springing away from the bottom die to some extent in due course.

Some typical figures for steel might be as follows,

Put $Y = 25 \cdot 10^3$ lb/in^2 ($172 \cdot 10^6$ N/m^2), $c_1/c_0 = \frac{1}{10}$ and take $V = 60$ ft/sec ($18 \cdot 3$ m/sec)

Then, if $c_0 = (E/\rho_0)^{1/2} \simeq 2 \cdot 10^5$ in/sec ($5 \cdot 10^3$ m/sec), so that

$$\rho_0 c_1 V = \frac{E}{c_0^2} \cdot c_1 V = 10,800 \text{ lb/in}^2 \ (75 \cdot 10^6 \text{ N/m}^2).$$

$$Y\left(1 + \frac{c_1}{c_0}\right) = 25(1 + \tfrac{1}{10}) \cdot 10^3 = 27 \cdot 5 \cdot 10^3 \text{ lb/in}^2 \ (190 \cdot 10^6 \text{ N/m}^2)$$

and

$$Y\left(1 - \frac{c_1}{c_0}\right) = 25(1 - \tfrac{1}{10}) \cdot 10^3 = 22 \cdot 5 \cdot 10^3 \text{ lb/in}^2 \ (155 \cdot 10^6 \text{ N/m}^2)$$

Also, $c_0 e_Y = 2 \cdot 10^5 \cdot \dfrac{25 \cdot 10^3}{30 \cdot 10^6} = 167$ in/sec $\simeq 14$ ft/sec ($4 \cdot 3$ m/sec)

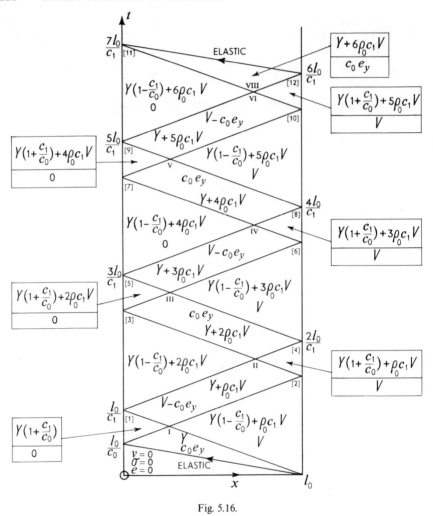

Fig. 5.16.

Stress in the zones identified in Fig. 5.16 in 000s lb/in^2 (or $7 \cdot 10^6$ N/m^2) are,

[1] 27·5

[2] 22·5 + 10·8 = 33·3

[3] 22·5 + 21·6 = 44·1

[4] 27·5 + 10·8 = 38·3

[5] 27·5 + 21·6 = 49·1

[6] 22·5 + 32·4 = 54·9

[7] 22·5 + 43·2 = 65·7

[8] 27·5 + 32·4 = 59·9

[9] 27·5 + 43·2 = 70·7

[10] 27·5 + 54·0 = 76·5

[11] 22·5 + 64·8 = 87·3

[12] 27·5 + 54·0 = 81·5

If $l_0 = 2$ in (~ 5 cm) then $l_0/c_1 = 2/2 \cdot 10^4 = 10^{-4}$ sec and the time of the operation is $6l_0/c_1 = 6 \cdot 10^{-4}$. The amount of compression in this time is $\Delta h = 6 \cdot 10^{-4} \cdot 720 = 0.432$ in (11 mm) and the engineering strain is $e = 0.432/2 = 0.216$. The stress on the upper die at the close of the operation is given by,

$$(\sigma - Y)/P = e$$

or

$$\sigma = Pe + Y$$
$$= 3 \cdot 10^5 \cdot 0 \cdot 216 + 25 \cdot 10^3$$
$$= 89 \cdot 8 \cdot 10^3 \text{ lb/in}^2 \ (618 \cdot 10^6 \text{ N/m}^2)$$

High speed normal impact of short rigid-perfectly plastic solid cylindrical blocks with a flat rigid anvil

(i) *Taylor's momentum approach*

In this section we consider the normal, high speed impact with consequent plastic deformation of a short, solid cylindrical bar with a rigid anvil. The end at which impact takes place 'mushrooms', see Plate 27a, and this shape is characteristic of this type of process[5.2]. For steel bars, by 'high speed' we mean a few hundred feet or metres/second; the bar is said to be short because for length to diameter ratios of greater than three, buckling would be expected as opposed to compression.

The analysis which follows is originally due to Taylor[5.3] and though not entirely successful in accounting for the mode of deformation revealed by experiment, it is highly instructive and suggestive.

The approach is applicable in cases where $\rho_0 v_0^2 \simeq Y$ where v_0 is the initial bar or projectile speed and for a typical mild steel, $v_0 \simeq 1000$ ft/sec (~ 300 m/sec); ρ_0 denotes the density of the material and Y the yield stress (or alternatively is interpreted as the tensile strength, and therefore takes strain-hardening into account to some degree). The aim is to account for the 'mushrooming' of bullets or projectiles during the impact process.

The discussion in the first place considers the projectile as made of elastic/perfectly-plastic material but subsequently considers the analysis in terms of the rigid/perfectly-plastic material. At impact with the rigid anvil, see Fig. 5.17, two waves are initiated and move out from the anvil; one travels with the elastic wave speed c_0 and the other—a plastic wave—at a much slower speed which is to be determined. The stress in the bar immediately rises to the elastic

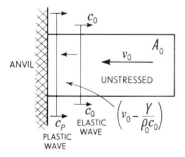

Fig. 5.17   Elastic and plastic waves are both initiated at moment of impact.

limit and particularly the elastic compressive stress, travels to the free end of the bar, giving rise to a change in particle speed of $Y/\rho_0 c_0$ to the right; if the initial speed of the bar was v_0 the speed of the particles in the bar through which this wave has travelled relative to the fixed anvil, is reduced to $(v_0 - Y/\rho_0 c_0)$, see Fig. 5.18(a). At the free end of the bar the compressive elastic wave is reflected as a wave of tension whose intensity is equal to that of the compressive wave; it travels to the left and is superimposed on the compressive wave so progressively unloading the bar, i.e. reducing the stress in it to zero, starting from the free end, see Fig. 5.18(b). There are three regions in the bar throughout this sequence; one which is plastically strained, i.e. through which the plastic wave has advanced, a second which is not strained at all and a third—between the plastic wavefront and the elastic wavefront in which *elastic* strains of magnitude Y/E are imposed.

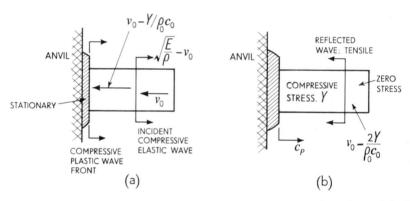

Fig. 5.18   Stress waves initiated at impact, indicating zone of plastic deformation and the first reflection of the elastic wave.

The head of the tensile wave, moving with speed $\sqrt{E/\rho_0}$ to the left, eventually encounters the compressive, slow moving plastic wave which is advancing along the bar to the right behind the compressive elastic wave. The reflected wave of tension moving to the left, of itself causes a change in particle speed of magnitude $Y/\rho_0 c_0$ to the right, so that the speed of the unloaded rear end of the bar is as a whole $(v_0 - 2Y/\rho_0 c_0)$. Thus, when the rightward-moving compressive plastic wave and the leftward-moving, unloading, tensile elastic wave meet, the whole of the bar to the right of the plastic wave front has the speed $(v_0 - 2Y/\rho_0 c_0)$. This sequence of events is described in different terms elsewhere. If representative figures, say for mild steel where $Y = 30\,000$ lb/in^2 ($207 . 10^6$ N/m^2). $\rho_0 g = 0.28$ lb/in^3 (8000 kg/m^3) and $c_0 = 2 . 10^5$ in/sec ($5 . 10^3$ m/sec) are used to calculate $2Y/\rho_0 c_0$, then it appears as only about 30 ft/sec (~ 9 m/sec).

The continuous passage of the elastic wave up and down the rear portion of the bar, which is reflected from the slowly advancing plastic wavefront and the free end of the bar, feeds energy forward for its subsequent dissipation plastically, and slowly, after many traversals of the rear part of the bar, brings it to rest. This rear portion, i.e. that which is not plastically deformed at a given time, may thus reasonably be treated as a continuously retarded *rigid* body whose motion is determined by events at the plastic wavefront. The momentum flux at the plastic wavefront decreases with time and hence the plastic strain developed also decreases with time; thus a mushroom shape is expected. As our concern is with plastic deformation we now confine attention to behaviour at the plastic wavefront.

A simple theoretical model may now be conceived in which the portion of the bar moving through the plastic wavefront (or shock) is brought to rest and, in doing so, the material spreads out laterally undergoing compressive plastic deformation, the necessary compressive force being derived from the change of momentum undergone by the rigid oncoming portion of the bar whose speed, v, is steadily reduced. The 'mushroomed' projectile as finally seen, is the terminal state of a deformation history which at a moment in the period of deformation appears as in Fig. 5.18; note that this simple model requires a discontinuity in cross-sectional area at the plastic wavefront.

(ii) *Basic equations*

In Fig. 5.19(a) for simplicity, bring the plastic wave front, *PF*, which has an absolute speed of c_p to relative rest, so that rigid material from the right moves across it with speed $(v + c_p)$; v is the instantaneous absolute speed of the end of the bar of initial cross-sectional area A_0, see Fig. 5.19(b). We denote by A the

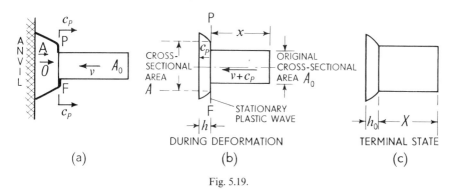

Fig. 5.19.

current cross-sectional area of the bar when brought to rest, it having been plastically deformed after moving through plane *PF*. Thus, the equation for no change in volume gives

$$A_0(v + c_p) = Ac_p \qquad (5.34)$$

Also at *PF*, the net force is $Y(A - A_0)$; the pressure in the 'shock' is everywhere the same at magnitude Y; this is equal to the rate of change of momentum across the shock plane, i.e. the mass arriving per unit time is $\rho_0 A_0(v + c_p)$ and its change in velocity is from $(v + c_p)$ to c_p. Hence

$$\rho_0 A_0 (v + c_p) \cdot \{(v + c_p) - c_p\} = Y(A - A_0)$$

or

$$\rho_0 A_0 (v + c_p) v = Y(A - A_0). \tag{5.35}$$

ρ_0 assumes an unchanging density. (Compare equations (5.41i) and (5.41iii) below.) If the longitudinal compressive engineering strain in any element of original length dl_0 which has been plastically compressed to length dl is e, then

$$e = \frac{dl_0 - dl}{dl_0} = \frac{\dfrac{V}{A_0} - \dfrac{V}{A}}{\dfrac{V}{A_0}} = \frac{A - A_0}{A} = 1 - \frac{A_0}{A} \tag{5.36}$$

where V is the volume of the element.

Now from (5.34)

$$c_p = \frac{v}{\dfrac{A}{A_0} - 1} \tag{5.37}$$

and thus substituting for c_p in (5.35),

$$\rho_0 A_0 \left\{ v + \frac{v}{\dfrac{A}{A_0} - 1} \right\} = Y\left(\frac{A}{A_0} - 1\right) A_0$$

which on simplifying reduces to

$$\frac{\rho_0 v^2}{Y} = \frac{\left(\dfrac{A}{A_0} - 1\right)^2}{\dfrac{A}{A_0}} = \frac{\left(\dfrac{1}{1 - e} - 1\right)^2}{\dfrac{1}{1 - e}} = \frac{e^2}{1 - e} \tag{5.38}$$

This relationship is shown in Fig. 5.20.

(iii) *Current deformed and undeformed length during deformation*

From Fig. 5.19(b) for the two principal portions of the bar which are of current increasing length h and decreasing length x, we have

$$\frac{dh}{dt} = c_p \tag{5.39}$$

and

$$\frac{dx}{dt} = -(v + c_p) \tag{5.40}$$

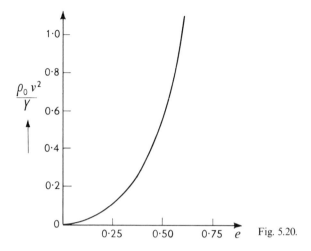

Fig. 5.20.

Further, for the undeformed portion of the rod, applying Newton's Second Law,

$$YA_0 = -\rho_0 A_0 x \cdot \frac{d}{dt}(v + c_p)$$

$$= -\rho_0 A_0 x \frac{dv}{dt} \tag{5.41i}$$

or

$$\frac{dv}{dt} = -\frac{Y}{\rho_0 x} \tag{5.41ii}$$

[Note incidentally that,

$$Y \cdot A = -\rho_0 A_0 \cdot \frac{d}{dt}(x(v + c_p)) \tag{5.41iii}$$

so that together (5.41i) and (5.41iii) give (5.35).]

Eliminating dt between (5.40) and (5.41ii)

$$\frac{dx}{dv} = \frac{v + c_p}{Y/\rho_0 x} \tag{5.42}$$

But from (5.37) and (5.36)

$$c_p = \frac{v}{\dfrac{A}{A_0} - 1} = \frac{v}{\dfrac{1}{1 - e} - 1} = \frac{1 - e}{e} \cdot v \tag{5.43}$$

and putting this into (5.42)

$$\frac{dx}{dv} = \frac{v\rho_0 x}{eY} \quad \text{or} \quad \frac{dx}{x} = \frac{\rho_0 v \cdot dv}{eY} \tag{5.44}$$

The term $v \cdot dv$ in (5.44) can be eliminated after differentiating (5.38) thus,

$$\frac{2\rho_0 v \cdot dv}{Y} = \frac{2e - e^2}{(1 - e)^2} \cdot de \tag{5.45}$$

so that (5.44) becomes,

$$2\frac{dx}{x} = \frac{2 - e}{(1 - e)^2} \cdot de \tag{5.46}$$

We may now integrate (5.46), noting that when $x = L$, i.e. at the beginning of the plastic deformation, $e = e_0$. Hence,

$$\left[\ln x^2 \right]_L^x = \left[-\ln (1 - e) + \frac{1}{(1 - e)} \right]_{e_0}^e$$

i.e.

$$\ln \left(\frac{x}{L}\right)^2 = \ln \left(\frac{1 - e_0}{1 - e}\right) + \frac{e - e_0}{(1 - e)(1 - e_0)} \tag{5.47}$$

Also at the end of plastic deformation $e = 0$ and we may denote the remaining undeformed length of bar by X so that from equation (5.47)

$$\ln \left(\frac{X}{L}\right)^2 = \ln (1 - e_0) - \frac{e_0}{(1 - e_0)} \tag{5.48i}$$

or

$$\ln \frac{L}{X} = \frac{1}{2} \left[\frac{e_0}{(1 - e_0)} + \ln \left(\frac{1}{1 - e_0}\right) \right] \tag{5.48ii}$$

Figure 5.21 shows how X/L varies with e_0.

The procedure for determining all the various quantities is now clear, but as an example we shall work through a series of calculations. Consider $e_0 = 0.5$;

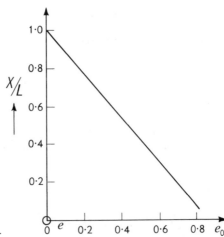

Fig. 5.21.

then from equation (5.38),

$$\frac{\rho_0 v_0^2}{Y} = \frac{e_0^2}{1 - e_0} = \frac{0.5^2}{1 - 0.5} = 0.5$$

Using (5.48i)

$$\ln \left(\frac{X}{L}\right)^2 = \ln(1 - 0.5) - 0.5/(1 - 0.5) = -1.69$$

and $X/L = 0.43$.

During this process, the plastic deformation as reflected through e, or loosely, the spread at the head of the advancing plastic wave—the plane across which the discontinuity occurs—is determined through equation (5.47). The values of x/L for each value of e are given in Table 5.1

TABLE 5.1

e	0	0·1	0·2	0·3	0·4	0·5
x/L	0·43	0·48	0·54	0·635	0·7	1·0
h/L see (5.50) below	0·38	0·34	0·28	0·21	0·12	0·0
d/d_0	1·00	1·05	1·12	1·20	1·29	1·41
$v_0 t/L$	0·34	0·29	0·24	0·18	0·10	0·0

To facilitate depicting the sequence of states of deformation, the corresponding values of h are required. These are found with the aid of (5.39) and (5.40) from which,

$$\frac{dh}{dx} = -\frac{c_p}{c_p + v} = -1 + e \tag{5.49}$$

introducing equation (5.37), and

$$\frac{h}{L} = \int_{X/L}^{1} (1 - e)\, d(x/L) \tag{5.50}$$

The integral (5.50) can be graphically interpreted after plotting x/L versus $(1 - e)$, as in Fig. 5.22, using the entries in Table 5.1.

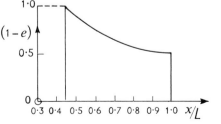

Fig. 5.22.

If the final height of the mushroom head is H and the undeformed length X then Fig. 5.26 shows how H/L and X/L vary with $\rho_0 v_0^2/Y$.

(iv) Profile shape

The profile of the 'mushroom' for each value of e or at each section x/L, is given by the ratio of plastically deformed diameter as it becomes stationary on crossing the plastic wave front d, to the original bar diameter d_0, and

$$\frac{d}{d_0} = \sqrt{\frac{A}{A_0}} = \frac{1}{\sqrt{1-e}} \tag{5.51}$$

Values of d/d_0 corresponding to values of e appear in Table 5.1.

(v) Time-wave position expressions

Finally, the time t which elapses since impact first occurred, for the plastic wave front to reach distance h from the anvil, is calculated using equation (5.41ii),

$$\int dt = \int -\frac{\rho_0 x \, dv}{Y} \tag{5.52}$$

But from (5.38),

$$v^2 = \frac{Ye^2}{\rho_0(1-e)} \quad \text{so that} \quad dv = \frac{1-e/2}{(1-e)^{3/2}} \cdot \sqrt{\frac{Y}{\rho_0}} \cdot de$$

and putting this into (5.52),

$$\int_0^t dt = -L\sqrt{\frac{\rho_0}{Y}} \int_{e_0}^e \left(\frac{x}{L}\right) \cdot \frac{(1-e/2)}{(1-e)^{3/2}} \cdot de$$

or

$$\frac{v_0 t}{L} = \frac{e_0}{\sqrt{(1-e_0)}} \int_e^{e_0} \left(\frac{x}{L}\right) \cdot \frac{1-e/2}{(1-e)^{3/2}} \cdot de, \tag{5.53}$$

with the help of (5.38) where $\rho_0 v_0^2 Y = e_0^2/(1-e_0)$.

The function $(x/L)(1-e/2)/(1-e)^{3/2}$ versus e, is plotted in Fig. 5.23 for the case considered, i.e. $\rho_0 v_0^2/Y = 0.5$, and the values of $v_0 t/L$ appear in Table 5.1.

In Fig. 5.24 three terminal profiles for $\rho_0 v_0^2/Y = 0.5$, 1·63 and 3·2 are shown as calculated by Taylor[5.3]; Fig. 5.24(b) indicates an envisaged instantaneous condition.

(vi) An alternative simplified calculation

Fig. 5.24(c) and (d) shows, for $\rho_0 v_0^2/Y = 0.5$, and 1·63 that the 'mushroomed' end appears as an almost straight-sided conical frustrum.

For each particular value of $\rho v_0^2/Y$, the final depth of the mushroomed head, H, requires to be numerically calculated as above. However, the amount of

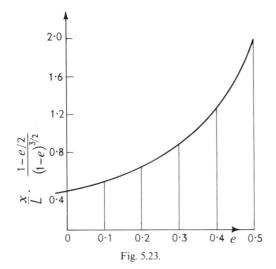

Fig. 5.23.

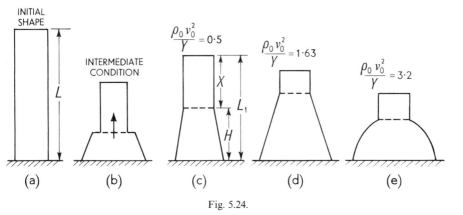

Fig. 5.24.

labour involved in calculating H/L may be avoided without too great an error. The volume of the deformed head, see Fig. 5.25, is expressed as,

$$(L - X)A_0 = \tfrac{1}{3}(A_1 H_1 - A_0 H_0)$$

and thus

$$1 - \frac{X}{L} = \frac{1}{3}\left(\frac{1}{1 - e_0} \cdot \frac{d_1}{d_1 - d_0} - \frac{d_0}{d_1 - d_0}\right) \cdot \frac{H}{L}$$

Hence,

$$\frac{H}{L} = \frac{3(1 - X/L)(1 - e_0)(1 - \sqrt{1 - e_0})}{1 - (1 - e_0)^{3/2}} \tag{5.54}$$

Figure 5.26 shows how H/L varies with e_0 or $\rho_0 v_0^2/Y$, following (5.54); X/L is of course obtained from (5.48). It is interesting to note that H/L has a maximum of about 0·43 when $\rho_0 v_0^2/Y \simeq 1$. The values of H/L obtained with (5.54)

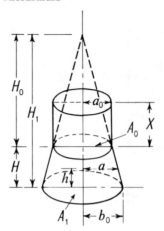

Fig. 5.25.

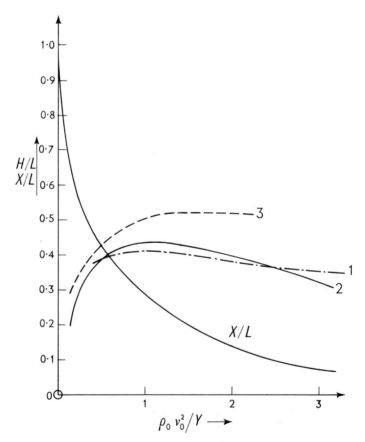

Fig. 5.26   Showing how H/L varies with $\rho_0 V_0^2/Y$ as
(1) calculated by Taylor[5.3],
(2) following equation (5.54) and
(3) following equation (5.65).

appear to be about the same as those given by Taylor and significant curvature of the sides of the mushroom, see Fig. 5.24(e), is evidently only taken on when $\rho_0 v_0^2/Y > 1.63$, a feature of no great importance since the solution is obviously in error at this level of $\rho_0 v_0^2/Y$.

(vii) *Plastic wave speed*

Plots of h/L against $v_0 t/L$ show that the plastic wave speed is nearly constant. For the particular case considered, i.e. $\rho_0 v_0^2/Y = 0.5$, if this is denoted by c_p then h/v_0 is the slope of the line made by plotting h/L by $v_0 t/L$ from Table 5.1; in this case $c_p \simeq 1.12\, v_0$. Reverting to equation (5.42) but treating c_p as constant,

$$\frac{1}{\rho_0} \cdot \frac{dx}{x} = \frac{(v + c_p)}{Y} \cdot dv,$$

or integrating,

$$\frac{Y}{\rho_0} \ln x = \tfrac{1}{2}v^2 + c_p \cdot v + c' \tag{5.55}$$

When $v = v_0$, $x = L$ and thus

$$c' = -\tfrac{1}{2}v_0^2 - c_p v_0 + (Y \ln L)\rho_0$$

Hence (5.55) becomes

$$\frac{Y}{\rho_0} \ln\left(\frac{x}{L}\right) + \tfrac{1}{2}(v_0^2 - v^2) + c_p(v_0 - v) = 0 \tag{5.56}$$

Since $v = 0$ when $x = X$,

$$\frac{Y}{\rho_0} \ln\left(\frac{X}{L}\right) + \tfrac{1}{2}v_0^2 + c_p \cdot v_0 = 0 \tag{5.57}$$

or

$$\frac{c_p}{v_0} = \frac{\ln(L/X)}{\rho_0 v_0^2/Y} - 0.5 \tag{5.58}$$

(viii) *Whiffen's experimental results*

In a paper by Whiffen[5.2], a room temperature steel projectile fired at 810 ft/sec (~ 246 m/sec) is identified with $\rho_0 v_0^2/Y = 0.5$ and, accordingly, for various values of $\rho_0 v_0^2/Y$, using (5.58), corresponding values of v, c_p/v and hence c_p may be found. In order to give an impression of the magnitudes involved these are presented in Table 5.2.

The duration of impact is H/c_p and thus this quantity in Table 5.2 is calculated using $L = 1$ in together with appropriate values of v_0.

Evidently for values of $\rho_0 v_0^2/Y \geq 0.267$, the duration of impact is nearly constant at about $5 \cdot 10^{-5}$ secs. In the experiments carried out by Whiffen at

TABLE 5.2

$\rho_0 v_0^2/Y$	0·011	0·050	0·128	0·267	0·500	0·900	1.633	3.200
c_p/v_0	4.23	4.27	2.57	1.71	1.19	0.84	0.575	0.40
v_0, ft/sec	120	256	505	590	810	1085	1460	2040
c_p, ft/sec	508	1094	1300	1010	965	912	840	816
H/L	—	—	0.19	0.34	0.38	0.425	0.409	0.310
$H/c_p \cdot v_0/L$	—	—	0·074	0·199	0·319	0·503	0·712	0·775
$10^5 \, H/c_p$ secs	—	—	1·44	4·1	4·7	5·5	5·9	4·7

1580 and 2045 ft/sec (or 480 and 622 m/sec), the measured impact durations were $6·8 \cdot 10^{-5}$ and $6·4 \cdot 10^{-5}$ seconds and thus strain rates of the order of 10^4/sec were attained.

Strain rate effects in deforming cylinders due to high speed impact at high temperature with a rigid anvil

Many of the above results originally derived by Taylor were utilised by Whiffen for trying to determine the yield stress of certain mild steels at room temperature at high rates of strain. Strain rate effects are the more pronounced the higher the homologous temperature at which a test is conducted and Fig. 5.27 shows how

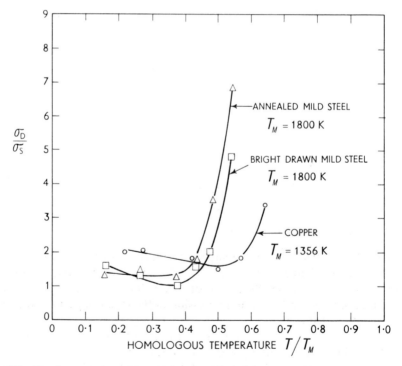

Fig. 5.27 Showing variation of dynamic/static mean yield stress ratios with homologous temperature (T/T_M).

the ratio of the yield stress σ_D, obtained in high speed impact tests, to quasi-static yield stress σ_S, varies with homologous temperature[5.4]. The considerable rate of increase in σ_D/σ_S at about half the absolute melting temperature of the steel should be noted.

Plate 27 shows the mushroom shapes obtained by firing, in effect hot bullets, at a nominally flat rigid target; note the deformation indicated in Plate 27(m), where straight wires inserted originally at right angles to the cylinder axis are deformed and appear curved after impact.

Energy method based on deformation into a frustum

(i) Non-hardening material

Without making any call at all on previous work, as on p. 237, e.g. taking X/L from (5.54), we may calculate H/L directly by an energy approach. If the final 'mushroomed' head of the projectile is assumed to be frustum-shaped, the compressive strain distribution may be presumed to be implicitly specified as proportional to distance from the anvil and thus the plastic work done in arriving at this state may be found.

From Fig. 5.25,

$$\frac{a - a_0}{b_0 - a_0} = \frac{H - h}{H} \quad \text{and thus} \quad \frac{da}{b_0 - a_0} = -\frac{dh}{H}. \tag{5.59}$$

For a transverse element of height dh at h from the anvil, the plastic work done in expanding its radius from a_0 to a is, using (4.41),

$$dW = Y . \ln\left(\frac{dh_0}{dh}\right) . \text{ volume of element.}$$

dh_0 is the original thickness of dh. For the whole frustum,

$$\frac{W}{Y} = \int_0^H \ln\left(\frac{dh_0}{dh}\right) . \pi a^2 . dh. \tag{5.60}$$

Now, $A_0 dh_0 = A dh$, where A and A_0 denote initial and final cross-sectional areas and hence

$$\frac{dh_0}{dh} = \frac{A}{A_0} = \frac{a^2}{a_0^2};$$

thus (5.60) becomes,

$$\frac{W}{Y} = 2\pi \int_0^H \ln\left(\frac{a}{a_0}\right) . a^2 \, dh$$

and using (5.59),

$$
\frac{W}{Y} = 2\pi \int_{b_0}^{a} - \frac{Ha^2}{b_0 - a_0} \cdot \ln\left(\frac{a}{a_0}\right) da
$$

$$
= \frac{2\pi H}{b_0 - a_0} \int_{a_0}^{b_0} a^2 \ln\left(\frac{a}{a_0}\right) \cdot da
$$

$$
= \frac{2\pi H a_0^3}{9(b_0 - a_0)} \cdot \left[3\left(\frac{b_0}{a_0}\right)^3 \ln\left(\frac{b_0}{a_0}\right) - \left(\frac{b_0}{a_0}\right)^3 + 1 \right],
$$

or

$$
\frac{W}{Y} = \frac{2\pi H a_0^3}{9(b_0 - a_0)} \cdot \phi\left(\frac{b_0}{a_0}\right) \tag{5.61}
$$

Now the energy for doing the plastic work is derived from the kinetic energy of the projectile and thus

$$
\frac{W}{Y} = \frac{1}{2} \cdot \frac{(\rho_0 \pi a_0^2 L)}{Y} \cdot v_0^2 = \frac{\pi a_0^2 L}{2} \cdot \frac{\rho_0 v_0^2}{Y} \tag{5.62}
$$

Equating (5.61) and (5.62) and simplifying,

$$
\frac{H}{L} = \frac{9(b_0 - a_0)}{4a_0} \cdot \frac{\rho_0 v_0^2/Y}{\left[3\left(\frac{b_0}{a_0}\right)^3 \ln\left(\frac{b_0}{a_0}\right) - \left(\frac{b_0}{a_0}\right)^3 + 1 \right]}. \tag{5.63}
$$

However, from previous work,

$$
\frac{\rho_0 v_0^2}{Y} = \frac{e_0^2}{1 - e_0} = \frac{\left(\frac{x^2 - 1}{x^2}\right)^2}{1 - \left(\frac{x^2 - 1}{x^2}\right)} = \frac{(x^2 - 1)^2}{x^2} \tag{5.64}
$$

where $x = b_0/a_0$. Putting (5.64) into (5.63), we have

$$
\frac{H}{L} = \frac{9}{4} \cdot \frac{(x - 1)(x^2 - 1)^2}{x^2[3x^2 \ln x - x^3 + 1]} \tag{5.65}
$$

A Table of values derived using (5.65) is given below:

TABLE 5.3

x	1·2	1·414	1·6	1·7	2·0	2·5
e_0	0·305	0·5	0·61	0·65	0·75	0·84
$\rho_0 v_0^2/Y$	0·135	0·5	0·975	1·24	2·25	4·42
H/L	0·29	0·42	0·505	0·51	0·515	0·52

A curve showing how H/L varies with $\rho_0 v_0^2/Y$, following equation 5.65, is given in Fig. 5.26. Evidently the outcome of the assumption on which (5.65) is based is only moderately in agreement with the predictions of the previous section over a narrow range of values of $\rho_0 v_0^2/Y$. Clearly small shape changes in the mushroom head have a relatively large influence; referring to Fig. 5.26, for values of $\rho_0 v_0^2/Y$ greater than about 1·5, the final predicted shape is significantly different from that of the frustum.

(ii) Linear strain-hardening material

By following a similar approach to that just presented, it may be shown for a material which is rigid/linear strain-hardening, i.e. $\sigma = Y + P\varepsilon$, where P is the plastic modulus, that the plastic work required to be done to attain the frustum shape of Fig. 5.25, determined on the same assumptions as before, is:

$$\frac{W}{Y} = \frac{2\pi Ha_0^3}{9(b_0 - a_0)}\left[3\left(\frac{b_0}{a_0}\right)^3 \ln\left(\frac{b_0}{a_0}\right) - \left(\frac{b_0}{a_0}\right)^3 + 1\right.$$
$$\left. + \frac{P}{Y}\cdot\left(\frac{b_0}{a_0}\right)^3\left\{\left(3\ln\left(\frac{b_0}{a_0}\right) - 2\right)\ln\frac{b_0}{a_0} + \frac{2}{3}\left(1 - \left(\frac{a_0}{b_0}\right)^3\right)\right\}\right] \quad (5.66)$$

Calculations of W/Y for non-linear strain-hardening curves are given in ref. 5.4.

(iii) Mean strain after impact

The mean strain ε_m imparted, for the non-hardening material, reverting to equation (4.42) is,

$$\varepsilon_m = \frac{W}{Y \cdot \text{volume of frustum}} = \frac{1}{3}\frac{\left[3\left(\frac{b_0}{a_0}\right)^3 \ln\left(\frac{b_0}{a_0}\right) - \left(\frac{b_0}{a_0}\right)^3 + 1\right]}{\left[\left(\frac{b_0}{a_0}\right)^3 - 1\right]}$$
$$= \frac{2\cdot\left(\frac{b_0}{a_0}\right)^3 \ln\left(\frac{b_0}{a_0}\right)}{\left(\frac{b_0}{a_0}\right)^3 - 1} - \frac{2}{3}$$

For $(b_0/a_0) = 1\cdot5, 2$ and 3, the corresponding values of ε_m are 0·48, 0·92 and 1·63 respectively.

Hawkyard's energy method

(i) Energy balance equation

In the previous section the fundamental principle employed was to use a *momentum balance* across the plastic wavefront (discontinuity) in order to determine the shape of the 'mushroom' head and other details when a short circular cylinder impinged against a rigid anvil. In this section, with all the same assumptions as before, the consequences of establishing an *energy balance* across the discontinuity at the plastic wavefront are examined—an investigation originally made by Hawkyard[5.5].

Figure 5.28 shows the events at an intermediate stage of deformation, which takes place in time dt. An elemental cylindrical length, dx, passes through the plastic wavefront and is so deformed as to acquire an area A, and height dy; the

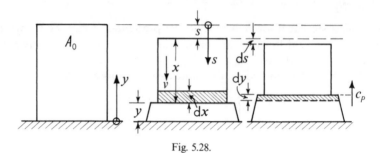

Fig. 5.28.

plastic wave speed is thus $c_p = dy/dt$. In the same time the rear portion of the cylinder moves forward a distance ds so that $v = ds/dt$. The rate at which plastic work is dissipated in crossing the wavefront is

$$\frac{dW}{dt} = \frac{d}{dt}(A_0 \, dx \, Y \ln A/A_0)$$

or

$$\frac{dW}{dt} = A_0(v + c_p) . \, Y \ln A/A_0 \tag{5.67}$$

since, $dx = ds + dy$ i.e.

$$dx/dt = ds/dt + dy/dt = v + c_p$$

The loss of kinetic energy in the undeformed rear portion in decreasing in speed from v to $(v - dv)$ is equal to the arresting force times the distance it moves, i.e. $YA_0 \, ds$ and the deformed element loses its entire kinetic energy, i.e. $A_0\rho_0 \, dxv^2/2$. Thus the rate of loss of energy of the projectile is

$$\frac{dE}{dt} = \frac{d}{dt}[\tfrac{1}{2}A_0\rho_0 \, dx \, v^2 + YA_0 \, ds] = A_0v[\tfrac{1}{2}\rho_0v(v + c_p) + Y] \tag{5.68}$$

Since $dE/dt = dW/dt$, using (5.67) and (5.68),

$$A_0(v + c_p)Y \ln \frac{A}{A_0} = A_0v[\tfrac{1}{2}\rho_0v(v + c_p) + Y] \tag{5.69}$$

Combining equations (5.69) and (5.34), gives

$$\tfrac{1}{2}\rho_0v^2 = Y\left[\ln \frac{A}{A_0} - \left(1 - \frac{A_0}{A}\right)\right] \tag{5.70}$$

(ii) *Velocity-strain equation*

Re-writing equation (5.70) using (5.36), we have

$$\tfrac{1}{2}\rho_0 v^2 = Y\left[\ln\left(\frac{1}{1-e}\right) - e\right].$$ (5.71)

With the initial condition $v = v_0$, the initial strain e_0 is given by

$$\tfrac{1}{2}\rho_0 v_0^2 = Y\left[\ln\left(\frac{1}{1-e_0}\right) - e_0\right].$$ (5.72)

(iii) *Relation between current undeformed length and strain*

The equation of motion for the rear undeformed portion of the cylinder is,

$$YA_0 = -\rho_0 A_0 x\left(v\cdot\frac{dv}{ds}\right).$$ (5.73)

But by differentiating with respect to s in equation (5.71), we have

$$\rho_0 v\frac{dv}{ds} = Y\left(\frac{e}{1-e}\right)\frac{de}{ds}.$$ (5.74)

Hence from (5.73) and (5.74),

$$-\frac{ds}{x} = \frac{e}{1-e}\cdot de$$ (5.75)

But $ds = -e\,dx$, so that (5.75) becomes

$$\frac{dx}{x} = \frac{de}{1-e}.$$ (5.76)

Integrating (5.76) and noting that $x = L$ when $e = e_0$,

$$\ln\frac{L}{x} = \ln\left(\frac{1-e}{1-e_0}\right)$$ (5.77)

or

$$x = L\left(\frac{1-e_0}{1-e}\right).$$ (5.78)

When $e = 0$, the remaining undeformed length X is

$$X = L(1 - e_0)$$ (5.79)

(iv) *Relation between current deformed length and strain*

We have for the element which crosses the plastic wavefront,

$$A_0\cdot dx = A\,dy$$

or

$$dy = \frac{A_0}{A} dx = -(1 - e) dx$$

and using (5.76),

$$dy = -(1 - e)x \cdot \frac{de}{(1 - e)} = -x \cdot de. \tag{5.81}$$

Substituting for x from (5.78)

$$dy = -L(1 - e_0)\frac{de}{1 - e}. \tag{5.82}$$

Integrating (5.82) and putting $y = 0$ at $e = e_0$

$$y = L(1 - e_0) \ln \left[(1 - e)/(1 - e_0) \right]. \tag{5.83}$$

The final deformed length is H and

$$H = L(1 - e_0) \ln \left[\frac{1}{(1 - e_0)} \right]; \tag{5.84}$$

and the final length $L_1 = X + H$.

(v) Terminal profile of the deformed cylinder

The final profile of the deformed end of the cylinder can be obtained by using equation (5.83), after finding e_0 from (5.72). Terminal profile shapes for various values of $\rho_0 v_0^2/Y$ as calculated by Hawkyard[5.5] are given in Fig. 5.29.

All profiles are of concave form and have the shape given by experimental results; the profiles differ significantly from those given by Taylor particularly for the larger values of $\rho_0 v_0^2/Y$.

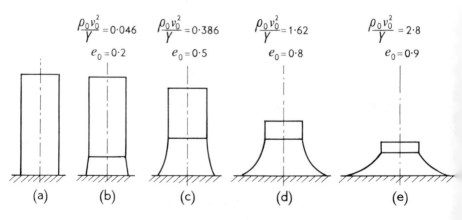

Fig. 5.29.

Comparisons between the results of Taylor and those of Hawkyard are made through Figs. 5.24 and 5.29.

(vi) *Plastic wave speed*

From equations (5.37) and (5.36),

$$c_p = \frac{1 - e}{e} \cdot v \tag{5.85}$$

and using (5.71) for v, (5.85) becomes

$$c_p = \left(\frac{Y}{\rho_0}\right)^{1/2} \left[2\left(\ln\left(\frac{1}{1 - e}\right) - e\right)\right]^{1/2} \cdot \left(\frac{1 - e}{e}\right). \tag{5.86}$$

The momentum balance theory gives, by combining (5.85) and (5.38),

$$c_p = \left(\frac{1 - e}{e}\right)\left[\frac{Ye^2}{\rho_0(1 - e)}\right]^{1/2} = \left(\frac{Y}{\rho_0}\right)^{1/2} \cdot (1 - e)^{1/2} \tag{5.87}$$

For a given value of e, the c_p of (5.87) is greater than that of (5.86) and the difference increases as e increases.

Work-hardening and work-softening materials

Work-hardening may easily be introduced into the above analysis, in which case the terminal profile shape depends on it and indeed *deformation of the whole projectile length* is predicted.

For small degrees of strain hardening the terminal shape is concave outwards, but for large degrees of hardening it becomes convex outwards. Work-softening materials provide a projectile profile which is exaggeratedly concave outwards.

Rigid striker impinging on a specimen of rigid linear work-hardening material supported by a rigid anvil

Figure 5.30 shows a short cylindrical specimen supported on a rigid anvil, and against which a rigid striker of mass M, moving with initial speed v_0, impinges

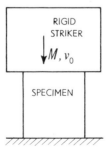

Fig. 5.30.

normally. The compression is supposed to take place frictionlessly so that the stress across each section is uniform; the material of the work-piece is rigid linear work-hardening.

At the instant of impact elastic and plastic waves are generated, so that at time t later, when the plastic wave moving with speed c_p has advanced through a length of cylinder $c_p t$, the equation of motion for this quantity of material is,

$$(M + \rho_0 A_0 c_p t)\frac{dv}{dt} = -A_0 \sigma \; ; \qquad (5.88)$$

σ is the stress just behind the plastic wave front and v is the speed to which the striker and the material between it and the plastic wave has been reduced. The stress just ahead of the plastic wave is the yield stress Y and the particle speed $Y/\rho_0 c_0$ is zero since c_0 is infinite. The particle speed is given by

$$v = \frac{\sigma - Y}{\rho_0 c_p} \; . \qquad (5.89)$$

Substituting in (5.88) using (5.89), gives

$$(M + \rho_0 A_0 c_p t)\frac{dv}{dt} = -A_0(Y + \rho_0 c_p v),$$

or

$$\frac{dv}{Y + \rho_0 c_p v} = -\frac{A_0 \, dt}{M + \rho_0 c_p A_0 t} \; .$$

Thus,

$$\left[\ln\,(Y + \rho_0 c_p v)\right]_{v_0}^{v} = \left[\ln \frac{1}{(M + \rho_0 A_0 c_p t)}\right]_{0}^{t}$$

i.e.

$$\frac{Y + \rho_0 c_p v}{Y + \rho_0 c_p v_0} = \frac{M}{(M + \rho_0 A_0 c_p t)} = \frac{M}{\left(M + m . \dfrac{c_p t}{l_0}\right)} \; , \qquad (5.90)$$

where m is the cylinder mass.

From (5.89) and (5.90),

$$\sigma = \frac{Y + \rho_0 c_p v_0}{\left(1 + \dfrac{m}{M} . \dfrac{c_p t}{l_0}\right)} \qquad (5.91)$$

if $\sigma > Y$. Equation (5.91) holds until σ reduces to Y and then,

$$c_p t = x = M c_p v_0 / A_0 Y.$$

Obviously the maximum value of x is the height of the cylinder, l_0. If plastic deformation does not cease during the first passage of the plastic wave through the cylinder, reflection of it at the anvil results in an enhanced compressive stress on the anvil and the material through which it has passed since leaving the anvil will have become stationary.

This topic and the approach in this Section is discussed at greater length in ref. 5.6.

REFERENCES

5.1 DONNELL, L. H. Longitudinal wave transmission and impact. *Trans. Am. Soc. mech. Engrs*, **52**, 153 (1930).

5.2 WHIFFEN, A. C. The use of flat-ended projectiles for determining dynamic yield stress, II: Tests on various metallic materials. *Proc. R. Soc.*, A.**194**, 300 (1948).

5.3 TAYLOR, G. I. The use of flat-ended projectiles for determining dynamic yield stress, I: Theoretical considerations, *Proc. R. Soc.*, A.**194**, 289 (1948).

5.4 EATON, D., HAWKYARD, J. B. and JOHNSON, W. The mean dynamic yield strength of copper and low carbon steel at elevated temperature from measurements of the "mushrooming" of flat-ended projectiles. *I.J.M.S.*, **10**, 929 (1968).

5.5 HAWKYARD, J. B. Mushrooming of flat-ended projectiles impinging on a flat rigid anvil. *I.J.M.S.*, **11**, 313 (1969).

5.6 LEE, E. H. and WOLF, H. Plastic wave propagation in high speed testing. *J. appl. Mech.*, **18**, 379 (1951).

6: Impulsive loading of beams

Introduction and historical note

Rawlings[6.1] identified four principal areas of interest to the engineer concerning the behaviour of steel structures under dynamic loading.

"Firstly, there are dynamic effects on stationary structures such as bridges, railway tracks and cranes, supporting moving loads which may cause impact conditions. This, of course, has been in the minds of designers for many decades. Secondly, the permanent damage and decelerations associated with the inelastic collisions of moving vehicles are of significance to mechanical, civil and aeronautical engineers. Then there are the problems associated with the design of building frames to resist the ground accelerations of earthquakes, and lastly the recent and very real challenge to the engineer in the design of buildings to resist bomb blasts."

Rather than collisions only, the mechanical engineer is interested in structural response to high rates of loading such as some of his structures undergo when an unintentional explosion takes place in a piece of equipment he has designed. A fifth category to be added to Rawlings' four, is the intentional dynamic loading of plates and shells and the like, in order to deliberately secure a specific amount of plastic deformation; this is the aim in high-rate sheet metal forming where explosive charges, and pulsed electro-magnetic fields, are used, see ref. 6.2.

Without doubt a great impetus was given to the study of the impulsive loading of structures, by the necessity to design structures which would stand up to blasts from bombs of all descriptions, during the Second World War as the following two extracts show. The first is taken from an American book "Aerial Bombardment Protection", by W. E. Wessman and W. A. Rose, published in 1942 by Whalley and Chapman. It referred to the existence of then unexplained behaviour and explicitly indicated useful areas of research, which were of course soon after considered. The whole of this chapter, in a sense, is concerned with the working out of the area of behaviour it identifies and the following quotation could well be re-read after this chapter has been covered.

"Not much is known about the phenomenon of localized bending which presumably accompanies the impact of a projectile travelling at a high velocity. There is considerable evidence based on observations of points which have been hit by bullets, shells, or bombs to indicate that dominant effects are localized, that structures as a whole because of their inertia do not have time to react to the sudden blow.

"A beam such as that in Fig. 6.1 would bend initially only over a small portion of its span length owing to the high energy load. Original span length has no significance in calculating initial bending moments due to an equivalent static load based on initial deflection. Presumably, the beam would eventually vibrate as a whole and assume a deflection curve associated with the fundamental mode . . . but it is the initial effects which are of major concern to the engineer. The following formula has been proposed by British Authorities for calculating the localized length, δ, ...

"Values of δ calculated by this formula are very small in comparison with actual span lengths. Just what significance may be attached to this beyond emphasizing the initial localized action is a matter for debate. There is no discussion of the derivation of the formula in the reference cited. It would seem as though the weight and velocity of the projectile would be a factor affecting the localized length.

"The extent of localized action might be determined by oscillograph records giving simultaneous readings from electric strain gages located at intervals along a span which is subjected to sudden impact. The use of high-speed photography, involving stroboscopic polarized light with transparent bakelite model beams subjected to weights dropped from different heights or even the penetration of a bullet, may also give additional information.

"This is a fascinating field for research . . . ."

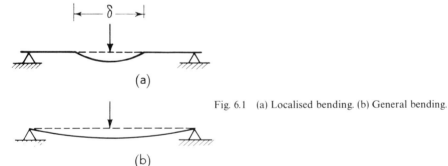

Fig. 6.1   (a) Localised bending. (b) General bending.

In the second quotation, the importance of studying dynamic plastic deformation during the Second World War was more generally instanced by J. F. Baker in "The Design of War-time Structures" (The Civil Engineer at War, *Instn of Civ. Engrs*, Vol. 3, 1948) who wrote ". . . protective structures must withstand severe impact loads or the effects of blast from explosions . . . the critical factor is not the stress distribution in the elastic range, but the capacity of the structure to absorb energy without collapse. The proof resilience of a ductile continuous structure is insignificant in comparison with the energy that can be absorbed in the elastic-plastic range . . .".

Rawlings' paper[6.1] should be referred to for an account of the early contributions to the study of impulsive structural behaviour.

Early investigations

Seeming to follow on from the first quotation above, the first theoretical and experimental consideration of the behaviour of a long beam due to transverse impact by a concentrated load which induces plastic deformation, is that by Duwez, Clark and Bohnenblust[6.3] reported in 1950. They extended a classical analysis of nearly a century earlier due to Boussinesq and discussed the case of an infinitely long beam, which after impact moved with constant speed at its centre. They showed that strain is not propagated along a beam at a uniform speed, as is the case for longitudinal impact; bending only was shown to be of primary importance and shear and tension secondary. The strain was shown to depend on the ratio of the square of the distance from the point of impact to the time from first contact.

The experimental work was carried out on 10 ft (3·05 m) long beams of $\frac{3}{4}$ in $\times \frac{3}{8}$ in (19 mm $\times$ 9·5 mm) and 1 in $\times \frac{3}{8}$ in (25·4 mm $\times$ 9·5 mm) cross-section, struck centrally by $5\frac{3}{4}$ lb (2·6 kg) weights moving at speeds between 25 and 150 ft/sec (7·6 and 45·5 m/s) at impact.

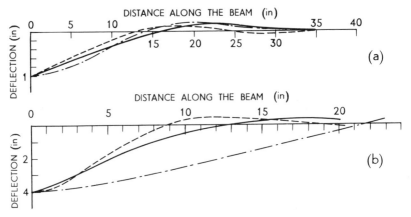

Fig. 6.2   (a)   Deflection curves for cold-rolled steel beam: Impact speed 100 ft/sec; duration of impact 0·87 m sec.
Experimental curve ——————
Theoretical curves

(i) assuming wholly elastic behaviour
— — — — — — — — — — —

(ii) using the real moment–curvature relationship   — · — · — · — · — · —

(b)   Deflection curves for annealed copper beam: Impact speed 97 ft/sec; duration of impact 3·44 m/sec.

Photographs were taken of each test, from which the degree of deflection and its mode of deformation were apparent. Typical experimental results shown in Figs. 6.2(a) and (b) are compared with predicted curves when (i) elastic behaviour is assumed and (ii) the real moment-curvature relationship of the material of each beam is used.

Some assumptions

In the sections below and in Chapters 7 and 8, the fast loading of rigid-perfectly plastic beams, rings and flat plates is analysed, introducing the concept of a travelling plastic hinge. The beam, ring or plate is subjected to a dynamic load which is so large and sudden that the inertia of the structure governs the manner of its deformation. A plastic hinge occurs at a section of a beam or ring, or at a location in a plate where the bending moment is equal to the full plastic bending moment at, usually, the position where the shear force is zero. An abrupt change in the shape of a beam, or a kink, often occurs at a hinge, and due to the change in angular speed of elements of the structure the location of this hinge, in accordance with the requirements of classical dynamics, will move. In dynamically loaded structures it is common to recognise three or four phases, or modes, of deformation. Several cases are treated below and in subsequent Chapters, and an understanding of these will familiarise the reader with the ideas of plastic hinges, their mobility, and their subsequent stationary location and behaviour. The plastic work done in these hinges derives, of course, from the original kinetic energy delivered to or possessed by the system.

Several considerations need to be kept in mind when judging the accuracy and the likely realistic applicability of the work described.

(i)   Nearly all the analyses are restricted to consideration of bending stress only; plastic failure or yielding which includes shear and/or direct stress is usually neglected.

(ii) The material is taken to be rigid-perfectly plastic and all elastic strains are omitted.

(iii) Local effects, i.e. the local deformation surrounding the region where a striker impinges on a structure, are neglected.

(iv) All analyses proceed on the assumption that the initial or given configuration is unchanged throughout the period of impact.

(v)   Strain-rate effects and strain-hardening do not enter into the analyses directly. It is often claimed that these two are likely to increase the static room temperature yield stress in mild steel by a factor of as much as 2 to 3, and because some experimental and theoretical results only agree when a strain-rate factor (of say 2 or 3) has been used, and, having been derived for other experimental work, it follows that there may naturally be some reluctance to accept this work as of great value and reliability.

(vi) Experimental investigations in this field are not plentiful and where reported seldom match theoretical predictions to any high degree. The use of high speed photography and short time measurements are seldom used and much reliance is placed on terminal results.

There is a need for more experimental work to ascertain the limitations and to test the validity of the theory of the rigid-perfectly plastic solid when applied to the study of the kinematic behaviour of simple structures.

Central impact of free-ended beams of finite length

The work of Duwez, Clark and Bohnenblust was continued for different boundary conditions and generally developed by Conroy, Bleich and Salvadori, Thomson, Alverson, Seiler, Cotter and Symonds, and Hopkins[6.8]. (See Rawlings[5.1], (1963), for detailed references.) It came to be appreciated that when the energy available for dissipation as plastic work on a beam—and usually presented as kinetic energy—exceeded by an order of magnitude the elastic strain energy it was possible to store in the beam, then it was reasonable to start from an assumption that the material of the beam was rigid-perfectly plastic. This also made the analysis tractable and meant that no complicating elastic vibration would need to be considered. Concurrently, it came to be appreciated that more than one single central hinge could be formed in a beam, and that under certain circumstances shear force effects could predominate.

One of the earliest and most elementary analyses is that of Lee and Symonds[6.4] which considers a perfectly free uniform beam AB—not simply supported or clamped at its ends but free at both of them—subjected to a transverse force, P, applied at C, the centre of its length. We endeavour to predict the behaviour of the beam according to the intensity of P. If m denotes the mass per unit length of the beam, then in the first place, with the application of P—which we repeat is of rigid-perfectly plastic material—the beam will accelerate in the direction of P, as a rigid body; let its acceleration be f_0 then, see Fig. 6.3(a),

$$P = 2mlf_0$$

or

$$f_0 = \frac{P}{2ml} \tag{6.1}$$

There is no rotation of the beam since external force P acts at the beam centroid and there are no external couples acting on it.

Each element of the beam possesses inertia, or reluctance to increase its speed, and thus the accelerating beam behaves as if it was carrying a *downwards* (opposite to the direction of motion) uniformly distributed load of mf_0 per unit length. Each section of the accelerating beam thus sustains a shear force, F, and, see Fig. 6.3(b), the magnitude of F at λ from the centre of the beam is given by,

$$F = \int_\lambda^l mf_0 \, dx = mf_0(l - \lambda) \tag{6.2}$$

The bending moment at each section of the beam is M, see Fig. 6.3(c), and

$$M = \int_\lambda^l mf_0(l - x) \, dx = mf_0\left[lx - \frac{x^2}{2} \right]_\lambda^l$$

$$= \frac{mf_0(l - \lambda)^2}{2} \tag{6.3}$$

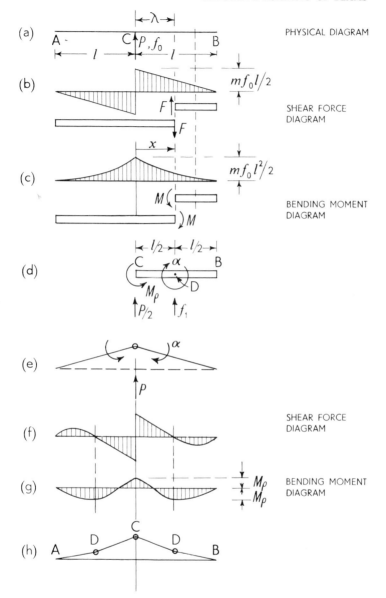

Fig. 6.3 Free-free beam impulsively loaded at its centre.

M is greatest at the beam centre, C, where $\lambda = 0$ and then $M_c = mf_0l^2/2$. When $M_c = M_p$, the full plastic bending moment of the beam,

$$M_p = mf_0l^2/2 = m \cdot \frac{P}{2ml} \cdot \frac{l^2}{2} = \frac{Pl}{4} \qquad (6.4)$$

and thus when $P = 4M_p/l$, the beam will contain a plastic hinge at C.

The discussion above applies to loads in which $0 < P < 4M_p/l$. The next portion of our examination concerns the case in which $P > 4M_p/l$; in this instance the beam will accelerate as a whole, each half also rotating about C as a rigid body. The free body diagram for the right hand half of the beam is shown in Fig. 6.3(d); the applied external force is $P/2$ at the left hand end and this causes the centroid D, of CB to have an acceleration of f_1; we have,

$$\frac{P}{2} = mlf_1 \tag{6.5}$$

On the left hand end of CB there will be an external moment, M_p, due to the action of the left hand portion of the beam AC on CB; we assume P is so large that the limiting bending moment M_p is sustained at C. The moment M_p and the moment of force $P/2$ about D, give rise to an angular acceleration in CB of α, so that

$$\frac{P}{2} \cdot \frac{l}{2} - M_p = I\alpha; \tag{6.6}$$

I, the moment of inertia of CB about D is $ml^3/12$. Thus (6.6) becomes

$$\frac{Pl}{4} - M_p = \frac{ml^3}{12} \cdot \alpha \tag{6.7}$$

The acceleration of a point at x from C is

$$f = f_1 - \left(x - \frac{l}{2}\right)\alpha$$

$$= \frac{P}{2ml} - \frac{\left(\dfrac{Pl}{4} - M_p\right)}{\dfrac{ml^3}{12}} \cdot \left(x - \frac{l}{2}\right) \tag{6.8}$$

The shear force distribution throughout the beam is found using (6.8) and is given by,

$$F = \int_\lambda^l mf\, dx$$

$$= \int_\lambda^l m\left[\frac{P}{2ml} - \frac{3(Pl - 4M_p)}{ml^3} \cdot \left(x - \frac{l}{2}\right)\right] dx$$

$$= m\left[\left(\frac{P}{2ml} + \frac{3(Pl - 4M_p)}{ml^3} \cdot \frac{l}{2}\right)(l - \lambda) - \frac{3(Pl - 4M_p)}{ml^3} \cdot \frac{(l^2 - \lambda^2)}{2}\right] \tag{6.9}$$

It is easily shown that $F = 0$ at λ when

$$\frac{l + \lambda}{2} \cdot \frac{3(Pl - 4M_p)}{ml^3} = \frac{P}{2ml} + \frac{3(Pl - 4M_p)}{ml^3} \cdot \frac{l}{2}$$

i.e.

$$\frac{\lambda}{l} = \frac{Pl/M_p}{3\left(\dfrac{Pl}{M_p} - 4\right)} \qquad (6.10)$$

Note the change in shape of the shear force diagrams as between Figs. 6.3(b) and 6.3(f); the angular acceleration is so large that the downward acceleration of the outer portion of the half beam, exceeds the upward acceleration due to force $P/2$. This gives rise to upward acting inertia loading and hence upward acting shear force. The bending moments in the outer portion of the half beam will thus act counter-clockwise—opposite to what they were in the case when $P < 4M_p/l$—compare Figs. 6.3(c) and 6.3(g).

Since we are investigating the situation in which $Pl/M_p > 4$, and evidently $\lambda/l < 1$, then because the bending moment will be a continuous function between $\lambda = 0$ and $\lambda = l$, it is clearly a maximum at the location given by (6.10). (Recall from elementary bending theory that $dM/d\lambda = 0$ for a maximum is the same as $F = 0$). Equation (6.10) thus defines the position at which another plastic hinge is to be expected. Writing $\lambda/l = z$, (6.10) gives,

$$\frac{M_p}{Pl} = \frac{3z - 1}{12z}, \qquad (6.11)$$

which will be used later.

The bending moment at section λ is,

$$M = \int_\lambda^l mf(l - x)\, dx \quad \text{and, using (6.8),}$$

$$= m \int_\lambda^l (l - x)\left[\frac{3(Pl - 4M_p)}{ml^3} \cdot \frac{l}{2} + \frac{P}{2ml} - \frac{3(Pl - 4M_p)}{ml^3} \cdot x\right] \cdot dx \qquad (6.12)$$

Substituting from (6.10), Pl^2/λ for $3(Pl - 4M_p)$ in (6.12),

$$M = \int_\lambda^l (l - x)\left[\left(\frac{P}{2\lambda} + \frac{P}{2l}\right) - \frac{P}{l\lambda} \cdot x\right] dx$$

or

$$\frac{2M}{P}l\lambda = \int_\lambda^l (l - x)(-2x + l + \lambda)\, dx = \frac{(l - \lambda)^3}{6} \qquad (6.13)$$

The limiting value of M is of course M_p, and hence substituting in (6.13),

$$(l - \lambda)^3 = 12 \cdot \frac{M_p}{Pl} \cdot l^2\lambda$$

or

$$(1 - z)^3 = 12 \cdot \frac{M_p}{Pl} \cdot z$$

$$= (3z - 1), \tag{6.14}$$

using equation (6.11).

Equation (6.14) when expanded provides the cubic equation

$$z^3 - 3z^2 + 6z - 2 = 0, \tag{6.15}$$

which possesses only one real root, which is $z \simeq 0.404$. Hence two further plastic hinges form

(i) at a distance $0.404l$ on either side of the beam centre, and

(ii) by substituting this value of z in (6.11), Pl/M_p is then found to be 22·8.

In Figs. 6.3(f) and 6.3(g), diagrams of the shear force and bending moment distribution are shown for values of Pl/M_p at this high level. Figure 6.3(h) shows diagrammatically the shape of the deformed beam when $Pl/M_p > 22·8$, after the hinges have formed; it behaves as a system of four rigid links possessing three hinges.

If the load exceeds $22·8M_p/l$, the hinge that was at $0.404l$ from the mid-point of the beam is moved; it shifts towards the mid-point and does so as a consequence of the dynamical and kinematical equations which apply to all sections of the beam. This possible third mode of motion is dealt with at length in the 1952 paper by Lee and Symonds.

The hinge systems will change as Pl/M_p falls from its maximum value of say greater than 22·8, to zero, until all the four portions of the beam attain the same angular speed. Firstly, the two outer hinges would disappear and then bending would continue at the central hinge only. Eventually the angular speed would fall to such a low level, that bending at the centre ceases, and only a rigid body uniform translational motion would persist thereafter.

Position of the plastic hinge for a jet striking the end of a cantilever

If a uniform circular jet of cross-sectional area A, density ρ, travelling with speed v, strikes the tip of a cantilever of length l, ($\sqrt{A} \ll l$), and sprays laterally, then suppose the plastic hinge which forms to be at distance X from the tip, see Fig. 6.4.

The equation for vertical motion is

$$F + R = mX \cdot (f/2), \tag{6.16}$$

where f is the acceleration of the tip, m the mass of the beam per unit length, R the shear force at distance X from the tip and $F = A\rho v^2$. (This always assumes $v \gg 2u$, the tip speed. Note that at the moment of impact the force applied by a square ended jet is $A\rho vc$; $A\rho v^2$ is just the steady state force, see p. 83.) The

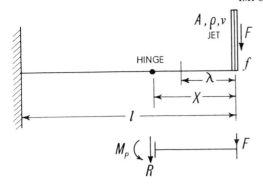

Fig. 6.4   Cantilever loaded
at its tip by a jet.

equation for rotation of the beam length X about the hinge is,

$$F \cdot X = M_p + \int_0^X m \cdot d\lambda \cdot (X - \lambda) \cdot f\left(\frac{X - \lambda}{X}\right)$$

$$= M_p + \frac{mf X^2}{3},$$
(6.17)

where M_p is the fully plastic bending moment. But at a plastic hinge $R = 0$ and thus from (6.16)

$$f = \frac{2F}{mX}$$
(6.18)

Putting (6.18) into (6.17),

$$F \cdot X = M_p + \frac{2F}{X} \cdot \frac{X^2}{3}$$

or,

$$X = \frac{3M_p}{F} = \frac{3M_p}{A\rho v^2}$$
(6.19)

If a lead bullet, mass M, length b moving with speed v, spreads out laterally on impinging with the cantilever tip, it would be necessary to treat the impact as if the bullet was a jet rather than a rigid body; then, $M = A\rho b$ and hence (6.19) becomes $X = 3bM_p/v^2 M$, an expression originally due to Parkes[6.6].

This last result could be obtained directly from considerations of the impulsive force F acting for time t, i.e. when an impulse $F \cdot t$ is delivered. If there is zero shear at the hinge,

$$F \cdot t = (mX)u$$
(6.20)

where u denotes the downward speed of the centroid of length X at the end of time t. The rotational equation of motion is,

$$(Ft) . \frac{X}{2} - M_p . t = I\omega, \qquad (6.21)$$

where I denotes the moment of inertia of the length X about its centroid and ω is the angular speed. However, $\omega = u/(X/2)$, and thus putting (6.20) over (6.21),

$$\frac{F}{F . \frac{X}{2} - M_p} = \frac{mXu}{I . \frac{u}{X/2}}$$

$$= \frac{mX^2}{2I} = \frac{mX^2}{2 . \frac{mX^3}{12}} = \frac{6}{X}$$

or

$$\frac{FX}{6} = \frac{FX}{2} - M_p$$

i.e.

$$X = 3M_p/F \qquad (6.22i)$$

and

$$u = \frac{Ft}{mX} = \frac{Ft}{3 . \frac{M_p}{F} . m}$$

$$= \frac{F^2 t}{3m . M_p} \qquad (6.22ii)$$

The tip acceleration,

$$f = \frac{2u}{t} = \frac{2F^2}{3mM_p} \qquad (6.23)$$

Note that equation (6.19) is valid only for $X \le l$. For $v^2 < 3M_p/Al\rho$, the hinge must always be at the root of the cantilever.

Plastic deflection of a constant width cantilever due to a transverse dynamic load applied at its end

A cantilever of rigid-perfectly plastic material is subjected to transverse impact at its end by a rigid (point) mass M moving at some initial speed v_0, see Fig. 6.5(a), and which adheres to the cantilever tip. The cantilever is of length l,

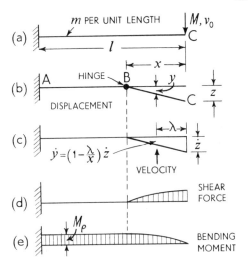

(a) m PER UNIT LENGTH M, v_0 C
l

(b) A   HINGE   B y z
DISPLACEMENT   C

(c) $\dot{y} = \left(1 - \dfrac{\lambda}{x}\right)\dot{z}$ λ $\dot{z}$
VELOCITY

(d)   SHEAR FORCE

(e) M_p BENDING MOMENT

Fig. 6.5   A uniformly wide cantilever, tip loaded by a mass M moving with speed v_0.

mass m per unit length, and M_p denotes the bending moment required to cause the whole of a section to become fully plastic. The kinetic energy of the impinging mass can only be dissipated by plastic bending and this therefore implies a plastic hinge. At the instant the mass hits the cantilever a hinge is created in it at C under the mass, and thereafter moves along the beam towards the built-in end, A. If the hinge was first created in the cantilever away from C, this would imply that the rigid portion of the beam between the hinge and C would instantly rotate, and for this an impossibly high inertia torque or moment would be required.

The high speed photographs in Plate 28 show the initiation of a plastic hinge, its motion along the cantilever, subsequent root rotation and elastic vibration when a vertical cantilever, trapezoidal in plan (see below), is end-loaded by a magneto-motive impulse[6.5].

The following analysis is due to Parkes[6.6]. Figure 6.5(b) shows a plastic hinge, initiated at the cantilever tip, after it has travelled a distance x in time t to reach point B. The portion of the beam of length x at the instant t, rotates about B; the portion of the beam AB is supposed still to be in an undeflected state, whilst BC is curved though rotating as a rigid body, the cantilever tip having a downward speed of v or $\dot{z}$. Assuming that all deflections are small, the speed of any point in BC at instant t is just proportional to its distance from B, see Fig. 6.5(c), and at distance λ from the end of the cantilever, the downward speed $\dot{u} = (x - \lambda)\dot{z}/x$. The downward acceleration, f, is obtained by differentiating the last expression, with respect to time; thus,

$$f = \frac{x - \lambda}{x} \cdot \ddot{z} - \frac{\lambda}{x^2} \cdot \dot{x}\dot{z}$$

(Dots above letters denote differentiation with respect to time.)

That the plastic hinge moves, is reflected in the second term on the right hand side of the last equation and it arises as a Coriolis-like component of the acceleration.

The impinging mass applies a finite (shear) force at the cantilever tip and it is offset by the inertia of the beam contributing a distributed load as far as x. The bending moment increases from zero at the end and as far as the section at x where the hinge lies, where it is a maximum at the full plastic bending moment M_p; at this location, i.e. x, the shear force is zero. Obviously thereafter, i.e. from B to A, the moment is of constant magnitude, M_p.

The mechanics of the system is developed after writing down the equation for vertical force equilibrium and the equation for rotational equilibrium by considering the inertia force for each element of BC. For the former, add the applied force and the reversed effective force, where the latter is given by the time rate of change of momentum of the cantilever length BC, thus,

$$M\ddot{z} + \int_0^x m\, d\lambda \cdot \frac{d}{dt}\left(\frac{x - \lambda}{x} \cdot \dot{z}\right) = 0. \tag{6.24}$$

z is the vertical or transverse displacement undergone by the cantilever end C. Equation (6.24) provides

$$M\ddot{z} + \int_0^x m\left(\ddot{z} - \frac{\lambda \ddot{z}}{x} + \frac{\lambda \dot{x}\dot{z}}{x^2}\right) d\lambda = 0$$

or,

$$M\ddot{z} + m\left[\ddot{z}\lambda - \frac{\lambda^2 \ddot{z}}{2x} + \frac{\lambda^2 \dot{x}\dot{z}}{2x^2}\right]_0^x = 0$$

i.e.

$$M\ddot{z} + m\left(\frac{x \cdot \ddot{z}}{2} + \frac{\dot{x}\dot{z}}{2}\right) = 0 \tag{6.25}$$

For rotational equilibrium, consider moments taken about C, for length BC, thus,

$$-M_p + \int_0^x (m\, d\lambda)\frac{d\dot{u}}{dt} \cdot \lambda = 0 \tag{6.26}$$

where $\dot{u}$ is the transverse speed of mass element $m\, d\lambda$ at section λ. Substituting in (6.26) for $\dot{u}$, we have

$$M_p = \int_0^x m \cdot d\lambda \frac{d}{dt}\left(\frac{x - \lambda}{x} \cdot \dot{z}\right)\lambda$$

$$= \int_0^x m\left[\ddot{z} - \frac{\lambda \ddot{z}}{x} + \frac{\lambda \dot{x}\dot{z}}{x^2}\right]\lambda \cdot d\lambda$$

$$= m\left[\frac{\lambda^2}{2} \cdot \ddot{z} - \frac{\lambda^3}{3} \cdot \frac{\ddot{z}}{x} + \frac{\lambda^3 \cdot \dot{x}\dot{z}}{3x^2}\right]_0^x$$

Hence,

$$M_p = m\left[\frac{x^2 \cdot \ddot{z}}{6} + \frac{x\dot{x}\dot{z}}{3}\right] \tag{6.27}$$

Two fundamental equations are now obtained by solving (6.25) and (6.27), using appropriate boundary conditions. From (6.25),

$$M\ddot{z}\left(1 + \frac{mx}{2M}\right) + \frac{m\dot{x}\dot{z}}{2} = 0 \tag{6.28}$$

Write v for $\dot{z}$ and (6.28) becomes,

$$\frac{dv}{dt}\left(1 + \frac{mx}{2M}\right) + \frac{m}{2M} \cdot \frac{dx}{dt} \cdot v = 0$$

Hence,

$$\int_{v_0}^{v} \frac{dv}{v} = -\int_{0}^{x} \frac{\frac{m}{2M}}{1 + \frac{m}{2M}x} \cdot dx$$

where v_0 denotes the initial speed at the tip of the cantilever at $t = 0$ and v is the speed at time t. Hence,

$$\ln\frac{v_0}{v} = \ln\left(1 + \frac{m}{2M}x\right) \tag{6.29i}$$

and thus,

$$v = \dot{z} = \frac{v_0}{1 + \frac{m}{2M}x} \tag{6.29ii}$$

From (6.29ii),

$$\ddot{z} = -\frac{v_0\dot{x} \cdot m/2M}{(1 + x \cdot m/2M)^2}$$

and the shear force at the tip of the cantilever is $-mv_0\dot{x}/2(1 + x \cdot m/2M)^2$; when $x = 0$, the shear force is infinite.

When the plastic hinge reaches the cantilever root, $x = l$, and the velocity is then,

$$v_R = \frac{v_0}{1 + ml/2M} \tag{6.29iii}$$

Also, starting with (6.27)

$$\frac{m}{6}(x^2\ddot{z} + 2x \cdot \dot{x}\dot{z}) = M_p$$

or

$$\frac{m}{6} \cdot \frac{d}{dt}(x^2 \ddot{z}) = M_p$$

Integrating,

$$x^2 \dot{z} = \frac{6M_p}{m} \cdot t + \text{constant}$$

As stated above, at $t = 0$, $x = 0$ and therefore the constant is zero. Hence,

$$t = \frac{mx^2 \dot{z}}{6M_p} \tag{6.30}$$

Substituting in (6.30) for $\dot{z}$ from (6.29ii),

$$t = \frac{mv_0}{6M_p} \cdot \frac{x^2}{\left(1 + \dfrac{m}{2M}x\right)} \tag{6.31}$$

The time taken for the hinge to travel from the cantilever tip to the built-in end A, designated T is given by putting $x = l$ in (6.31); thus,

$$T = \frac{1}{3} \cdot \frac{Mv_0}{M_p/l} \cdot \frac{1}{(1 + 2M/ml)} \tag{6.32}$$

The speed with which the plastic hinge progresses from C to A can be deduced using (6.31), thus

$$\frac{dt}{dx} = \frac{1}{\dot{x}} = \frac{mv_0 l}{6M_p} \left[\frac{2 \cdot \dfrac{x}{l}}{\left(1 + \beta \cdot \dfrac{x}{l}\right)} - \frac{\left(\dfrac{x}{l}\right)^2 \cdot \beta}{\left(1 + \beta \cdot \dfrac{x}{l}\right)^2} \right] \tag{6.33i}$$

Hence,

$$\dot{x} = \frac{6M_p}{mlv_0} \cdot \frac{(1 + \beta\mu)^2}{\mu(2 + \beta\mu)}, \tag{6.33ii}$$

where $\mu = x/l$ and $\beta = ml/2M$. This expression shows that the hinge speed is infinite at $t = 0$ (which, of course, is theoretically admissible if we recall that the material is rigid-plastic; elastic wave speeds in a rigid material are infinite), but by the time it reaches A it has slowed down to become,

$$6M_p(1 + \beta)^2/mlv_0(2 + \beta) \tag{6.33iii}$$

To find the curve into which the beam deflects when the hinge has just reached the built-in end, observe from Fig. 6.5 that,

$$\dot{y} = \frac{dy}{dt} = \frac{x - \lambda}{x} \cdot \dot{z}$$

and using (6.29ii),

$$y = \int \frac{x - \lambda}{x} \cdot \frac{v_0}{1 + \frac{m}{2M}x} \cdot dt;$$

substituting for dt from (6.33i) gives

$$y = \int_\lambda^l \left(1 - \frac{\lambda}{x}\right) \cdot \frac{v_0}{\left(1 + \frac{m}{2M}x\right)} \cdot \frac{mv_0}{6M_p} \left[\frac{2x}{\left(1 + \frac{m}{2M}x\right)} - \frac{\frac{m}{2M}x^2}{\left(1 + \frac{m}{2M}x\right)^2}\right] . dx \quad (6.34)$$

The limits of integration obviously apply from the time the hinge reaches the section at λ until it reaches the built-in end.

Put $(1 + mx/2M) = g$, so that $x = (g - 1)l/\beta$, and also put $\lambda/l = \xi$. Hence (6.34) simplifies to,

$$y \cdot \frac{6M_p}{mv_0^2} \cdot \frac{\beta^2}{l^2} = \int_{1+\beta\xi}^{1+\beta} \left(\frac{1}{g} - \frac{\beta\xi}{g^2} - \frac{1 + \beta\xi}{g^3}\right) dg,$$

$$= \ln \frac{(1 + \beta)}{(1 + \beta\xi)} + \beta\xi\left(\frac{1}{1 + \beta} - \frac{1}{1 + \beta\xi}\right)$$

$$+ \frac{(1 + \beta\xi)}{2} \cdot \left[\frac{1}{(1 + \beta)^2} - \frac{1}{(1 + \beta\xi)^2}\right]$$

This last equation may be rewritten thus,

$$y \cdot \frac{12M_p}{mv_0^2} \cdot \frac{\beta^2}{l^2} = 2\ln\frac{(1 + \beta)}{(1 + \beta\xi)} + \frac{2\beta\xi}{(1 + \beta)} - \frac{(1 + 2\beta\xi)}{(1 + \beta\xi)} + \frac{(1 + \beta\xi)}{(1 + \beta)^2}$$

$$= 2\ln\frac{(1 + \beta)}{(1 + \beta\xi)} - \frac{\beta\xi}{(1 + \beta\xi)} + \frac{\beta(3\xi - 2)}{(1 + \beta)} + \frac{\beta^2(1 - \xi)}{(1 + \beta)^2}$$

or, to write it in the form originally given by Parkes, as

$$y = \frac{(Mv_0)^2}{3M_p m}\left[2\ln\frac{(1 + \beta)}{(1 + \beta\xi)} - \frac{\beta\xi}{(1 + \beta\xi)} + \frac{\beta(3\xi - 2)}{(1 + \beta)} + \frac{\beta^2(1 - \xi)}{(1 + \beta)^2}\right] \quad (6.35i)$$

$$\equiv \frac{(Mv_0)^2}{3M_p m} \cdot D \quad (6.35ii)$$

When the travelling hinge reaches the built-in end at $t = T$ both the beam and the mass M still possess kinetic energy. This residual kinetic energy is assumed to be dissipated as plastic work by the plastic hinge at A, in rotating through, say, angle θ_R; the already deflected beam rotates as a rigid body about A through θ_R. Thus at section λ the further deflection is,

$$y_1 = (l - \lambda)\theta_R \quad (6.36i)$$

Now the rotational energy of the beam E_R at time T is,

$$E_R = \int_0^l \frac{1}{2}(m \, . \, d\lambda)\left(\frac{l - \lambda}{l} \, . \, \dot{z}_R\right)^2$$

$$= \frac{m\dot{z}_R^2}{2l^2} \, . \, \frac{l^3}{3} = \frac{mlv_R^2}{6} = \frac{mlv_0^2}{6\left(1 + \dfrac{ml}{2M}\right)^2} \, , \qquad (6.36\text{ii})$$

where suffix R refers to values when the plastic hinge reaches A.

Thus the total energy which remains to be plastically dissipated in the root hinge is the sum of E_R and that still possessed by M, i.e. $(E_R + Mv_R^2/2)$. Hence, assuming that all the kinetic energy of M is used in doing plastic work,

$$M_p \, . \, \theta_R = \frac{mlv_R^2}{6} + \frac{Mv_R^2}{2} \qquad (6.36\text{iii})$$

Rewriting (6.36iii), using (6.36i),

$$y_1 = \left(\frac{ml}{6} + \frac{M}{2}\right)\frac{v_R^2}{M_p} \, . \, (l - \lambda) \qquad (6.36\text{iv})$$

From (6.36iii) and (6.29ii), the angle turned through by the cantilever where it is built-in θ_R, is

$$\theta_R = \frac{2}{3} \, . \, Mv_0^2 \, . \, \frac{\left(3 + \dfrac{ml}{M}\right)}{M_p\left(2 + \dfrac{ml}{M}\right)^2} \qquad (6.36\text{v})$$

We have,

$$y_1 = \left(\frac{ml}{6} + \frac{M}{2}\right) . \frac{v_0^2}{(1 + \beta)^2} . \frac{(l - \lambda)}{M_p}$$

$$= \left(\frac{ml}{2M} + \frac{3}{2}\right) . \frac{v_0^2}{(1 + \beta)^2} . \frac{(1 - \xi)Ml}{3M_p} \qquad (6.37)$$

The final total deflection is, $\Upsilon = y_1 + y$, and

$$\Upsilon = \frac{\beta + \frac{3}{2}}{(1 + \beta)^2} . \frac{Mv_0^2}{3} . \frac{(1 - \xi)l}{M_p} + y$$

or,

$$\Upsilon = \frac{(Mv_0)^2}{3mM_p} . \left[\frac{ml}{2M} . \frac{2\beta + 3}{(1 + \beta)^2} . (1 - \xi) + D\right] \qquad (6.38)$$

where D is evident from (6.35i) and (6.35ii).

Equation (6.38) simplifies to provide,

$$\Upsilon = \frac{(Mv_0)^2}{3M_p \, . \, m}\left[\frac{\beta}{1 + \beta} - \frac{\beta\xi}{1 + \beta\xi} + 2\ln\frac{(1 + \beta)}{(1 + \beta\xi)}\right] \qquad (6.39\text{i})$$

or,

$$\frac{(\Upsilon/l)M_p}{\frac{1}{2}Mv_0^2} = \frac{1}{3(1+\beta)} - \frac{\xi}{3(1+\beta\xi)} + \frac{2}{3}\cdot\frac{1}{\beta}\ln\frac{(1+\beta)}{(1+\beta\xi)} \tag{6.39ii}$$

When the ratio of the striking mass to the cantilever mass is, (a), very large, i.e. $\beta \to 0$ and, (b), very small, i.e. $\beta \to \infty$, (6.39i) gives,

for (a),

$$\Upsilon \simeq \frac{(Mv_0)^2}{3M_pm} \cdot [\beta - \beta\xi + 2\ln(1+\beta)(1-\beta\xi)]$$

$$= \frac{(Mv_0)^2}{3M_pm}[\beta - \beta\xi + 2(\beta - \beta\xi)]$$

$$\doteqdot \frac{(Mv_0)^2}{M_pm} \cdot [\beta(1-\xi)]$$

$$= \frac{1}{2}\cdot\frac{Mv_0^2 l}{M_p}(1-\xi) \tag{6.40i}$$

or

$$\frac{(\Upsilon/l)M_p}{\frac{1}{2}Mv_0^2} = 1 - \xi; \tag{6.40ii}$$

and for (b),

$$\Upsilon \simeq \frac{(Mv_0^2)^2}{3M_pm} \cdot \left[1 - 1 + 2\ln\frac{1}{\xi}\right]$$

$$= \frac{1}{3\beta}\cdot\frac{Mv_0^2 l}{M_p}\cdot\ln\frac{1}{\xi} \tag{6.41i}$$

or

$$\frac{(\Upsilon/l)M_p}{\frac{1}{2}Mv_0^2} = \frac{1}{6\beta}\ln\frac{1}{\xi} \tag{6.41ii}$$

Figures 6.6 and 6.7 show how $\Upsilon M_p m/(Mv_0)^2$ and $(\Upsilon/l)M_p/\frac{1}{2}Mv_0^2$ vary with ξ using equations (6.39i) and (6.39ii) respectively; they are, in effect, non-dimensional curves of beams dynamically deformed by a mass striking the tip. Figure 6.6 (i.e. equation (6.39i)) shows the form taken up when a cantilever is struck by a relatively light mass; the extreme case—an infinitely light mass—is indicated by $\beta \to \infty$. Figure 6.7 (i.e. equation (6.39ii)) shows the deflected form taken up when a cantilever is struck by a relatively heavy mass at its tip; the straight line AB represents the extreme case, equation (6.40ii), of an infinitely heavy striker.

Figure 6.8 shows some of Parkes' experimental results and these should be compared with the curves of Fig. 6.7.

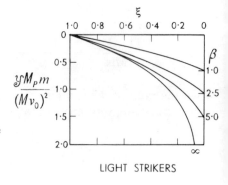

$$\frac{yM_p m}{(Mv_0)^2}$$

Fig. 6.6 Non-dimensional curves showing the form of cantilever deflection for light strikers.

LIGHT STRIKERS

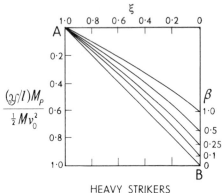

$$\frac{(y/l)M_p}{\frac{1}{2}Mv_0^2}$$

Fig. 6.7 Non-dimensional curves showing the form of cantilever deflection for heavy strikers.

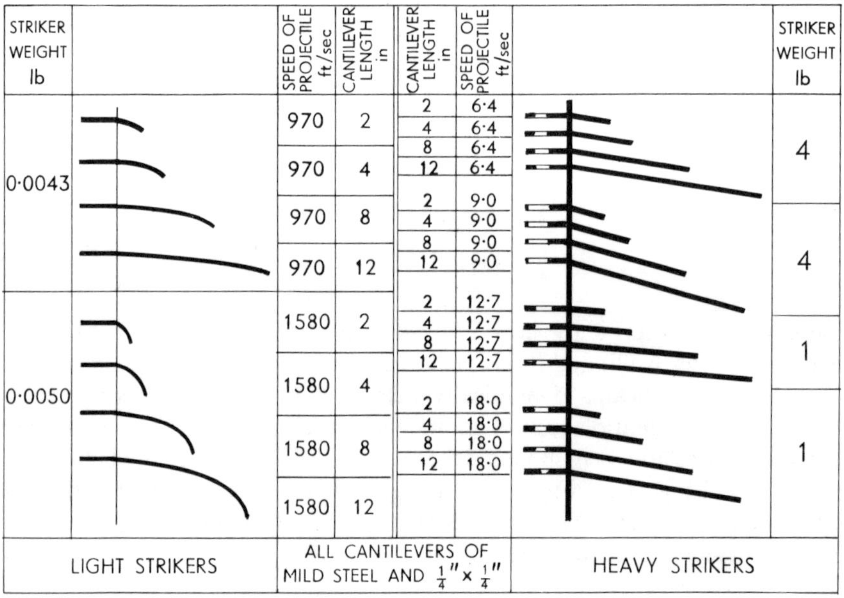

HEAVY STRIKERS

STRIKER WEIGHT lb			SPEED OF PROJECTILE ft/sec	CANTILEVER LENGTH in	CANTILEVER LENGTH in	SPEED OF PROJECTILE ft/sec		STRIKER WEIGHT lb
			970	2	2	6·4		4
					4	6·4		
			970	4	8	6·4		
					12	6·4		
0·0043			970	8	2	9·0		
					4	9·0		
			970	12	8	9·0		4
					12	9·0		
			1580	2	2	12·7		
					4	12·7		
					8	12·7		1
					12	12·7		
0·0050			1580	4	2	18·0		
					4	18·0		
			1580	8	8	18·0		1
					12	18·0		
			1580	12				
LIGHT STRIKERS			ALL CANTILEVERS OF MILD STEEL AND $\frac{1}{4}'' \times \frac{1}{4}''$				HEAVY STRIKERS	

Fig. 6.8 Showing the effect on the deflection of a cantilever of projectiles impinging at different speeds when their mass is relatively heavy or light.

The energy dissipated in the moving plastic hinge is,

$$\tfrac{1}{2}Mv_0^2 - \tfrac{1}{2}M\dot{z}^2 - E_R$$

$$= \frac{1}{2}Mv_0^2 - \frac{1}{2}\cdot M\dot{z}^2 - \frac{ml\dot{z}^2}{6}$$

$$= \frac{1}{2}Mv_0^2 - \frac{1}{6}\left(\frac{3M}{2M} + \frac{ml}{2M}\right)\cdot\frac{v_0^2}{(1+\beta)^2}\cdot 2M$$

$$= \frac{1}{2}Mv_0^2 - \frac{2\left(\tfrac{3}{2}+\beta\right)}{3(1+\beta)^2}\left(\frac{Mv_0^2}{2}\right)$$

$$= \frac{1}{2}Mv_0^2\left\{1 - \frac{(1+\tfrac{2}{3}\beta)}{(1+\beta)^2}\right\} \tag{6.42i}$$

Thus the fraction of the initial energy of the impinging mass which is dissipated in the travelling hinge, q, is

$$q = \frac{\gamma(8+3\gamma)}{3(2+\gamma)^2}, \tag{6.42ii}$$

where $\gamma = 2\beta$ is the ratio of the cantilever mass to the striking mass.

TABLE 6.1

γ	0	$\frac{1}{10}$	$\frac{1}{4}$	$\frac{1}{2}$	$\frac{3}{4}$	1	2	5	8	$12\frac{1}{3}$	18	198
q	0	0·063	0·138	0·25	0·31	0·41	0·58	0·78	0·85	0·90	0·93	0·99

Dynamic loading of a uniformly thick symmetrical cantilever, triangular in plan

The methods of dealing with the case in the preceding section may easily be used for the consideration of the plastic deflection of a uniformly thick cantilever, which in plan has a symmetrical triangular form of small apex angle, when dynamically loaded at its end, as shown in Fig. 6.9(a). The notation is largely the same as that used earlier, but note that

$$b = \frac{Bx}{l} \quad \text{and} \quad M_p = Y\cdot\frac{Bh^2}{4}\cdot\frac{x}{l} \tag{6.43}$$

Proceeding as before, the equation for the transverse motion of the beam when the plastic hinge has reached BB' from $x = 0$ is,

$$M\ddot{z} + \frac{d}{dt}\left(\int_0^x \rho bh\, d\lambda \cdot \frac{x-\lambda}{x}\cdot\dot{z}\right) = 0 \tag{6.44}$$

where ρ is the density of the material of the beam. Substituting for b from (6.43), equation (6.44) reduces to,

$$M\ddot{z} + \frac{\rho hB}{6l}\cdot(2x\dot{x}\dot{z} + x^2\ddot{z}) = 0 \tag{6.45}$$

Taking moments about C (this eliminates the moment of the force applied by M at the tip) to derive the equation for the rotation of CBB', Fig. 6.9(b),

$$M_p = \int_0^x \lambda \cdot \frac{d}{dt}\left\{\frac{\rho h B}{l} \cdot \lambda \cdot \ddot{z}\left(1 - \frac{\lambda}{x}\right)\right\} d\lambda$$

$$= \frac{\rho h B}{l} \cdot \int_0^x \left\{\ddot{z}\left(1 - \frac{\lambda}{x}\right) + \frac{\dot{z}\lambda\dot{x}}{x^2}\right\} \cdot \lambda^2 \cdot d\lambda$$

or

$$M_p = \frac{\rho h B}{12l}(\ddot{z}x^3 + 3\dot{z}x^2\dot{x}) \tag{6.46}$$

The mass of the cantilever, $\mu = \rho h B l/2$, and on writing v for $\dot{z}$ in (6.45),

$$M\dot{v} + \mu(2x\dot{x}v + x^2\dot{v})/3l^2 = 0 \tag{6.47}$$

The solution to (6.47) with $v = v_0$ when $x = 0$, is

$$\dot{z} = v = \frac{v_0}{1 + \frac{1}{3} \cdot \frac{\mu}{M} \cdot \left(\frac{x}{l}\right)^2} \tag{6.48i}$$

The magnitude of v when the hinge just reaches the root of the cantilever is,

$$v_r = v_0 \Big/ \left(1 + \frac{1}{3}\frac{\mu}{M}\right) \tag{6.48ii}$$

Equation (6.48i) confirms what would be expected, namely, that v/v_0 for given ratios of x/l and μ/M, and which are the same for a triangular plan beam and one of constant width—so that the influence of mass distribution is, to some extent, being considered—that the former gives rise to a less rapid decay of the velocity than the latter.

Equation (6.46) with (6.43) provides,

$$6M_p^* l/\mu = \ddot{z}x^2 + 3\dot{z}x\dot{x} \tag{6.49}$$

where M_p^* is the fully plastic moment at the root of the cantilever.

Substituting for $\dot{z}$ and $\ddot{z}$ in (6.49) and (6.48i) gives

$$\frac{6M_p^* l}{\mu v_0} \int_0^t dt = \int_0^x \left[\frac{3x}{1 + \alpha x^2} - \frac{2\alpha x^3}{(1 + \alpha x^2)^2}\right] dx \tag{6.50}$$

where $\alpha = \mu/3Ml^2$. After integrating (6.50)

$$t = \frac{\frac{1}{4}Mv_0 l}{M_p^*}\left[\ln\left(1 + \frac{1}{3} \cdot \frac{\mu}{M} \cdot \left(\frac{x}{l}\right)^2\right) + \frac{\frac{2}{3}\frac{\mu}{M}\left(\frac{x}{l}\right)^2}{1 + \frac{1}{3}\frac{\mu}{M}\left(\frac{x}{l}\right)^2}\right] \tag{6.51i}$$

The time for the hinge to reach the cantilever root after the mass M first made impact is,

$$T = \frac{\frac{1}{4}Mv_0 l}{M_p^*}\left[\ln\left(1 + \frac{1}{3}\frac{\mu}{M}\right) + \frac{2}{3\frac{M}{\mu} + 1}\right] \tag{6.51ii}$$

For a mild steel beam, for which the specific weight is 0·28 lbf/in³ (0·77 kg/m³) and which has $B = 4$ in (0·1 m), $l = 16$ in (0·41 m), $h = \frac{1}{4}$ in (6·35 mm), $Y = 20\,000$ lbf/in² (13·78 . 10^4 kN/m²), $v_0 = 32$ ft/sec (9·7 m/sec) and assuming $\mu/M = 3$ (so that the striker weight is $\frac{3}{4}$ lb (0·34 kg)), $T \simeq 2\cdot4$ msec. For a constant width cantilever of otherwise the same dimensions, and for the same velocity of impact and mass ratio, i.e. 3:1, time $T = 5$ milliseconds.

As before, the above analysis pertains only to the phase of beam motion during which the plastic hinge travels from the cantilever tip to its root.

The rotational energy of the triangular cantilever when the plastic hinge has just reached the built-in end is,

$$E_R = \int_0^x \frac{1}{2} \cdot \frac{B\lambda}{l} \cdot h \, d\lambda\rho \cdot \left(\frac{l - \lambda}{l} \cdot \dot{z}_R \right)^2$$

$$= \frac{1}{2} M v_0^2 \cdot \frac{\dfrac{\mu}{M}}{6 \left(1 + \dfrac{1}{3} \dfrac{\mu}{M} \right)^2} \tag{6.52i}$$

the kinetic energy of the impinging mass, M, which remains at this time is,

$$= \frac{\frac{1}{2} M v_0^2}{\left(1 + \dfrac{1}{3} \dfrac{\mu}{M} \right)^2} \tag{6.52ii}$$

Thus the angle θ_R through which the cantilever turns as a whole at its built-in end is given by,

$$\theta_R = \frac{M v_0^2}{12 M_p^*} \left\{ \frac{6 + \dfrac{\mu}{M}}{\left(1 + \dfrac{1}{3} \dfrac{\mu}{M} \right)^2} \right\} \tag{6.52iii}$$

Inserting the numerical values assumed above, $\theta_R \simeq 2\frac{1}{2}°$ whilst for the constant width cantilever $\theta_R \simeq 3\cdot8°$.

Whilst the derivation of the form of the deflected beam is straightforward, as in the previous section, it is too lengthy and tedious to be worth pursuing here.

The amount of work which would be required to be done in order that this triangular beam should be elastically stressed but so that the top and bottom surface layers just reach the yield point Y, is given by $BhlY^2/12E$, where E is Young's Modulus. For the numerical problem discussed above, the energy stored at this critical stage is $\simeq 18$ in/lb (2·035 J); this is equivalent to the energy that would be possessed by the striker, of weight $\frac{3}{4}$ lb (0·340 kg), after falling vertically 2 ft (0·6 m).

Other plan shapes of cantilever may be analysed as in the two cases above. It may easily be shown, for instance, that for the trapezoidal plate in Fig. 6.9(c) corresponding to (6.48i) and (6.48ii).

$$v = \dot{z} = \frac{v_0}{1 + \dfrac{\rho h}{3M} \left(\dfrac{B - b_0}{l} x^2 + 3 b_0 x \right)} \tag{6.53}$$

Since the principles of the approach are always the same, we shall not proceed further.

Plastic response of a simply supported beam to an impact load at the centre

Two cases immediately above have already been discussed using the concept of moving yield hinges and in this section we follow a paper of Ezra[6.7], (1958), and consider a uniform simply supported beam dynamically loaded at its midspan by a rigid striker. The deflections induced are everywhere supposed small, but the kinetic energy delivered by the striker and dissipated in the plastic hinges is taken to be an order of magnitude greater than the elastic strain energy which the beam can store.

Photographs of one half of a simply supported beam taken very soon after being struck indicate that the central half of the beam takes up a more-or-less

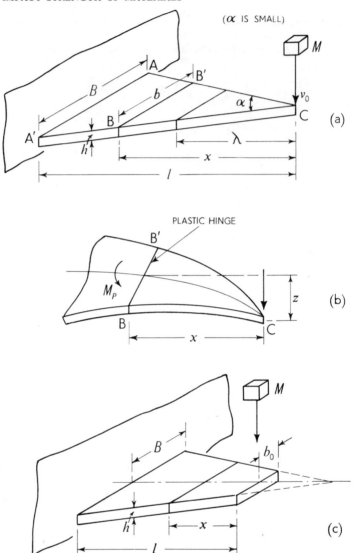

Fig. 6.9   Triangular shaped cantilever subject to impact at its tip by a mass M moving with speed v_0.

symmetrical vee-shaped deflection curve about the striker, the other two portions of the beam remaining essentially undeflected. From the moment of impact plastic hinges form under the striker; also, two plastic hinges travel outwards from it, the portions of the beam between the hinges remaining rigid. Between the travelling hinges and the supports there are two portions of undeformed beam, each of which rotates about its support; these rotations must occur because, as the free body diagram of Fig. 6.11 indicates, the yield moment only, acts in OB, there being no shear force at B. The bending moment is greatest, i.e. is the yield moment, at the plastic hinges B and B', see Fig. 6.10, and, since there is no concentrated load between O and A, the shear force diagram is continuous, which implies zero shear force at B and B'.

It will be shown that the moving plastic hinges only move a little more than half way towards the supports before they become stationary; at this moment the first stage of deformation ceases and the second ensues, during which each 'bent' portion of the beam, acting as a rigid body, rotates about the stationary hinge below the striker. The unspent kinetic energy of the striker at midspan and the rotational energy of each half of the beam are then dissipated in doing plastic work in the stationary hinges. The situation depicted in Fig. 6.10 applies some short time after the striker impinges on the beam; the notation is obvious and follows that previously used.

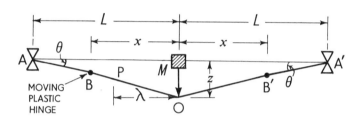

Fig. 6.10   Impulsive load applied at centre of a simply supported beam.

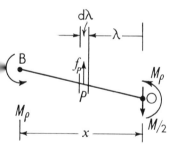

Fig. 6.11   Free body diagram pertaining to Fig. 6.10.

The downwards motion of OB

The downwards velocity, v_p, at a point P between O and B is given by

v_p = velocity of B + velocity of P relative to B

$$= (L - x)\dot\theta + [\dot z - (L - x)\dot\theta]\left(\frac{x - \lambda}{x}\right) \tag{6.54}$$

$$= \dot z\left(1 - \frac{\lambda}{x}\right) + \frac{\lambda}{x}(L - x)\dot\theta \tag{6.55}$$

Thus, the acceleration at P, f_p, is

$$f_p = \frac{dv_p}{dt} = \ddot{z}\left(1 - \frac{\lambda}{x}\right) + \dot{z}\left(\frac{\lambda \dot{x}}{x^2}\right) - \frac{\lambda}{x^2}(L - x)\dot{x}\dot{\theta} + \frac{\lambda}{x}(-\dot{x})\dot{\theta} + \frac{\lambda}{x}(L - x)\ddot{\theta} \quad (6.56)$$

The inertia force of OB is upwards, and this, together with the downwards force $M\ddot{z}/2$ is zero, noting that there is no shear force at B. Hence, if m is the beam mass per unit length,

$$\frac{M}{2}\ddot{z} + \int_0^x m \, d\lambda \cdot f_p = 0 \quad (6.57)$$

and,

$$\frac{M}{2}\ddot{z} + m\left[\ddot{z} \cdot \frac{x}{2} + \frac{\dot{z}\dot{x}}{2} - \frac{(L - x)\dot{x}\dot{\theta}}{2} - \frac{x\dot{x}\dot{\theta}}{2} + \frac{x(L - x)\ddot{\theta}}{2}\right] = 0$$

This reduces to,

$$(M + mx)\ddot{z} + mx\ddot{\theta}(L - x) + m\dot{x}(\dot{z} - L\dot{\theta}) = 0 \quad (6.58)$$

The rotation of OB

The equation of rotation for OB is, taking moments about O, see Fig. 6.11,

$$2M_p = \int_0^x m \, d\lambda \cdot f_p \lambda \quad (6.59)$$

and substituting for f_p from (6.56)

$$2M_p = m\int_0^x \left[\left(1 - \frac{\lambda}{x}\right)\ddot{z} + \frac{\lambda}{x^2} \cdot \dot{x}\dot{z} + (L - x)\ddot{\theta}\frac{\lambda}{x} - \frac{\dot{\theta}\dot{x}\lambda}{x} - \frac{(L - x)\dot{\theta}\lambda\dot{x}}{x^2}\right]\lambda \, d\lambda$$

and hence,

$$12M_p = m[x^2\ddot{z} + 2x^2(L - x)\ddot{\theta} + 2x\dot{x}(\dot{z} - L\dot{\theta})] \quad (6.60)$$

The rotations of AB

For the portion AB, see Fig. 6.10, rotating about the position-fixed support A, there is only the yield moment applied at B to cause angular acceleration $\ddot{\theta}$. The moment of inertia of AB about A is $I_A = m(L - x)^3/3$ and since $I_A \cdot \ddot{\theta} = M_p$, then

$$m(L - x)^3\ddot{\theta} = 3M_p \quad (6.61)$$

The extreme position of the travelling plastic hinge

If (6.58) is multiplied by $2x$ and subtracted from (6.60), we obtain

$$\ddot{z} = -12M_p/(2Mx + mx^2) \quad (6.62)$$

Next, substituting in (6.58) for $\ddot{z}$ from (6.62) and for $\ddot{\theta}$ from (6.61), it is found that,

$$\dot{x}(\dot{z} - L\dot{\theta}) = \frac{3M_p}{m}\left[\frac{2}{x} + \frac{2}{2\frac{M}{m} + x} - \frac{x}{(L-x)^2}\right] \tag{6.63}$$

When $\dot{x}$ is zero, so also is $\dot{z} - L\dot{\theta} = 0$; these two equations both hold simultaneously, for if $x = 0$ then each half of the beam behaves as a rigid body and thus the second one also holds. The right hand side of (6.63) equated to zero, gives then the values of x for which the plastic hinge ceases to move and we have,

$$\frac{2}{x} + \frac{2}{2\frac{M}{m} + x} = \frac{x}{(L-x)^2} \tag{6.64}$$

(i) When $M/m \to \infty$, (6.64) gives

$$\frac{2}{x} = \frac{x}{(L-x)^2} \quad \text{and} \quad x = (2 - \sqrt{2})L \simeq 0.59L \tag{6.65i}$$

(ii) When $M/mL \to 0$, (6.64) gives

$$\frac{2}{x} + \frac{2}{x} = \frac{x}{(L-x)^2} \quad \text{or} \quad x = \tfrac{2}{3}L \tag{6.65ii}$$

(iii) When $M/mL = 1$, $x = 0.61L$ \tag{6.65iii}

For all values of M/mL, the distance from midspan, at which the plastic hinge becomes stationary, lies between $0.67L$ and $0.59L$.

For small values of t, i.e. for small values of x also, (6.62) shows that $\ddot{z}$ is large. Also, referring to (6.63), because $\dot{\theta} = 0$ at $t = 0$, and since $x = 0$ and $\dot{z}$ is finite and equal to v_0, therefore $\dot{x} \to \infty$. From (6.61), $\ddot{\theta}$ is seen to have a finite value when $x \to 0$.

High speed photographs of simply supported beams show that in the early stages of deformation the two extreme portions rotate about the supports and remain almost straight and undeflected.

Thus by deleting terms $\dot{\theta}$ and $\ddot{\theta}$ in (6.58), (6.60) and (6.61), we arrive at a set of differential equations which, if solved, should *approximately* describe the motion of the beam in the early stages of motion, i.e. equation (6.58) becomes

$$(M + mx)\ddot{z} + m\dot{x}\dot{z} = 0. \tag{6.66}$$

(6.60) becomes

$$m\ddot{z}x^2 + 2mx\dot{x}\dot{z} = 12M_p. \tag{6.67}$$

(6.66) becomes

$$d(M\dot{z} + mx\dot{z})/dt = 0 \tag{6.68}$$

and (6.67) becomes

$$d(mx^2\dot{z})/dt = 12M_p \tag{6.69}$$

Hence, integrating and noting that at $t = 0$, $x = 0$ and $\dot{z} = v_0$, (6.68) gives

$$\dot{z} = \frac{Mv_0}{M + mx} \tag{6.70}$$

and (6.69),

$$mx^2\dot{z} = 12M_pt \tag{6.71}$$

Substituting for $\dot{z}$ in (6.71) from (6.70), and differentiating with respect to t,

$$\dot{x} = \frac{12M_p}{Mmv_0} \cdot \frac{(M + mx)^2}{x(2M + mx)} \tag{6.72}$$

The deflection at midspan

Dividing (6.70) by (6.72), we find

$$\frac{dz}{dx} = \frac{Mv_0}{M + mx} \cdot \frac{Mmv_0}{12M_p} \cdot \frac{x(2M + mx)}{(M + mx)^2} \tag{6.73}$$

Put, $M + mx = s$ and (6.73) becomes,

$$z = \int_0^x \frac{M^2v_0^2}{12M_pm} \cdot \frac{s^2 - M^2}{s^3} \cdot ds$$

Thus,

$$z = \frac{M^2v_0^2}{12M_pm} \cdot \left[\ln\left(1 + \frac{m}{M}x\right) - \frac{mx(2M + mx)}{2(M + mx)^2} \right] \tag{6.74}$$

Some recent work

Symonds and Mentel[6.9] in 1958 examined the impulsive loading of beams, the *whole* length of which were subjected to a very short pulse of uniform pressure which imparts a uniform transverse velocity to them, taking into account the axial constraint imposed by the fixing of the ends of the beam, in the case of both pin-ended and built-in beams.† Their solution utilises a yield relation between the bending moment at a section and a normal force acting on the same section, e.g. equation (4.138). Their analysis identified three modes of deformation.

    (i) Hinges first formed at the end of a beam move inwards; the two end portions of the beam rotate as rigid links whilst the centre portion is subject to tension only and continues to move at its initial speed.

---

† See, 'Impulsive loading of fully clamped beams with finite plastic deflections and strain rate sensitivity', by P. S. Symonds and N. Jones, *I.J.M.S.*, **14**, 49, 1972.

(ii) The two hinges eventually meet at the centre of the beam and subsequently the two halves of the beam rotate about a support, hinges being contiguous with one another at the central plastic hinge, where permanent curvature change and axial extension occur.
It is shown that after such beams as these are deflected by an amount greater than their own thickness, axial forces become important and tend to greatly reduce further deflection.

(iii) In the third phase of loading, which prevails if the intensity of loading is great enough, the beam behaves as a plastic string; the bending moments in the beam become unimportant by comparison with the tensile forces.

In 1955 Symonds[6.10] had analysed this problem neglecting the effect of axial restraint. The rotation of the outer portion of the beam, between the moving hinges and the supports, was considered, the central portion of the beam not carrying any tension. When the two hinges met at the centre of the beam, the two halves of the beam then rotated as rigid bodies about the supports until all the kinetic energy of the system was dissipated as plastic work at the hinges.

Witmer, Balmer, Leech and Pian[6.11] have studied the dynamic deformation of beams, rings and plates and shells. In their paper they present many results showing how these structural elements deflect with time when subjected to explosive loading.

A very interesting set of experiments was reported by Bodner and Spiers[6.12] in 1963 in which aluminium cantilevers carrying a tip mass were impulsively loaded by detonating capsules of lead azide powder on the tip mass; the cantilevers were held at room temperature, 212 °F (100 °C) and 400 °F (204 °C). It transpired that the strain-rate dependence of the yield stress became increasingly important at elevated temperatures. The usual rigid-plastic theory neglects this feature, though most experimenters have noted that some allowance had to be made for it in their room temperature work in order to obtain good correlation between theory and experiment. The increasingly important effect of strain rate on yield stress at elevated temperatures is now well known (see Chapter 4).

Ting[6.13] (1964), more or less re-analysing Parkes' problem, pp. 260 to 269 above, but introducing a stress-strain rate law, showed that the two uncoupled phases—the period of the moving hinge and the final phase during which the hinge is stationary at the cantilever root—are not called for. According to Ting's analysis beam deflection is a single, continuous motion with the plastic region initially extending the full length of the beam and shrinking to zero when motion ceases.

The effect of geometry changes when a cantilever carrying an end mass is dynamically loaded by causing the tip to move off with some initial speed and where the kinetic energy acquired by the system greatly exceeds that which could be elastically sustained in bending the beam, has been rigorously treated by Ting[6.14] in a paper in 1965. He has shown that part of the discrepancies between Parkes' theory and experiments can be attributed to the neglect of changes in geometry.

Humphreys[6.15] (1965) conducted a series of tests on flat steel beams, built-in at both ends, using sheet explosive to give high uniform impulsive loading which lasted $\frac{1}{2}$ msec, sufficient to produce plastic deformation. The beams were made part of a ballistic pendulum so that the applied impulse could be measured. A high speed camera, operating at about 10 000 frame/sec, was used to photograph the deforming beams, and the deformation mode based on the rigid-plastic model which includes axial constraint appeared to correspond well with what was observed, i.e. in the first phase hinges are just formed where the beam is built-in and move in towards the beam centre as the beam moves downwards; the region between the hinges remained straight. In the second phase, after the hinges have met, the hinge pattern remained fixed until all the kinetic energy was dissipated as plastic work. The final observed plastic deflection was found to be consistently lower than that predicted by the Symonds–Mentel theory by 20% to 50%. It was believed that lack of knowledge of the effect of strain-rate on yield stress may have been largely responsible for the discrepancies observed.

An experimental investigation to test the reliability of the rigid-plastic theory, without axial constraints and as developed for pin-ended and built-in beams, carrying a uniformly distributed dynamic load, was made by Florence and Firth[6.16] (1965). They found the theory to be good for engineering purposes for predicted central deflection and for the slope at the supports. Little improvement in predicted deflections occurs when geometry changes are allowed for, but significant improvements are found when some account of strain-hardening is taken. High speed photographs of deforming beams well substantiate the Symonds–Mentel theory, though an interaction of elastic and plastic effects was observable.

The influence of strain-hardening and strain rate sensitivity in impulsively loaded rigid-plastic beams has been investigated by Jones[6.17] (1967), and it shows, as would be expected, that strain-hardening is relatively unimportant but strain rate much more so.

Cantilevers subject to a uniform blast load

The consequences of applying an impulsive uniform load to a cantilever with or without a tip mass using a magneto-motive 'blast', are seen in Plates 29 and 30. These show high speed photographs of cantilevers in process of deflection[6.18]. Plate 31 shows the terminal form of some impulsively loaded cantilevers carrying different tip masses.

For comparative purposes Figs. 6.12 and 6.13 show, on the same graph, the deflection curves as taken from Plates 29 and 30 and the position of the plastic hinge at each stage of deflection.

Figure 6.14 shows a cantilever blast-loaded along a portion of its length and carrying a tip mass, so that at the instant of loading, the loaded length has a uniform downward speed. Immediately, two contiguous plastic hinges

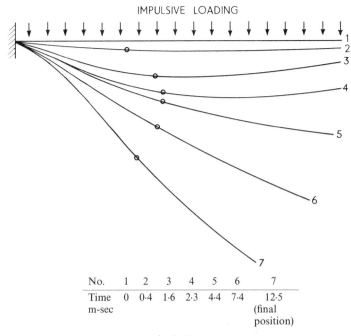

Fig. 6.12   Instantaneous profile of cantilever as obtained from high speed photographs.

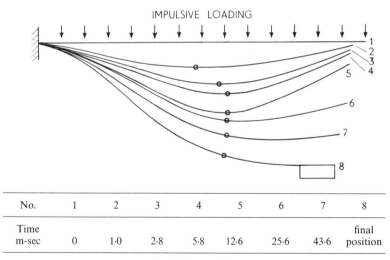

Fig. 6.13   Instantaneous profile of cantilever as obtained from high speed film.

develop and commence travelling in opposite directions. Depending on the parameters of the situation, any one of five possible modes of deformation may ensue; as a full discussion of this topic is long it is not pursued here but is dealt with in ref. 6.18.

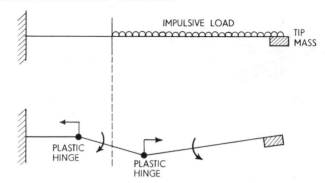

Fig. 6.14   Indicating plastic hinge movement after uniform impulsive loading.

REFERENCES

6.1   RAWLINGS, B. The present state of knowledge of the behaviour of steel structures under an impulsive load. *Civ. Engng Trans. Instn Engrs Aust.*, 89 (1963).

6.2   DAVIES, R. and AUSTIN, E. R. *Developments in High Speed Metal Forming.* Machinery Publishing, pp. 284 (1970).

6.3   DUWEZ, P. E., CLARK, D. S. and BOHNENBLUST, H. F. The behaviour of long beams under impact loading. *J. appl. Mech.*, **72**, 27 (1950).

6.4   LEE, E. H. and SYMONDS, P. S. Large plastic deformation of beams under transverse impact. *J. appl. Mech.*, **74**, 308 (1952).

6.5   HALL, R. G. *Plastic Response of Cantilevers to Dynamic Loading.* M.Sc. thesis, Univ. Manchester Inst. Sci. Technol. (1970).

6.6   PARKES, E. W. The permanent deformation of a cantilever struck transversely at its tip. *Proc. R. Soc.*, Series A, **228**, 462 (1955).

6.7   EZRA, A. A. The plastic response of a simply supported beam to an impact load at its center. *Proc. Third U.S. Nat. Congr. appl. Mech., Am. Soc. mech. Engrs*, 513 (1958).

6.8   HOPKINS, H. G. On the behaviour of infinitely long rigid-plastic beams under transverse concentrated load. *J. Mech. Phys. Solids*, **4**, 38 (1955).

6.9   SYMONDS, P. S. and MENTEL, T. Impulsive loading of plastic beams with axial constraints. *J. Mech. Phys. Solids*, **6**, 186 (1958).

6.10   SYMONDS, P. S. Brown Univ. Rep. UERD-3 (1955).

6.11   WITMER, E. A., BALMER, H. A., LEECH, J. W. and PIAN, H. H. Large dynamic deformation of beams, rings, plates and shells. *J.A.I.A.A.*, **1**, 1848 (1963).

6.12   BODNER, S. R. and SPIERS, W. G. Large deformation of a rigid, ideally plastic cantilever beam. *J. appl. Mech.*, **32**, 295 (1965).

6.13   TING, T. C. The plastic deformation of a cantilever beam with strain rate sensitivity under impulsive loading. *J. appl. Mech.*, **11**, 38 (1964).

6.14   TING, T. C. Large deformation of a rigid, ideally plastic cantilever beam. *J. appl. Mech.*, **32**, 295 (1965).

6.15   HUMPHREYS, J. S. Plastic deformation of impulsively loaded straight clamped beams. *J. appl. Mech.*, **32**, 7 (1965).

6.16   FLORENCE, A. L. and FIRTH, R. D. Rigid plastic beams under uniformly distributed impulses. *J. appl. Mech.*, **32**, 481 (1965).

6.17   JONES, N. Influence of strain-hardening and strain-rate sensitivity on the permanent deformation of impulsively loaded rigid-plastic beams. *I.J.M.S.*, **9**, 777 (1967).

6.18   VICKERS, G. W. *The Dynamic Deformation of a Cantilever.* M.Sc. thesis, Univ. Manchester Inst. Sci. Technol. (1970).

7: Dynamic loading of rings and frames

The plastic deformation of circular rings and frames under static load and due to low speed impact was discussed on p. 181; in those cases the inertia of the structure played a negligible role in the mode of plastic deformation enforced. In this chapter we consider several examples, theoretically and experimentally, where the inertia of the material of the structure plays a considerable part.

Initial position of the plastic hinges in a free thin circular ring under concentrated dynamic loading

The subject of this Section is taken from the first part of a paper by Owens and Symonds[7.1].

The mass of a circular ring, which is radially loaded by a suddenly applied force P, is assumed to be concentrated along its middle line and distributed at a rate of m per unit length. Immediately after impact the ring moves as a rigid body until such time as the inertia loading is great enough to cause the bending moment at certain sections of the ring to attain the value M_p—the full plastic bending moment—i.e. to develop plastic hinges. Obviously, for reasons of symmetry, see Fig. 7.1(a), one hinge will develop under the load at A and another diametrically opposite at B. To permit plastic deformation of the ring as a mechanism, at least four hinges must be present; let the two additional hinges arise symmetrically at angle ϕ_0 on either side of AB.

The free body diagram for one half of a ring is shown in Fig. 7.1(b), the whole ring supposedly moving with an acceleration f, as shown; the loading on the

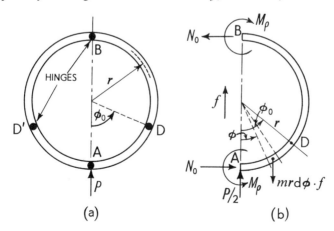

(a) (b)

Fig. 7.1   Thin circular ring loaded at A by force P.

ring is then just due to inertia and acts in the direction opposite to that of motion. The equation of translational motion gives,

$$P = 2\pi r m f \tag{7.1}$$

where r is the mean radius of the ring.

Taking moments about A, the normal force on a section at $\phi = 0$ and π, i.e. N_0, is

$$N_0 . 2r = \int_0^\pi m . r \, d\phi . f . r \sin \phi$$

or

$$N_0 = mrf \tag{7.2}$$

The plastic moments at A and B, because they annul one another, do not appear in equation (7.2). The bending moment at D is M_ϕ and is given by,

$$M_\phi = M_p + N_0 r(1 - \cos \phi_0) - \frac{P}{2} r \sin \phi_0 + \int_0^{\phi_0} mr \, d\phi fr(\sin \phi_0 - \sin \phi)$$

$$-M_\phi = M_p \left\{ -1 + \frac{Pr}{2M_p} . \sin \phi_0 - \frac{Pr}{2M_p} . \frac{\phi_0}{\pi} . \sin \phi_0 \right\} \tag{7.3}$$

after introducing (7.1) and (7.2).

Obviously the two further hinges at D and D' will occur where M_ϕ is greatest and thus putting $dM_\phi/d\phi_0 = 0$ in (7.3), we find

$$\tan \phi_0 = \pi - \phi_0 \tag{7.4i}$$

Hence on solving (7.4i), the value of ϕ_0 is found to be 1·11 radians or about 64°. When $M_\phi = M_p$ in (7.3), (negative, since the plastic bending moment must obviously apply in the clockwise sense), by putting $\phi_0 = 1·11$,

$$\frac{Pr}{M_p} = \frac{4}{(1 - 1·11/\pi) \sin 64°} = 6·9 \tag{7.5i}$$

Also,

$$f = 1·1 \frac{M_p}{mr^2} \left. \vphantom{\frac{M_p}{mr^2}} \right\}$$

and

$$N_0 = 1·1 \frac{M_p}{r} \tag{7.5ii}$$

In the above analysis it is assumed that the normal force and the shear force across each section are of negligible importance as regards yield; bending only is judged important. We now justify this. First, the shear force at a hinge is, in fact, zero because $dM/d\phi_0 = 0$. Second, if the normal force on the section at D is N_ϕ, then strictly, for a rectangular section ring, the yield inequality (4.138)

$$\frac{M_\phi}{M_p} + \left(\frac{N_\phi}{N_Y}\right)^2 \leq 1$$

applies, see p. 180, N_Y is the normal force on the section when the whole of it is subject only to a normal stress equal to the yield stress Y.

Now,

$$N_\phi = N_0 \cos \phi + \frac{P}{2} \sin \phi - mr\phi . f . \sin \phi$$

$$= \frac{M_p}{r}\left[1\cdot1 \cos 64° + 3\cdot45 \sin 64° - \frac{mr^2 f}{M_0} . 1\cdot1 . \sin 64° \right]$$

$$= \frac{M_p}{r}[0\cdot48 + 3\cdot11 - 1\cdot11] \simeq 2\cdot5\frac{M_p}{r} \qquad (7.6)$$

Suppose the thin ring under consideration is of unit width and is one in which the thickness to diameter ratio, i.e. $h/2r = \frac{1}{10}$, then $N_Y = hY = Yr/5$, $M_p = h^2 Y/4 = Yr^2/100$ and $N_\phi = Yr/40$. Thus $N_\phi/N_Y \simeq 0\cdot12$ and $M_\phi/M_p \simeq 0\cdot98$. Hence, since $M_\phi \simeq 0\cdot98M_p$ at the collapse load, we are well justified in neglecting the effects of direct stress over a section, and considering bending stresses only.

The analysis by Owens and Symonds shows that after the two hinges at 64° to the centre line have formed, they move, but depending on how P changes with time; the calculation of this movement is long and tedious and is not pursued here.

It is easily shown that for a ring simultaneously loaded by given forces P and Q ($P > Q$), see Fig. 7.2(a), that the initial hinge location is given by

$$\frac{P/Q}{P/Q - 1} = \frac{\phi_0 + \tan \phi_0}{\pi}$$

Also

$$\frac{PR}{4M_p} = \frac{\phi_0 + \tan \phi_0}{\sin \phi_0 . \tan \phi_0}$$

and

$$\frac{QR}{4M_p} = \frac{\phi_0 + \tan \phi_0 - \pi}{\sin \phi_0 . \tan \phi_0}$$

$$(7.4ii)$$

When $P = Q$, $\phi_0 = \pi/2$ (as would be expected from symmetry considerations) and $PR/M_p = 4$, which value is the same as given by (4.141). For comparison with (7.4ii), the static force P to give a plastic hinge at ϕ_0 is

$$\frac{PR}{M_p} = \text{cosec } \phi_0$$

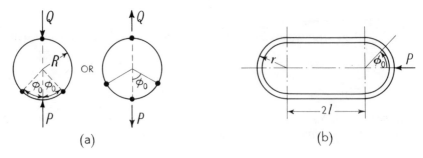

Fig. 7.2   A shackle suddenly subject to a load P.

Figure 7.2(b), which shows the centre line of a shackle subject to a dynamic load, may be treated as for the simple circular ring, and it shows that ϕ_0, the angle to the centre line at which the two additional plastic hinges occur, is given by

$$\tan \phi_0 = c\pi - \phi_0 \qquad (7.4\text{iii})$$

where

$$c = 1 + (2l/\pi r).$$

Some experimental results

Below, a collection of experimental results is presented concerning the impulsive loading of rings and frames[7.2].

(i) *Lead ring falling on to a sharp indenter*

A 5 in (12·7 cm) o.d., $\frac{3}{8}$ in (9·6 mm) thick and 0·5 in (1·27 cm) wide ring when allowed to fall freely from a height of 9 ft (2·75 m), i.e. to impinge at a speed of 24 ft/sec (7·3 m/s), on to a rigid sharp indenter deforms with time after the moment of impact as shown in Fig. 7.3; these results were obtained using a high speed camera. It was found that the vertical diameter contracted and the horizontal diameter extended, see Fig. 7.4, at nearly constant rates of 26 ft/sec (7·93 m/sec) and 18 ft/sec (5·48 m/sec). Comparisons with theoretical results for force, etc., are difficult in tests on lead because very significant strain rate effects occur to give an inconstant yield stress; in tests such as these the greatest rate of strain is about $10^2/\text{sec}$. The terminal state of a deformed ring is seen in Plate 32.

(ii) *Anvil-supported rings hit by a sharp indenter or a flat hammer*

Plate 33 shows the final form taken up by rings of copper, aluminium and mild steel supported on a rigid anvil after impact at an initial speed of 24 ft/sec (7·3 m/s) by a pointed indenter. The mechanics of this set-up is discussed in

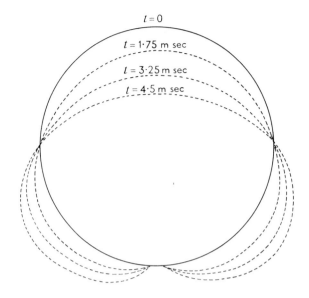

Fig. 7.3   Showing the instantaneous profile of a lead ring at various times t after impact, when falling freely and encountering a sharp indenter (5·0 in outer diameter; $\frac{3}{8}$ in radial thickness).

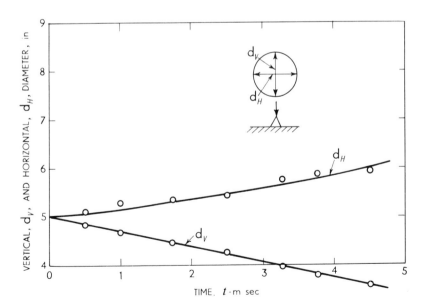

Fig. 7.4   Showing how the horizontal and vertical diameters of the ring of Fig. 7.3 and Plate 32 alter with time when freely falling on to a sharp indenter of 40° nose angle, with an initial speed of 24 ft/sec.

ref. 7.2. The consequent deformation from having two contiguous supported lead rings on to which falls an identical ring is seen in Plate 34. The different shapes taken up by rings, (a) when falling freely onto a flat anvil and (b) when supported on a flat anvil and then subjected to impact from a heavy flat rigid hammer is evident from Plate 35. How the shape of the deformed ring alters with time is shown in Fig. 7.5.

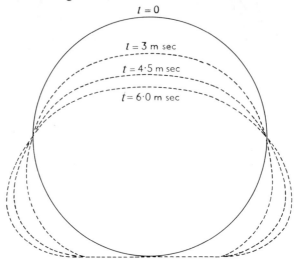

Fig. 7.5   Showing the instantaneous profiles of a 2·5 in radius lead ring at various times after first impact when falling freely on to a flat rigid anvil; initial speed at $t = 0$ is 24 ft/sec.

(iii) *Ring hit by bullets*

Plate 36 shows a freely suspended copper ring which has been hit radially by a long mild steel bullet moving at about 700 ft/sec (214 m/s). The asymmetry of plastic hinge formation is well indicated in the Plate; the general shape of the terminal deformation is similar however to that inflicted by a heavy but slower moving mass as in Plate 32.

(iv) *Multipoint loading of rings*

If a ring is very rapidly loaded, simultaneously at several points around its circumference, then forms as shown in Plate 37 arise; the concentrated loading in these cases was achieved explosively using detonators.

(v) *Impulsive loading of rings to which masses are added*

The influence of mass distribution on terminal deformation shape is seen through Plate 38 where to each of four aluminium rings two masses each of weight $\frac{1}{4}$ lb (0·113 kg) were symmetrically clamped at the locations indicated in black. Each ring was suspended and then explosively loaded at the top. The closer are the masses to the impact point, the closer they are to the hinge positions, off the centre-line.

If M_R denotes the mass of a ring and $M_w/2$ the mass of each of the two concentrated masses attached at a location where $\phi = \theta_0$, then the side hinge initial locations are, if $\theta_0 > \phi_0$, given by

$$\tan \phi_0 = \frac{\pi\left(1 + \dfrac{M_w}{M_R}\right) - \phi_0}{1 + \dfrac{M_w}{M_R} \cdot \dfrac{\pi \sin \theta_0}{2}} \qquad (7.7\text{i})$$

When $\theta_0 = 180°$, then if $M_w/M_R = 1$ or $\frac{1}{4}$, $\phi_0 \simeq 78\frac{1}{2}°$ and $70°$ respectively. If $\theta_0 < \phi_0$, then

$$\tan \phi_0 = \frac{\pi - \phi_0}{1 + \dfrac{M_w}{M_R} \cdot \dfrac{\pi \sin \theta_0}{2}} \qquad (7.7\text{ii})$$

(vi) *Impulsive loading of Perspex rings*

Fast loaded Perspex behaves in a brittle manner. A ring loaded by a detonator may suffer local fracture as the lower ring in Plate 39 shows; bending appears negligible by comparison with shear force effects. However, when the Perspex ring is supported on a flat anvil and subject to a falling pointed indenter, two fractures occur as the upper ring in Plate 39 shows.

(vii) *Magnetomotive loading of frames*

Simple metal structures, e.g. frames and cantilevers, may be loaded at very high rates by use of high strength transient magnetic fields; the magnetic field is produced by the discharge of a bank of capacitors through a coil adjacent to a part of the structure and the deforming force arises from the interaction of the eddy current induced in the structural member and the magnetic field produced by the coil; ref. 7.3 describes the details of this technique.

Plate 40 shows two cases of a square frame symmetrically loaded but to different degrees of intensity and in Plate 41 one frame asymmetrically loaded.

Roots-blower impeller forming

Besides interest in fast ring compressive 'point loading' as a structural problem, note may be taken of its potential employment as a manufacturing technique, e.g. for the free implosive forming of Roots-blower impellers, see Fig. 7.6.

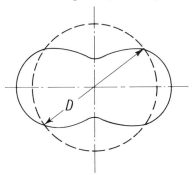

Fig. 7.6   Basic profile of Roots blower impeller.

Usually these impellers are made by welding together two halves of pre-formed plate, but by starting with a short length of seamless metal tubing and affixing and then detonating suitably shaped and located high-explosive charges, see Fig. 7.7, the required form may be arrived at, see Plate 42. To achieve the required shape 'constraining' explosive charges may be used on the horizontal axis, or some other physical restraint. The distinct hinges or regions of large plastic bending are evident in Fig. 7.6. The shapes shown in Plate 42 are as given in Blazinski's original paper[7.4].

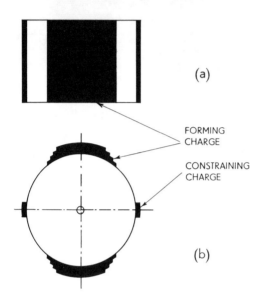

Fig. 7.7   Positioning of explosive charges to give impeller shape.

REFERENCES

7.1   OWENS, R. H. and SYMONDS, P. S. Plastic deformation of a free ring under concentrated dynamic loading. *J. appl. Mech.*, **22**, 523 (1955).

7.2   HASHMI, Md. Plastic response of simple structures to dynamic load. M.Sc. Thesis, U.M.I.S.T. 1970.

7.3   AL-HASSANI, S. T. S. and JOHNSON, W. The magnetomotive loading of cantilevers, beams and frames. *I.J.M.S.*, **12**, 711 (1970).

7.4   BLAZINSKI, T. Z. *Scabbing Problems in the Development of Free Implosive Forming of Roots-Blower Impellers. Proc. 10th M.T.D.R. Conf.*, Pergamon Press, 511 (1970).

8: Dynamic plastic deformation of plates

We now consider some cases of the impulsive loading of thin metal plates. First, a simple situation in which an exponential shock wave impinges on a thin plate, in no way restrained at its boundary or elsewhere. Second, an annular plate, firmly restrained over an inner circular area by a boss and subject to a specific peripheral speed; there are three phases of motion here, as for the cantilever beam, see p. 260. Third, a clamped square plate is impulsively loaded and dished to become a shallow shell.

In the last two cases, the plastic deformation is supposed brought about by bending only and combined bending and tension is not analytically considered. Such analyses as exist are usually long, involved and of doubtful practical value. Basic data about strain-rate and strain-hardening at appropriate levels is seldom immediately available. At no point in these analyses are elastic strains considered, so that it follows that the greater the plastic deflections or strains in relation to the elastic ones, the more realistic are these approaches likely to be.

Exponential shock wave loading of a free, flat, air-backed thin plate in water

Consider a free, flat, air-backed circular plate subject to a plane exponential shock wave at normal incidence and let our objective be to determine the maximum speed acquired by the plate. The pressure in the shock wave may be assumed to be given by,

$$p = p_m \exp(-t/\tau) \tag{8.1}$$

where p_m is the peak pressure at a point at the head of the wave, t denotes time and τ is a time constant—the time taken for the pressure to fall to p_m/e, which for high explosives is ~ 30 μsecs. This situation may arise when an underwater metal plate is subject to explosive shock from a high explosive charge also detonated under water; this arises destructively as when a mine is set to attack an underwater vessel or constructively as in explosive metal forming operations, compare p. 177.

It will be observed that the analysis below is basically the same as that on p. 36.

The incident shock wave will be reflected and we assume that the plate always takes the speed possessed by the particles of the wave transmitting medium in contact with it. At time t after first falling upon the plate, the pressure due to the incident compressive wave is p and that due to the reflected wave p'' so that the total plate pressure is $(p + p'')$. Suppose the plate has been moved a distance x from its initial position at time $t = 0$, and let m denote the mass of the plate per unit area, so that the equation of motion per unit area of plate is,

$$m \cdot \frac{d^2x}{dt^2} = p + p'' \tag{8.2}$$

Assuming the shock wave is sonic and linear (i.e. that the transmitted pressures are not too high), we have from elementary theory,

$$p = \rho_0 c_0 v \quad \text{and} \quad p'' = \rho_0 c_0 v'' \tag{8.3}$$

where c_0 denotes the elastic wave speed in the transmitting medium and v and v'' are particle speeds at the plate-medium interface; v and v'' are measured in the same direction as that in which the incident and reflected waves travel, so that the plate speed $dx/dt = v - v''$. Hence,

$$\frac{dx}{dt} = v - v'' = (p - p'')/\rho_0 c_0 \tag{8.4}$$

Adding (8.2) and (8.4), we find

$$m\frac{d^2x}{dt^2} + \rho_0 c_0 \frac{dx}{dt} = 2p \tag{8.5i}$$

Substituting in (8.5i) for p from (8.1), and integrating, we obtain,

$$\frac{dx}{dt} = \frac{2p_m}{m(1-\beta)} \cdot \left[\exp\left(-\beta\frac{t}{\tau}\right) - \exp\left(-\frac{t}{\tau}\right) \right] \tag{8.5ii}$$

and

$$p + p'' = \frac{2p_m}{(1-\beta)} \left[\exp\left(-\frac{t}{\tau}\right) - \beta \exp\left(-\beta \cdot \frac{t}{\tau}\right) \right], \tag{8.6}$$

where $\beta = \rho_0 c_0 \tau / m$. Note that at $t = 0$, $p + p'' = 2p_m$; this is the greatest pressure on the plate. The pressure on the plate falls to zero when $p + p'' = 0$, and (8.6) then gives the time which has elapsed since the head of the incident wave arrived at the plate; thus,

$$t_c = \frac{\tau \ln \beta}{\beta - 1} \tag{8.7}$$

If negative pressures, or tension, cannot be transmitted to the plate, then the greatest speed that can be acquired by the plate is given by substituing (8.7) in (8.5ii). We have,

$$v_{max} = \frac{2p_m}{\rho_0 c_0} \cdot \frac{\beta}{1-\beta} \left[\exp\left(\frac{\beta}{1-\beta} \cdot \ln \beta\right) - \exp\left(\frac{1}{1-\beta} \ln \beta\right) \right]$$

$$= \frac{2p_m}{\rho_0 c_0} \cdot \frac{\beta}{1-\beta} [\beta^{(1/1-\beta)}(\beta^{(\beta/1-\beta)-1/(1-\beta)} - 1)]$$

$$= \frac{2p_m}{\rho_0 c_0} \beta^{(1/1-\beta)} \tag{8.8}$$

A simple arrangement for testing the accuracy of the above calculations, is shown in Fig. 8.1; a metal plate is held in the surface of water contained in a

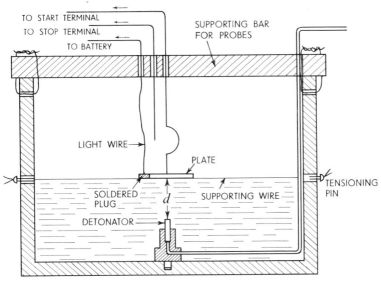

Fig. 8.1.

tank, and beneath the plate at a specified distance, d, a charge of explosive of weight W is detonated. Reference 8.1 states that,

$$p_m = 22\,500 \left(\frac{W^{1/3}}{d} \right)^{1 \cdot 13} \text{ lb/in}^2,$$

and

$$\tau = 73 \cdot 5 \, . \, W^{0 \cdot 29} \, d^{1 \cdot 4} \ \mu \text{sec.,}$$

when W is stated in lb and d in ft.

For $W = 0 \cdot 00055$ lb (0·29 g) of P.E.T.N. and $d = 0 \cdot 16$ ft (48·6 mm), the above expressions give $p_m = 10\,800$ lb/in² $(74 \, . \, 10^6 \text{ N/m}^2)$ and $\tau = 6.56 \, . \, 10^{-6}$ sec. For $\frac{1}{8}$ and $\frac{1}{4}$ in (3·18 and 6·35 mm) thick mild steel plates, $\beta = \rho_0 c_0 \tau / m$ is 0·39 and 0·195 respectively so that using (8.7), the time after the arrival of the shock wave at the plate at which the plate leaves the water is $10 \cdot 1 \, . \, 10^{-6}$ and $13 \cdot 3 \, . \, 10^{-6}$ sec respectively. The maximum speed acquired by the plates using (8.8) is 70·3 and 43·4 ft/sec (21·4 and 13·4 m/s). When the charge is detonated, the plate leaves the water and by having a probe above the plate at a known distance it is possible, with the help of a microsecond counter, to determine the time to traverse the known distance and hence find the average speed. The experimental results obtained by Travis[8.1] were close to the calculated ones.

Annular plate subject to an impulsive load

In this Section we consider the axi-symmetrical dynamic bending of an annulus of rigid-plastic material clamped along its inner edge $r = a$ and free along its outer edge $r = R$, see Fig. 8.2, following Shapiro[8.2]. The outer periphery is

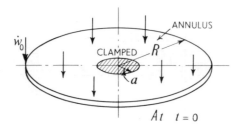

Fig. 8.2.

suddenly given a downward speed of $\dot{w}_0$ which persists and is constant for time $t = T$, after which time the driving force is removed. Three phases of motion are to be recognised:

(i) First phase: A plastic hinge circle appears at $r = R$ at time $t = 0$ and travels radially inward—a converging circular hinge—until it reaches the clamped inner periphery at time $t = t_1$. Assume $t_1 < T$.

(ii) Second phase: The plate rotates uniformly about the stationary plate hinge at $r = a$ for period $(T - t_1)$.

(iii) Third phase: The impulse is removed at $t = T$ and for a further period t_3, until the plate comes to rest, the inertia of the plate is responsible for further deflection. The kinetic energy of the annulus is dissipated in doing plastic work as the plate comes to rest, rotation about the stationary hinge at $r = a$ persisting as for phase (ii).

The existence of these phases of motion can be inferred from a high speed photographic record made by Kiyota and Fujita[8.3] and reproduced as Plate 43. A thin circular plate of lead, firmly clamped over some inner radius by a rigid boss, was given a certain vertical speed and then suddenly arrested at the central boss. The figure shows the initiation at the boss and the propagation outwards of a *diverging* hinge circle; this is followed by rotation about the central boss. In the circumstance analysed below the hinge circle is initiated at the periphery and *converges* onto the boss.

The plastic yielding of the plate is supposed to follow Tresca's yield criterion and the deflections from the initial position are not large enough to cause buckling.

For ease of understanding (and as far as possible), the comparable situation regarding beams should be kept in mind.

The situation which it is proposed to analyse, and the mode of deformation outlined above, is analogous to that considered earlier, in which a rigid-perfectly-plastic cantilever is struck by a mass at its tip.

The moment to secure full plastic bending is M_p per unit length of plate and this is taken to be strain-rate independent. All deflections are supposed to be small.

(i) *First phase*

When $0 < t < t_1$, the situation is as shown in Fig. 8.3 and in particular the plastic hinge has progressed from $r = R$ to $r = \rho$.

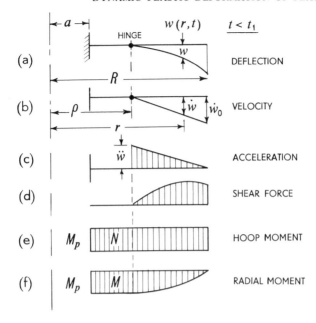

Fig. 8.3.

The velocity field for $r > \rho$ is assumed to be given by,

$$\frac{\dot{w}}{\dot{w}_0} = \frac{r - \rho}{R - \rho} \tag{8.9}$$

where w denotes the deflection and $\dot{w}$ the downward speed at r, at time t, and where $\dot{w}_0$ is the speed of the outer edge of the plate at the same instant. Differentiating with respect to time in (8.9) the downward acceleration of a particle at r is

$$\ddot{w} = -\dot{\rho}\dot{w}_0 \cdot \frac{R - r}{(R - \rho)^2} \tag{8.10}$$

For the inner portion of the plate not yet traversed by the travelling plastic hinge circle, i.e. for $r < \rho$,

$$w = 0 \quad \text{and} \quad \dot{w} = 0$$

Consider an element of the annulus at radius r as shown in Fig. 8.4. On the boundary there are radial moments, hoop moments and shear forces; M and N refer to the line intensity of these moments respectively and Q is the shear stress. The plate thickness is T and m denotes plate density. In Fig. 8.4, M and N are moments represented vectorially; Q is the shear stress, also shown as a vector.

If the material yields, then
(i) M varies from zero at $r = R$ to $M = M_p$ at $r = \rho$, see Fig. 8.3(f).

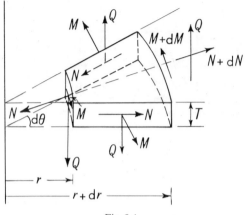

Fig. 8.4.

(ii) $N = M_p$ for all r. Especially, $N = M_p$ for $R > r > \rho$, otherwise the plate would not be plastic, because $M < M_p$, in as far as $r = \rho$. Also, at the same time, we may have both $N = M_p$ and $M = M_p$, for $r \le \rho$.

The dynamic equation for moment equilibrium in a radial plane, by taking moments about the centroid of the element, is

$$(M + dM)(r + dr)\,d\theta - Mr\,d\theta - N\,dr\,.\,d\theta - Q\,.\,T\,.\,r\,.\,d\theta\,.\,dr = 0 \qquad (8.11)$$

The effects of inertia do not enter into equation (8.11) because the rotatory inertia of the element, with respect to the centroid, gives rise to a moment which is negligible in comparison with the other moments. Second order quantities such as $dM\,.\,dr$ and those in dQ are also negligible. Thus (8.11) becomes,

$$r\,.\,dM + M\,.\,dr - N\,.\,dr - Qr\,dr = 0$$

or,

$$\frac{d}{dr}(rM) - N = Qr \qquad (8.12)$$

Now, the shear force Q at radius r, is given by

$$Q\,.\,2\pi r\,.\,T + \int_{\rho}^{r} 2\pi r\,dr\,Tm\ddot{w} = 0$$

or,

$$Qr = -\int_{\rho}^{r} mr\ddot{w}\,dr \qquad (8.13)$$

Recall that the shear force must be zero at the plastic hinge; thus to find the total shear force at r we must integrate from ρ to r, see Fig. 8.3(d).

Substituting in (8.13) for $\ddot{w}$, using (8.10) and integrating,

$$Qr = \int_\rho^r mr \cdot \dot{\rho} \dot{w}_0 \cdot \frac{R - r}{(R - \rho)^2} \, dr$$

$$= \frac{m\dot{\rho}\dot{w}_0}{(R - \rho)^2} \left(\frac{Rr^2}{2} - \frac{r^3}{3} - \frac{R\rho^2}{2} + \frac{\rho^3}{3} \right) \tag{8.14}$$

Substituting in (8.12) for Qr from (8.14) above, and recalling that throughout this outer region $N = M_p$, (8.12) gives,

$$\int_{\rho M_p}^0 d(rM) = \int_\rho^R \left[\frac{m\dot{\rho}\dot{w}_0}{(R - \rho)^2} \left(\frac{Rr^2}{2} - \frac{r^3}{3} - \frac{R\rho^2}{2} + \frac{\rho^3}{3} \right) + M_p \right] dr$$

or,

$$-\rho M_p = \frac{m\dot{\rho}\dot{w}_0}{(R - \rho)^2} \left(\frac{R^4 - 6R^2\rho^2 + 8R\rho^3 - 3\rho^4}{12} \right) + M_p(R - \rho)$$

i.e.,

$$M_p \cdot R = -\frac{m\dot{\rho}\dot{w}_0}{12(R - \rho)^2} \{(R - \rho)^2(R^2 + 2R\rho - 3\rho^2)\}$$

and the hinge circle radial speed,

$$\dot{\rho} = -\frac{12M_p}{m\dot{w}_0 R} \cdot \frac{1}{(1 - \xi)(1 + 3\xi)} \tag{8.15}$$

where $\xi = \rho/R$.

The time t_1 for the hinge to reach the clamped radius $r = a$ is, using (8.15),

$$\frac{-12M_p}{m\dot{w}_0 R^2} \int_0^{t_1} dt = \int_1^{a/R} (1 + 2\xi - 3\xi^2) \, d\xi$$

or

$$t_1 = \frac{m\dot{w}_0 R^2}{12M_p} \left(1 - \left(\frac{a}{R}\right) - \left(\frac{a}{R}\right)^2 + \left(\frac{a}{R}\right)^3 \right) \tag{8.16i}$$

$$= \frac{m\dot{w}_0 R^2}{12M_p} \left[\left(1 - \frac{a}{R}\right)\left(1 - \left(\frac{a}{R}\right)^2\right) \right] \tag{8.16ii}$$

The shear force is given by (8.14) after substituting for $\dot{\rho}$ from (8.15) as,

$$Q = -\frac{m\dot{w}_0}{r(R - \rho)^2} \cdot \frac{2M_pR^2}{m\dot{w}_0 R} \left[\frac{3R(r^2 - \rho^2) - 2(r^3 - \rho^3)}{(R - \rho)(R + 3\rho)} \right] \tag{8.17}$$

In particular, around the periphery, i.e. at $r = R$,

$$Q = \frac{-2M_p}{(R - \rho)^3} \cdot \frac{3R(R^2 - \rho^2) - 2(R^3 - \rho^3)}{(R + 3\rho)} = \frac{-2M_p}{R - \rho} \cdot \frac{R + 2\rho}{R + 3\rho} \tag{8.18}$$

Note that the shear force is zero at the clamped edge for the whole time, to t_1.

Briefly, recapitulating, because the plate has been given an initial velocity $\dot{w}_0$ which is maintained up to time T, it follows that a finite (shear) force of, as yet, unknown magnitude must be applied for this time. However, the inertia of the plate between its circumference and the plastic hinge acts so as to counteract this shear force and, indeed, at the hinge the shear force is zero. The inertia force also causes the radial moment M to increase from zero at the outside until it reaches a maximum value M_p at the hinge.

We may determine the curve of deflection, during this first stage of motion, between ρ and r as follows.

From (8.9) we have,

$$dw = \frac{r - \rho}{R - \rho} . \dot{w}_0 . dt$$

and from (8.15)

$$d\rho = -\frac{12M_p}{m\dot{w}_0} . \frac{R}{(R - \rho)(R + 3\rho)} . dt$$

so that, eliminating dt,

$$dw = \frac{r - \rho}{R - \rho} . \dot{w}_0 . \frac{m\dot{w}_0(R - \rho)(R + 3\rho)}{-12M_pR} d\rho$$

and hence,

$$w = \frac{m\dot{w}_0^2}{24M_pR} . (\rho - r)^2(R - r + 2\rho) \tag{8.19}$$

(ii) Second phase

In the second phase of motion the annulus rotates uniformly about the clamped inner radius a for the period of time t_2, so that the deflection added during t_2 is,

$$w_2 = t_2 . \dot{w}_0 \frac{r - a}{R - a} \tag{8.20}$$

The shear force and the bending moments are the same as for the limiting static loading.

(iii) Third phase

The plate will have acquired a certain kinetic energy by the time the second phase of motion is complete and this will be dissipated in doing plastic work; we require to calculate the time of this third phase, i.e. the time during which the plate is retarded by rotating about the inner radius. We assume that the kinetic energy is spent entirely in plastic bending; no energy is supposed to be spent in plastically stretching or compressing elements of the plate, by the membrane forces. The kinetic energy of the plate at the end of phase two, or the beginning of phase three, is

$$\int_a^R \frac{1}{2} \cdot (2\pi r \, drmT) \cdot \left(\frac{r-a}{R-a}\right)^2 \cdot \dot{w}_0^2 = \frac{mT \cdot \dot{w}_0^2 \cdot \pi}{12}(3R^2 - 2Ra - a^2) \quad (8.21)$$

If the tip deflection is w_3, then following the results on p. 197, because only the moment M along $r = a$ and N throughout the annulus do work, therefore the work done in plastic deformation is

$$(2\pi a \cdot M_p)\frac{w_3}{R-a} + (R-a)M_p\left(2\pi \cdot \frac{w_3}{R-a}\right) = 2\pi R M_p w_3/(R-a) \quad (8.22)$$

Equating (8.21) and (8.22), we find

$$w_3 = \frac{mT\dot{w}_0^2 R^2}{24M_p} \cdot \left(3 - 5\left(\frac{a}{R}\right) + \left(\frac{a}{R}\right)^2 + \left(\frac{a}{R}\right)^3\right) \quad (8.23)$$

The time of duration of the third phase, t_3, is $w_3/(\dot{w}_0/2)$, i.e.

$$t_3 = \frac{mT\dot{w}_0 R^2}{12M_p} \cdot \left(3 - 5\left(\frac{a}{R}\right) + \left(\frac{a}{R}\right)^2 + \left(\frac{a}{R}\right)^3\right) \quad (8.24)$$

The analysis above is not substantially different from that given by Wang[8.4] (1955) who dealt with the permanent deflection of a plastic plate subjected to a strong blast.

The dynamic plastic deformation of a position-fixed uniform square plate at medium load

We may obtain simply, some of the results of Cox and Morland[8.5] (1959), who theoretically investigated the dynamic deformation of square plates, side length $2a$, position-fixed at their periphery, when subject to a uniform *constant* transverse pressure p for time τ, using the approach described on p. 194. Their detailed examination showed that two categories of load may be distinguished; medium load when $p_s \le p \le 2p_s$ and high load when $2p_s \le p$, where p_s denotes the pressure required just to enforce plastic collapse of the plate, statically. For p_s we have, see Fig. 8.5,

$$4a\sqrt{2} \cdot \omega\sqrt{2} \cdot M_p = \tfrac{1}{3} \cdot 4a^2 \cdot a\omega \cdot p_s$$

i.e.

$$p_s = 6M_p/a^2, \quad (8.25)$$

For simplicity we deal only with their first case, and for the second, more complicated one, the reader is referred to the original source. For this medium range of loading two sub-divisions are required: (i) when $0 < t < \tau$ and (ii) when $t > \tau$. Use is made of the results obtained above for static situations using hinge lines, and we take over whatever results may be useful. As previously, the analysis pays no special attention to material rate effects. Further, it is implicit in this approach that the static and dynamic modes of deformation are identical.

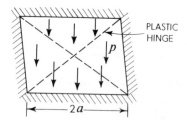

Fig. 8.5.

(As remarked, this is not so for high loadings). We denote by m the mass of the plate per unit area, and v is the plate speed at its centre at time t.

(i) Medium load: $0 < t < \tau$

Assume the mode of deformation of the plate is that of Fig. 8.5 and that the plate diagonals become hinge lines. Since p is constant and greater than p_s, and because the four equal parts of the plate act as rigid bodies each rotating about its boundary or side, they must undergo an angular acceleration, α. If changes in plate geometry throughout the deformation are neglected, the resistance to deformation, which arises from the yielding taking place in the hinge lines, will be constant; this resistance is related to p_s, the pressure to cause static yield. Thus the excess load is constant and hence α must be constant. The work done by the excess load will manifest itself as kinetic energy acquired by the four rigid regions of the plate, i.e. $4 \times \frac{1}{2}I\omega^2$, where I is the moment of inertia of a triangle about a side of the plate and ω is its current angular velocity. Because α is constant, at the end of time t the plate centre will have descended through a distance $vt/2$, where v is its current speed. Thus, an equation involving the work available for giving rise to rotational kinetic energy of the plate triangles is,

$$(p - p_s)4a^2 \cdot \frac{vt/2}{3} = 4 \cdot \frac{1}{2}I\omega^2 \tag{8.26}$$

Hence, substituting for p_s from (8.25), noting that $I = ma^4/6$ and simplifying,

$$\left(p - \frac{6M_p}{a^2}\right)t = mv/2 \quad \text{or} \quad v = 2\frac{(p - p_s)t}{m} \tag{8.27}$$

or directly by momentum considerations, thus,

$$\left((p - p_s) \cdot t \cdot \frac{a \cdot 2a}{2}\right)\frac{a}{3} = \frac{ma^4}{6} \cdot \frac{v}{a} \cdot$$

The deflection w_1 at the end of time τ is,

$$w_1 = v\tau/2 = (p - p_s)\tau^2/m \tag{8.28}$$

(ii) Medium load: $\tau < t$

After the removal of pressure p at $t = \tau$, further deflection, w_2, is added to w_1, because the rotational kinetic energy of the four plate segments must be dissipated in doing plastic work in the hinges. Let the segments rotate through further angle ϕ before coming to rest, then,

$$4 \cdot \left(\frac{1}{2} I \cdot \frac{v^2}{a^2} \right) = 4a\sqrt{2} \cdot M_p(\phi\sqrt{2})$$

$$= 8aM_p \cdot w_2/a$$

Hence,

$$w_2 = \frac{ma^2v^2}{24M_p} = \frac{mv^2}{4p_s} = \frac{(p - p_s)^2\tau^2}{mp_s} \tag{8.29}$$

using (8.27). Thus the total central deflection is,

$$w = w_1 + w_2 = p(p - p_s)\tau^2/mp_s \tag{8.30}$$

If the total response time of the plate is τ_t, note that $\tau_t \cdot p_s = p\tau$.

In the original paper of Cox and Morland it is argued that when $p > 2p_s$, a mode of deformation prevails which is different from that discussed above. (See footnote on p. 301.)

Dynamic deformation of thin plates clamped along their outside edges

In the case of thin plates clamped at their outer periphery it is clear that after a significant amount of deflection there must be stretching. An analysis of the dishing of peripherally clamped metal plates when given a transverse initial speed of a few hundred feet per second has been given by Hudson[8.8]. Descriptively, Hudson's model is easily understood by reference to Fig. 8.7. Central portions of the plate maintain their given transverse speed until overtaken by a bending wave propagated radially inwards from the clamping ring. Figure 8.7(a) shows the imagined plate configuration at successive intervals during the deformation process; Kiyota's set of high speed photographs of a lead plate which has been explosively attacked in air and which confirms this model is shown in Plate 44. Figure 8.7(b) shows the situation at a specific instant and points out how material in the central region is progressively, radially stretched and thinned whilst that in the conical region is rigid and stationary. When the plate deflection is significant, the process is predominantly one of stretching and for many practical purposes the technological approach on p. 176 is adequate.

Plate 45(a) shows the terminal state taken up by a thin rectangular copper plate clamped around its periphery after being subjected to the uniform but intense impulsive loading, generated electromagnetically by a robust coil close to, but beneath, the plate[8.6]. The maximum speed of the plate soon after delivering the impulse was 350 ft/sec (107 m/s). In this instance measurements of vertical displacement-time showed a more-or-less flat plateau moving upwards at a few hundred feet per second, but contracting in area with time; the dynamic situation during deformation, with plastic hinges moving into the plate from the clamped edges and intersecting along lines equally inclined to the sides from the corners, is indicated diagrammatically in Fig. 8.6. For comparison, Plate 45(b) shows an identical rectangular copper plate after being deformed due to steadily increasing lateral hydrostatic pressure. The contrast as between Plate 45(a) and 45(b) is quite marked.

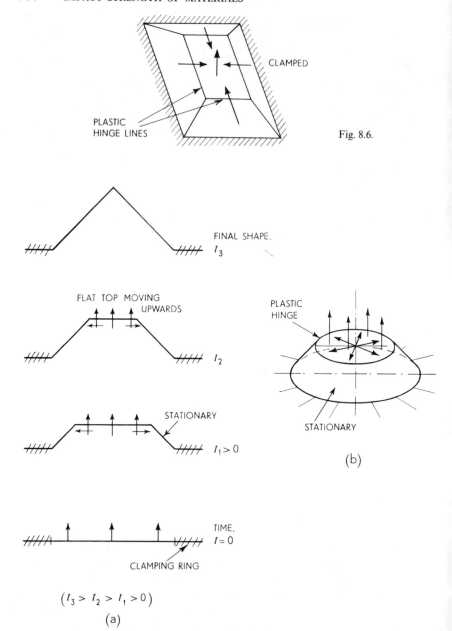

Fig. 8.6.

FINAL SHAPE.
t_3

FLAT TOP MOVING UPWARDS
t_2

PLASTIC HINGE

STATIONARY
$t_1 > 0$

STATIONARY

(b)

TIME.
$t = 0$

CLAMPING RING

$(t_3 > t_2 > t_1 > 0)$

(a)

Fig. 8.7.

Dynamic deformation of thin spherical shells

Plate 46 shows a hemispherical aluminium shell of thickness 0·010 in (0·254 mm) and radius 2 in (50·8 mm) after being statically loaded by a concentrated force at the pole; Pian[8.7], from whose paper this figure is taken, remarks that during the deformation the mode gradually developed from a circular to a triangular shape at large deflections. When the shell is impact loaded, by mounting it as the bob of a ballistic pendulum, the 'deformation mode becomes a polygon of five or more sides at large deflections'. Pian remarks that a specimen may absorb 20% more energy during dynamic loading than it does under static loading for the same maximum deflection.

REFERENCES

8.1   TRAVIS, F. W. Experiments in explosive metal forming, *Bull. mech. Engng Educ.*, **5**, 3, 11 (1966).
8.2   SHAPIRO, G. S. On a rigid-plastic annular plate under impulsive load. *J. appl. Math. Mech.*, **23**, 234 (1959). (English translation of Russian Journal *P.M.M.*)
8.3   KIYOTA, K. and FUJITA, M. Diverging plastic wave generated at the centre of a plate by an impulsive load. *Proc. 13th Jap. natn. Congr. for appl. Mech.*, 90 (1963).
8.4   WANG, A. J. The permanent deflection of a plastic plate under blast loading. *J. appl. Mech.*, **77**, 375 (1955).
8.5   COX, A. D. and MORLAND, L. W. Dynamic plastic deformations of simply-supported square plates. *J. Mech. Phys. Solids*, **7**, No. 4, 229–241 (1959).
8.6   DUNCAN, J. L. *Non-Symmetric Sheet Metal Forming Processes*. Ph.D. thesis, Univ. Manchester Inst. Sci. Technol. (June 1968).
8.7   PIAN, T. H. H. *Dynamic Response of Thin Shell Structures, Plasticity*, Ed. E. H. Lee and P. Symonds, Pergamon Press, 443 (1960).
8.8   HUDSON, G. E. A theory of the dynamic plastic deformation of a thin diaphragm. *J. appl. Phys.*, **221** (1951).

Prompted by the Ronan Point collapse, a similar approach to that on p. 298 is used by S. J. Alexander and E. C. Hambly, (Concrete, 62–65 and 107–116, 1970) for, "The design of (building) structures to withstand (internal) gaseous explosions". They start by considering a slab (beam) having a clear span, l, and mass m per unit length, subject at time t to uniformly distributed pressure p, where $p > p_s$, the pressure to cause static yielding. Using the deformation mode of Fig. 4.37 and considering angular momentum,

$$p - p_s = ml\alpha/3 \qquad (8.31)$$

where α is the angular acceleration of each half of the slab. The vertical equation of motion for the slab and (8.31) above, combine to give the instantaneous shear force, F, at the supports as

$$F = \frac{1}{2}l\left(\frac{p}{4} - mg + \frac{3}{4}p_s\right) \qquad (8.32)$$

9: Plastic deformation in a semi-infinite medium due to impact

Introduction

In this Chapter we discuss some of the aspects of the penetration of relatively large blocks of material—nominally semi-infinite masses—by projectiles. The possible relative speeds at normal impact extend over the vast range of 0 to 100 000 ft/sec (say 0 to 10^5 m/s) so that the phenomena encountered at different speed levels can be very different. It is not only relative speed of impact that is important; all the physical properties of both targets and projectiles—Young's modulus, strain-hardening or softening behaviour at high and low rates of strain, density and volumetric compressibility of the materials, specific heat and conductivity—are important too, as is the shape of the projectile and other aspects of the geometrical configuration presented (e.g. a pointed projectile at any impact speed causes plastic deformation). Whilst all these factors play differently important roles at different levels of speed, there are further complications introduced because many of them actually change significantly during the course of an impact—as is conspicuously the case in hypervelocity impact.

At this stage in our treatment of impact problems it will be obvious that it is not possible to present a simple unified treatment and thus the contents of the next two Chapters, both of which deal with penetration problems, will emphasise this.

The material presented below is often only partially quantitative, but the range of phenomena described is so varied that this will not be surprising. Many of the features described will be new to many students of engineering and if only for reasons of curiosity therefore, it is hoped that the imperfections of theories and explanations will not weigh too heavily. The approach adopted is to briefly discuss facets of the penetration problem, at successively higher levels of impact speed. Such lacunae as manifest themselves can be made up for by pursuing such references as 1.2, 2.8, 4.40, 9.1 and 9.2.

Many attempts have been made to categorise impact behaviour and none are wholly successful. One criterion which is used, especially when very high impact speeds are involved, is that of the ratio, the relative impact speed to the *elastic* (usually dilatational) wave speed in one or other of the materials. Obviously conspicuous shock effects must occur when this ratio is of order unity. The latter criterion is of rather limited value however in that shock effects must enter when impact speed and *plastic* wave speed—a function of the degree of strain imposed—are of comparable magnitude. And in the case of fast and intense loadings, temperature must affect material properties to such a degree as to make calculations of the latter wave speeds in the circumstances prevailing, rather obscure.

$\rho v^2 / \overline{Y}$ as an indication of behaviour regime: a damage number

A useful guide for assessing the regime of behaviour of metals in impact situations is to determine that non-dimensional number $\rho v^2/\overline{Y}$, which is the larger as between target and projectile materials where the relative speed at normal impact is v, the density ρ and the mean flow stress $\overline{Y}$. This number—a damage number—can be understood as a measure of the order of strain imposed in the region where severe plastic deformation occurs. For mild steel at room temperature, if we give $\overline{Y}$ a typical value of 40 000 lb/in^2 (275 . 10^6 N/m^2), then by reference to impact by a square-ended projectile, we may make up Table 9.1 and identify various regimes.

TABLE 9.1

ft/sec	$\rho v^2/\overline{Y}$	Regime
2·5	10^{-5}	{quasi-static {elastic
25	10^{-3}	plastic behaviour starts
250	10^{-1}	slow bullet speeds
2 500	10^1	extensive plastic deformation —ordinary bullet speeds
25 000	10^3	hypervelocity impact
—	—	laser, electron beam

The number $\rho v^2/\overline{Y}$ facilitates useful comparison as between individual metals and other materials and helps in the anticipation of the behaviour regime. For example, for Plasticine (or American play-dough) projectiles impinging against Plasticine semi-infinite targets, the specific gravity is 0·17, and at high speed $\overline{Y} \simeq 200$ lb/in^2, so that when $v = 1500$ ft/sec and $\rho v^2/\overline{Y} \simeq 400$, a form of hypervelocity impact behaviour may be expected; that this is so, see ref. 9.11.

Correspondingly, for metals both ρ and $\overline{Y}$ are much larger than for Plasticine and thus, to arrive at the regime number appropriate to hypervelocity behaviour of the Plasticine, we would not be surprised to find what is indeed the fact, namely, that speeds of 10 000 ft/sec and over are necessary.

Some weaknesses attaching to the use of this damage number are (i) that no account is taken of projectile nose shape, (ii) it is not clear what meaning or value is to be given to $\overline{Y}$ when the damage number is large, the pressures extremely great and strain rates high with consequent temperatures large, and (iii) in predominantly elastic situations $\rho v c_0/\overline{Y}$ may provide a more useful number.

The mean adiabatic temperature rise due to the total conversion of an initial kinetic energy $\rho v^2/2$ in unit mass of metal is readily calculated as

$$\tfrac{1}{2}\rho v^2 = \rho c g J . \Delta T \quad \text{or} \quad \Delta T = v^2/2cgJ$$

where c denotes specific heat and J is Joule's constant. Assuming that c changes little with temperature, speeds of about 1000 ft/sec (300 m/s) are necessary to cause 100 °C temperature rise in metals such as mild steel, copper and aluminium.

Slow speed indentation

We consider the slow speed indentation of a large block by a small indenter neglecting elastic effects and mainly in anticipation of high speed indentation work later on. Suppose a rigid *conical-ended tool, indenter* or *projectile* of semi-angle θ, impinges normally on the flat surface of a semi-infinite block of metal with speed v_0 and mass M and leaves a permanent impression of diameter d. Let the indenter mass be m and denote by $\overline{Y}$ the mean pressure of resistance of the metal. ($\overline{Y}$ will be nearly $3Y$ where Y is the uniaxial flow stress of the metal block after about 10% extension.)

The equation of motion for the impinging tool is, see Fig. 9.1,

$$M\frac{d^2x}{dt^2} = Mv \cdot \frac{dv}{dx} = -\overline{Y}\frac{\pi d^2}{4} \tag{9.1}$$

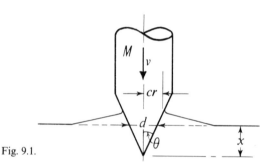

Fig. 9.1.

In (9.1) d is the current crater diameter in the original plane of the block and v is the projectile speed after the tip has penetrated a distance x. Substituting in (9.1), $d/2 = x \tan \theta$, and integrating,

$$\overline{Y} \cdot \pi \tan^2 \theta \cdot \frac{x^3}{3} = \frac{M}{2}(v_0^2 - v^2);$$

the final crater diameter d_0 and depth x_0 are

$$d_0 = 2 \tan \theta \left[\frac{3}{2} \cdot \frac{M}{\overline{Y}\pi \tan^2 \theta} \right]^{1/3} \cdot v_0^{2/3} \Bigg\}$$

and

$$x_0 = d_0 \cot \theta/2 \tag{9.2}$$

The volume of the crater below the original surface, V_c is $\pi d_0^2 x_0/12$ so that using (9.2),

$$V_c = \tfrac{1}{2}Mv_0^2/\overline{Y} \tag{9.3}$$

From equation (9.3), $\overline{Y}$ is seen to be just the work required to form unit volume of the crater and it could well have been written down without any analysis at all.

The work above has some particular limitations[9.3] : the height of rebound of the projectile is neglected, the volume V_c may be different from the final observable volume due to elastic recovery after impact is complete and $\overline{Y}$ is a dynamic value, somewhat greater than the static value. Energy radiated as elastic waves can be assumed negligible. Provided the rebound speed is only a small fraction of the initial speed, the result given in (9.3) is very useful.

If a rigid *spherical projectile* of diameter D impinges on the semi-infinite block, see Fig. 9.2, then the equation of motion for the sphere is,

$$Mv\frac{dv}{dx} = -\overline{Y}.\pi r^2$$

$$\simeq -\overline{Y}\pi x.D; \tag{9.4}$$

this assumes that $r^2 \simeq x.D$, which is true only when x/D is small. Hence,

$$\tfrac{1}{2}M(v_0^2 - v^2) = \overline{Y}.\pi r^4/2D$$

and if r_0 is the final cavity radius measured on the original surface,

$$Mv_0^2/2 = \overline{Y}.\pi r_0^4/2D$$

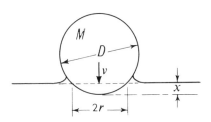

Fig. 9.2.

The final penetration x_0 is,

$$x_0 = [M/\overline{Y}.\pi D]^{1/2}.v_0 \tag{9.5}$$

or

$$x_0 = \left(\frac{D^2}{6}\right)^{1/2}.\left(\frac{\rho v_0^2}{\overline{Y}}\right)^{1/2} \tag{9.6}$$

where ρ is the density of the sphere.

If a square-ended rod, of mass M impinges on the block, then for plastic penetration, taking the resistance to be constant at $\overline{Y}$,

$$Mv\frac{dv}{dx} = -\overline{Y}.A$$

and again the nominal impressed volume V_c is,

$$\tfrac{1}{2}Mv_0^2 = \overline{Y}.Ax_0 \quad \text{or} \quad V_c = \tfrac{1}{2}Mv_0^2/\overline{Y}. \tag{9.3}$$

If elastic considerations were kept in mind, then an energy balance taken at the termination of penetration would give,

$$E_R + \overline{Y}.Ax_0 + E_S = \tfrac{1}{2}Mv_0^2,$$ (9.7)

where E_R is the energy radiated through the block as stress waves, and E_S is the vibrational energy in the impact body.

The above expressions are useful when impact speeds exceed a few ft/sec and when a significant amount of plastic deformation occurs. It should be remembered however that the critical speed at which plastic deformation is *initiated* between, for example, ball bearings and steel specimens is only a few inches/sec. Also, Hunter[9.3] has shown in this connection that though for impact speeds small compared with the elastic wave speed, E_R in equation (9.7) is entirely negligible, relatively high rates of strain do occur in these simple impact situations and 'inelastic or viscous damping forces' are thought to be present to account for losses of 10%–20% of the initial kinetic energy.

The recent paper by Olubode and Crossland[9.4] describes and shows how even for static contact loads—a ball pressed into various steels—the precise value that may be expected for a yield stress is uncertain. The yielding which starts at about one half a contact diameter below the surface is well known to be in excess of that measured say in a tensile test—in mild steel by as much as 60% greater—and the diameter of the impressed ball is itself found to be a factor, (typically up to 0·75 in. dia.) This size effect is attributed to the necessity for a sufficiently large or critical volume of material to yield, say, 10 to 17 crystals.

The copious literature on low speed impact is reviewed in refs. 1.2 and 4.5.

Penetration of a homogeneous medium by a fast moving non-deforming projectile

The situation discussed in this Section refers to historical problems which have occupied the attention of many scientists who have been interested in the penetrating capabilities of ball ammunition especially with regard to relatively soft materials such as soils and sands.

(i) *Historical*[9.5]

The first penetration equation proposed seems to be due to Robins (c. 1742) and Euler (c. 1750); they assumed that the resistance to penetration is a constant, i.e. is independent of speed and depth of penetration. Their equation is of the form

$$-\frac{dv}{dt} = \gamma$$ (9.8)

where v and t denote speed and time respectively and γ is a positive constant.

An equation more general than (9.8), continually used is

$$-\frac{dv}{dt} = \alpha v^2 + \beta v + \gamma$$ (9.9)

It is most useful for low impact speeds.

Poncelet's equation (c. 1829/1835), in a form first suggested by Euler, is,

$$-\frac{dv}{dt} = \alpha v^2 + \gamma \tag{9.10}$$

Resal's well known equation (c. 1895) is, effectually,

$$-\frac{dv}{dt} = \alpha v^2 + \beta v \tag{9.11}$$

(ii) *Dynamic penetration of sand*

A projectile of mass m and presentation area† A passing through a fluid medium at speed v and of density ρ is subjected to a drag force and it is usual to write

$$-m\frac{dv}{dt} = \frac{1}{2}C_D A \rho v^2 \tag{9.12}$$

Using the same approach to analyse the situation of dry quartz sand penetration, a method typical of aero-dynamics is followed where C_D is a dimensionless drag coefficient which is a function of speed v; we may write, using (9.9),

$$C_D(v) = \frac{2m}{\rho A}\left(\alpha + \frac{\beta}{v} + \frac{\gamma}{v^2}\right) \tag{9.13i}$$

noting that $C_D(\infty) = 2m\alpha/\rho A$.

Allen, Mayfield and Morrison[9.5] carried out tests by firing bullets at an initial speed of about 700 m/sec (2300 ft/sec) from a machine gun into a sand box containing a copper grid for facilitating time measurement. The total conical angle of the bullets used, varied between 10° and 180°, but 16 out of the 19 tests applied where the angle was between 60° and 180°; their mass for this range of angles was between 81 and 77 gm (0·18 and 0·17 lb). The bullet diameter was 0·51 in (1·3 cm) and its length 5·11 in (13 cm), a hole having been drilled in the rear portion of the bullet to give it stability in flight. The projectiles were fired into a long horizontal sand box so that the sand was equally confined on all sides. (A top to the box had to be fitted to ensure symmetrical confinement, for otherwise the flight path of the bullet was curved). From position versus time measurements of the projectile path, values of α, β and γ of (9.13i) were calculated using (9.12).

Projectiles with nose-cone angles of less than 90° were unstable. Maximum penetration occurred for the 100° angle cone with a striking speed of 2100 ft/sec (645 m/sec) and was ~ 5 ft (156 cm). Each projectile left a trail of powdered quartz in its wake, thus indicating its trajectory.

Typical values of the constants of equation (9.13i) were found to be

$$\alpha = 0\cdot025, \qquad \beta = 23 \quad \text{and} \quad \gamma = 55 \times 10^3,$$

for a test in which the bullet was flat-ended, the mass 0·18 lb (80·3 gm) and the striking speed 2054 ft/sec (674 m/sec).

---

† Presentation area is the cross-sectional area of the projectile orthogonal to its line of flight.

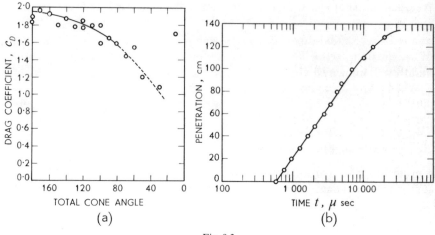

Fig. 9.3.

The Fig. 9.3(a) shows how $C_D(\infty)$ varies with cone angle using calculated values of α and shows that C_D varies little with angle; the dotted portion of the curve refers to unstable projectile flight. Figure 9.3(b) is a typical space-time plot for the flat-ended projectile referred to above when the penetration was 50·4 in (137 cm). Figure 9.4 shows the variation of C_D with v for the flat-ended round which is said to be typical and is intended to show that over most of the velocity range the drag force is nearly constant; a change in the value of C_D appears at about 328 ft/sec (100 m/sec) above which speed it is constant at about 2, but below which it increases rapidly, becoming 4 at 65 ft/sec (20 m/sec). Thus, experimental results were best described by two equations, as

$$-dv/dt = \alpha'v^2 \qquad \text{for} \qquad v_0 > v > v_c$$

and by

$$-dv/dt = \beta'v^2 + \gamma' \qquad \text{for} \qquad v_c > v > 0$$

(9.13ii)

where v_0 is the initial bullet speed and v_c is the transition speed. The $\alpha'v^2$ and $\beta'v^2$ terms are associated with the reaction motion of comminuted material as

Fig. 9.4 Drag coefficient of typical round. Dashed line corresponds to conventional theory. Solid line corresponds to proposed theory.

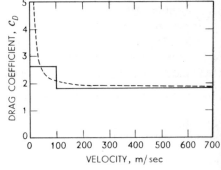

it accelerates to the projectile speed; γ' is associated with the fracturing of the structural framework of the material. $m\gamma'$ is the force required to draw a projectile at almost zero speed through the sand and the resistance is due to the binding of the medium; relief is afforded by the crushing of keystone grains, motion and then binding again.

When a sand grain impinges on the projectile nose it is broken-up into small particles that escape laterally through the interstices between the grains; these particles are assumed not to interact appreciably with oncoming flow.

In equation (9.13ii) for a flat nosed projectile for

$$v_0 > v > v_c, \qquad \alpha' = 0\!\cdot\!025$$

and for

$$v_c > v > 0, \qquad \beta' = 0\!\cdot\!0352 \quad \text{and} \quad \gamma = 49\!\cdot\!10^3$$

The transition critical speed, v_c is associated with the local speed of sound in the sand. There is a visual change in the powder or crushed sand trail at about 328 ft/sec (100 m/sec). For $v > v_c$ the trail is diffuse, and for $v < v_c$ it is sharp and distinct.

Referring to Fig. 9.5, which is a replot of Fig. 9.3(b) and shows experimental results together with a fitted curve for a typical round, for $v > v_c$, $C_D = 1\!\cdot\!85$ and for $v < v_c$, $C_D = 2\!\cdot\!61$.

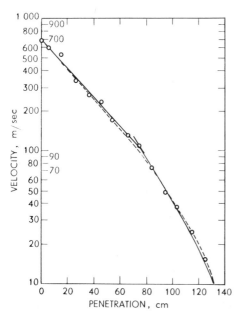

Fig. 9.5 Velocity plotted as a function of penetration for a typical round. Dashed line corresponds to conventional theory. Solid line corresponds to proposed theory.

In subsequent work these authors reported the existence of a powder cone formed on the leading end of a projectile, and this suggested that the m of equation (9.12) should be modified to take into account the mass of the powder cap. Further, the cap alters the blunt end of a projectile towards having a conical end.

(iii) *Dynamic penetration of a clay*

The analysis below pertains to problems of shell and bomb penetration into soil and protection against fast moving fragments of a few hundred feet per second. The results described in this Section arose from an attempt to determine the impact speed of an aircraft into Leda or quick clay, from the depth of burial of wreckage fragments[9.6].

We consider the normal penetration of a homogeneous plastic mass by a fast moving sphere or a short stable cylindrical rod. Until 90% of its initial speed is destroyed the dominating force resisting penetration is due to the inertia of the medium. The static strength of the medium gives rise to a force only comparable in magnitude with the inertia force towards the end of the penetration.

(a) Short cylindrical projectiles

In analysing penetration by a cylinder, the mass of the blunt-ended cylinder is increased by a hemipsherical mass of the medium which attaches itself to the end of the cylinder, see Fig. 9.6. The equation of motion for a cylinder penetrating a plastic medium end-on and maintaining a stable motion parallel to its axis, is

$$(M + M')U . \frac{dU}{dx} = -D - F \qquad (9.14)$$

where x is the penetration. The cylinder mass is $M = \pi a^2 l \rho_p$, its current speed is U, a is cylinder radius, l length, and ρ_p density; the added mass $M' = \frac{2}{3}\pi a^3 \rho_t$, where ρ_t is the target density and x denotes the penetration measured from the surface. D is the drag on the cylinder, and for a circular cylinder at zero incidence,

$$D = \tfrac{1}{2}C_D . \rho_t U^2 . \pi a^2 \qquad (9.15)$$

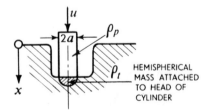

Fig. 9.6.

HEMISPHERICAL
MASS ATTACHED
TO HEAD OF
CYLINDER

The drag coefficient depends on the Reynolds number if the impact speed is well below the elastic or sonic speed in clay. It is made up of two terms, one due to viscous drag and the other due to form drag; the former depends on body shape but is negligible in this case because we are dealing with a sharp edge, i.e. the circular end of a cylinder, and separation takes place from the sharp edge. All the drag can be attributed to form drag and for this $C_D = C_{D_\infty}$. F is the force of resistance due to the plastic medium and we may write, if p_0 is the compressive strength of the clay,

$$F = \pi a^2 p_0 \qquad (9.16)$$

Normally in static indentation, F increases with penetration because of change in geometry; however, here p_0 will tend to decrease with penetration, since the rate of strain will fall off as x increases and hence a constant value of F will not be much in error. Note, that when penetrating a clay, the value of p_0 will depend on water content.

Substituting in (9.14) from (9.15) and (9.16),

$$(\pi a^2 l \rho_p + \tfrac{2}{3}\pi a^3 \rho_t)U \cdot \frac{dU}{dx} = -\tfrac{1}{2}\pi a^2 \rho_t \cdot U^2 \cdot C_D - \pi a^2 p_0 \tag{9.17}$$

Simplifying (9.17), and re-writing it in non-dimensional form, putting $x = l\xi$ and $U^2 = U_0^2 w$,

$$\frac{dw}{d\xi} + aw = b \tag{9.18}$$

where

$$a = \frac{C_{D_\infty}}{\left(\dfrac{\rho_p}{\rho_t} + \dfrac{2}{3}\dfrac{a}{l}\right)} \quad \text{and} \quad b = -\frac{p_0/\rho_t U_0^2}{\dfrac{1}{2}\left(\dfrac{\rho_p}{\rho_t} + \dfrac{2}{3}\dfrac{a}{l}\right)}$$

The solution to (9.18), also satisfying the initial condition that $\xi = 0$ when $w = 1$, is

$$w = \frac{b}{a} + \left(1 - \frac{b}{a}\right)\exp(-a\xi) \tag{9.19}$$

and

$$\xi_{max} = \frac{1}{a}\ln\left(1 - \frac{a}{b}\right) \tag{9.20}$$

Further, the speed of the cylinder at any time is

$$U = U_0\left[\frac{b}{a} + \left(1 - \frac{b}{a}\right)\exp(-a\xi)\right]^{1/2} \tag{9.21i}$$

or

$$\frac{U}{U_0} \simeq \exp\left(-\frac{a\xi}{2}\right) \tag{9.21ii}$$

because $b/a \simeq 0$.

(b) Spherical projectiles

In adapting the previous analysis for the cylindrical projectile, account needs to be taken of the fact that at the start of penetration, the surface area in contact with the clay increases with penetration; in this first regime this latter feature can be important because during this stage when the speed is high, the largest stresses will be set up. However, we consider only the second regime of the process when the area of contact does not alter substantially, see Fig. 9.7 (which is throughout most of the process) and we assume the area of contact is then always πa^2. In the original report[9.6], the force of resistance due to the material strength, F, is taken to be $(p + (\pi/2)\tau)$; p is 'the contribution due to hydrostatic pressure' and τ is 'the shear stress assumed constant'. As before there is an entrained mass of hemispherical shape, M', added to that of the M; $M' = \frac{2}{3}\pi a^3 \rho_t$.

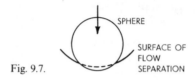

Fig. 9.7.

In place of (9.17) above, writing $\xi = x/a$, where a is the radius of the sphere, we have, with $u = U/U_0$,

$$\left(\frac{\rho_p}{\rho_t} + \frac{1}{2}\right) u \cdot \frac{du}{d\xi} = -\frac{3}{4} \cdot \frac{p + (\pi/2)\tau}{\rho_t U_0^2} - \frac{3}{8} \cdot C_{D_\infty} \cdot u^2 \tag{9.22}$$

Putting

$$b_1 = \frac{\frac{3}{4}C_{D_\infty}}{\left(\frac{\rho_p}{\rho_t} + \frac{1}{2}\right)} \quad \text{and} \quad c_1 = \frac{-\frac{3}{2}\dfrac{p + (\pi/2)\tau}{\rho_t U_0^2}}{\left(\frac{\rho_p}{\rho_t} + \frac{1}{2}\right)}$$

the solution to (9.22) is

$$u = \left[\frac{c_1}{b_1} + \left(u_1^2 - \frac{c_1}{b_1}\right) \exp\left(-b_1(\xi - 1)\right)\right]^{1/2} \tag{9.23}$$

Equation (9.23) is applicable only for $\xi \geq 1$ and $u = u_1$ at $\xi = 1$. It is strictly necessary to ascertain how u varies with ξ in the first regime because its terminal conditions, i.e. when $\xi = 1$, are the initial conditions for regime two, and it is necessary to satisfy a continuity condition at $\xi = 1$. The area over which p acts and which is associated with D, instead of being πa^2 would be $\simeq \pi x(2a - x)$.

From above,

$$\xi_{max} = 1 + \frac{1}{b_1} \ln\left(1 - \frac{b_1}{c_1} \cdot u_1^2\right) \tag{9.24}$$

(c) Experimental results

Using $p_0 = 400$ lb/ft^2 (19·1 . 10^3 N/m^2), $\rho_t = 100$ lb/ft^3 (1600 kg/m^3) and with $l = 40$ in (1·03 m) and $a = 20$ in (0·51 m) an approximate curve showing how, for steel and aluminium cylinders, the maximum predicted depth of penetration varies with original impact speed is shown in Fig. 9.8. Note that the curves flatten out with increase in impact speed and that penetration changes most rapidly at low impact speeds.

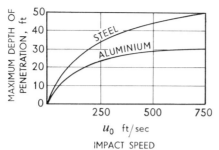

Fig. 9.8.

From experiments on Leda clay, C_{D_∞} was determined to be 0·850 and 0·350 for a cylindrical and a spherical projectile respectively.

With the help of the experimentally found coefficient C_{D_∞}, the theory gives good predictions of actual results, though there is room for improvement concerning the first regime of penetration by spherical projectiles.

The *shape* of a typical velocity-penetration curve shown in Fig. 9.9 is substantiated by experiment for initial speeds of about 1000 ft/sec (304 m/s).

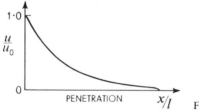

Fig. 9.9.

Craters or holes formed by projectiles are shown in Plate 47, and how their volume varies with the kinetic energy of the projectile is seen in Fig. 9.10.

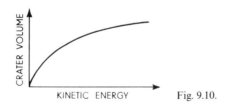

Fig. 9.10.

Lined-cavity† or hollow charges

A given mass of explosive detonated in contact with a block of metal succeeds in causing a greater crater in the block if a hollow is first made in the explosive, see Fig. 9.11. To increase the depth of the cavity and the effectiveness of the explosive, the hollow may be lined with sheet metal. The penetrating power of lined-cavity charges is very great when optimised proportions are determined.

† Also known as hayrick charges.

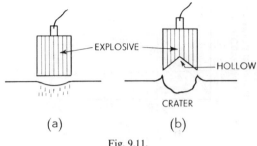

(a)   (b)

Fig. 9.11.

Figure 9.12(a) shows in section a plane wedge of two relatively thin sheets of metal which are backed-up on the outside with explosive; the figure could also be taken to refer to a cone of sheet metal. When the explosive is detonated the walls of the wedge or cone are caused to collapse so that the metal is forced to concentrate on the axis and to give rise to a slug and jet, see Fig. 9.12(b). If the angle of the wedge, or cone, and the explosives are correctly chosen, the jet ejected, though of small mass, may be caused to move at speeds of up to about 30 000 ft/sec ($\sim$ 9000 m/s). This set-up is a lined-cavity or hollow charge (also a shaped charge) and its effect is known as the Munroe effect in the UK and the USA, or as the Neumann effect in Germany: the phenomenon has been known for more than a century. There are very close similarities between the behaviour of lined-cavity charges and those of explosive-welding or cladding set-ups, see below.

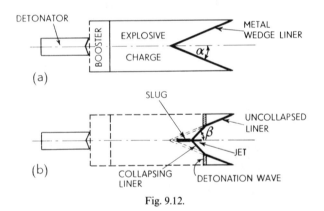

Fig. 9.12.

Fluid jet theory

The mechanism of wedge collapse described below is known from high speed radiographs and can be analysed following the method of Birkhoff, MacDougall, Pugh and Taylor[9.7]. The initial apex angle of the wedge is α but that part of it which has been traversed by the detonation wave, see Fig. 9.12(b), takes up an angle β and $\beta > \alpha$. A model of the progressive collapse of a liner due to Cousins[9.8], is seen in Plate 48. The pressure on the liner due to the explosive is very large and by comparison the yield strength of the metal is negligible; it is therefore proposed to analyse the system hydrodynamically assuming the metal to flow as a non-viscous fluid; this is *not* to say that the metal *is* in a fluid state when moving and deforming.

The pressure on the collapsing liner is assumed to act so that it does not increase the length of any portion of the liner. The consequences of this is clear from Fig. 9.13(a); if the head of the detonation wave has reached P in travelling along the sheet from A to B, then AP would have been moved to position $A'P$ and $A'P = AP$; all particles of AP after traversal by the detonation wave are impelled to move with the same velocity, say V_0, in an, as yet, unspecified direction. The direction taken by a particle at P, say PN, is as explained, parallel to AA'; now, obviously $B\widehat{P}N = P\widehat{A}A'$ and $N\widehat{P}A' = P\widehat{A'}A$, but because $PA = PA'$, then $P\widehat{A'}A = P\widehat{A}A'$ and hence $B\widehat{P}N = N\widehat{P}A'$. Thus P moves along the bisector of angle $B\widehat{P}A'$ with speed V_0, and every other particle in the moving wall PM has an identical motion. In the wedge in Fig. 9.13(a), let the current collision point M move to the right with speed V_1. Now Fig. 9.13(b) is a velocity diagram showing V_0 and V_1 and if we now bring the collision point to rest by imposing a uniform translational motion of V_1 to the left, all the particles of PM—velocity V_0—then have the velocity V_2 and move along the line PM. Thus in this stationary collision-point picture, at M, two streams or jets collide and

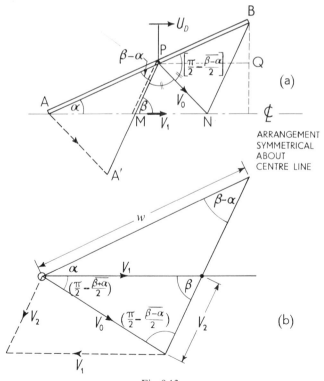

Fig. 9.13.

then bifurcate, the one which moves to the left being known as the 'slug' and that to the right as the 'jet'. Applying the sine rule to the velocity triangle of Fig. 9.13(b), we have

$$\frac{V_0}{\sin \beta} = \frac{V_1}{\sin\left(\dfrac{\pi}{2} - \dfrac{\beta - \alpha}{2}\right)} = \frac{V_2}{\sin\left(\dfrac{\pi}{2} - \dfrac{\beta + \alpha}{2}\right)}$$

or

$$V_1 = V_0 \frac{\cos \dfrac{\beta - \alpha}{2}}{\sin \beta} \quad \text{and} \quad V_2 = V_0 \frac{\cos \dfrac{\beta + \alpha}{2}}{\sin \beta} \tag{9.25}$$

The collision of two fluid jets, as in Fig. 9.14, is familiar to engineers, e.g. see ref. 2.14. In this stationary system the speed of particles in the slug or jet will be unchanged from what they were before collision; they will recede from M with identical speeds V_2.

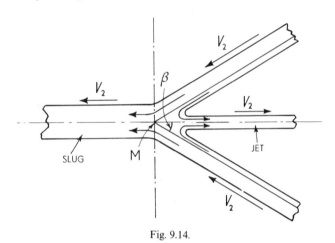

Fig. 9.14.

Reverting to the real system it follows that the absolute speed of the slug is $(V_1 - V_2)$ and that of the jet $(V_1 + V_2)$. Let the mass of the wedge material approaching point M be m per unit length, and let m_s of this enter the slug and m_j enter the jet. Applying the principle of linear momentum,

$$mV_2 \cos \beta = m_s V_2 - m_j V_2 \tag{9.26}$$

But

$$m = m_s + m_j \tag{9.27}$$

and thus

$$\left.\begin{aligned} m_j &= \tfrac{1}{2}m(1 - \cos \beta) \\[2mm] m_s &= \tfrac{1}{2}m(1 + \cos \beta) \end{aligned}\right\} \tag{9.28}$$

and

Hence,

$$\frac{m_j}{m_s} = \frac{1 - \cos \beta}{1 + \cos \beta} = \left(\tan \frac{\beta}{2}\right)^2 \tag{9.29}$$

so that if, as is usually the case, β is small, $m_j/m_s \simeq \beta^2/4$; for $\beta \simeq 14°$, $m_j/m_s \simeq$ 0·016. Evidently for small values of α and β only a very small fraction of the mass of the liner becomes jet material. The ratio of the speed of the jet V_j to the speed of the slug V_s is $V_j/V_s = (V_1 + V_2)/(V_1 - V_2) = \cot \alpha/2 \cot \beta/2$ using (9.25); again, if α and β are small, say 14°, then $V_j/V_s \simeq 16$.

The jet and slug speeds may be expressed in terms of the *forward* detonation speed U_D; in the time that a particle moves from P to N, Fig. 9.13(a), the detonation wave advances from P to Q, i.e. embraces length PB. Thus using Fig. 9.13(b), we have

$$\frac{w}{\sin \left(\dfrac{\pi}{2} - \dfrac{\overline{\beta - \alpha}}{2}\right)} = \frac{V_0}{\sin \overline{\beta - \alpha}}$$

Hence,

$$U_D = w \cos \alpha = V_0 \frac{\cos \dfrac{\overline{\beta - \alpha}}{2}}{\sin \overline{\beta - \alpha}} \cos \alpha = \frac{V_0 . \cos \alpha}{2 \sin \dfrac{\overline{\beta - \alpha}}{2}} \tag{9.30}$$

Thus,

$$V_j = V_1 + V_0 = V_0 \left(\frac{\cos \dfrac{\overline{\beta - \alpha}}{2} + \cos \dfrac{\overline{\beta + \alpha}}{2}}{\sin \beta}\right), \text{ using (9.25)}$$

$$= 2U_D \frac{\sin \dfrac{\overline{\beta - \alpha}}{2}}{\cos \alpha} \left(\frac{\cos \dfrac{\overline{\beta - \alpha}}{2} + \cos \dfrac{\overline{\beta + \alpha}}{2}}{\sin \beta}\right), \text{ using (9.30)}$$

$$= 2U_D \frac{\sin \dfrac{\overline{\beta - \alpha}}{2} . \cos \dfrac{\alpha}{2}}{\sin \dfrac{\beta}{2} . \cos \alpha} \tag{9.31}$$

and also,

$$V_s = 2U_D . \frac{\sin \dfrac{\overline{\beta - \alpha}}{2} . \sin \dfrac{\alpha}{2}}{\cos \alpha . \cos \beta/2}. \tag{9.32}$$

V_j increases as α decreases, since β also decreases. V_j is greatest when $\alpha \to 0$ and using (9.31), $V_j \to 2U_D$. Thus the jet speed cannot be greater than $2U_D$

and since high explosives usually have detonation speeds in the range 15 000 to 25 000 ft/sec, the maximum jet speeds usually lie in the 30 000 to 50 000 ft/sec range.

Penetration of a semi-infinite medium by a jet

The length of jet, l, which would be produced by the lined-cavity charge shown in Fig. 9.15 is,

$$l = h + h' = h\left(1 + \frac{b'}{h} \cdot \frac{h'}{b'}\right) = h\left(1 + \tan \alpha . \tan \overline{\frac{\beta + \alpha}{2}}\right) \qquad (9.33)$$

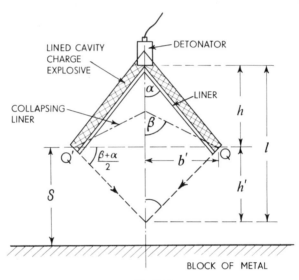

Fig. 9.15.

If this charge is stood-off at a distance S from a semi-infinite block and if $S < h'$, then maximum penetration would not be expected; greatest penetration will only occur when the whole of the collapsed liner is concentrated as a line jet along the axis of the wedge. Maximum penetration for a given liner would be expected for a stand-off distance of h' or $h \tan \alpha . \tan (\beta + \alpha)/2$. Since $\beta > \alpha$ the least value which h' can have is $h . \tan^2 \alpha$.

An expression for the penetration at normal incidence and speed V that a given length of jet l of density ρ_j can achieve in a semi-infinite target of density ρ_t is easily found by again using a hydrodynamic model. The process may be imagined to be similar to that of the penetration of a quasi-solid (say soil) by a high speed easily-deformed material or, say, a water jet. Figure 9.16 shows an idealised penetration process when the bottom of the hole being made by the jet is brought to rest. U denotes the absolute speed of penetration of the jet relative to the stationary target. With both jet and target conceived as fluids—again the pressures created during the impact are assumed so high that by

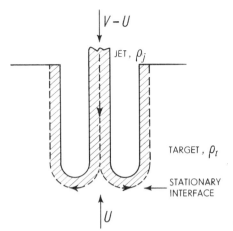

Fig. 9.16.

comparison static yield strength is altogether negligible—the pressure on both sides of the stationary interface, p, using Bernouilli's theorem, must be equal and hence,

$$p = \tfrac{1}{2}\rho_j(V - U)^2 = \tfrac{1}{2}\rho_t U^2 \tag{9.34}$$

This steady state is assumed to be reached almost instantaneously, and penetration is only considered to cease when the tail end of the jet has entered the target. The total penetration, P, is thus given by,

$$P = U \times \text{time of penetration}$$

$$= U \times \frac{l}{V - U}$$

or

$$\frac{P}{l} = \sqrt{\frac{\rho_j}{\rho_t}} \tag{9.35}$$

using (9.34) above. Note that in this expression, P is independent of V. Also, no indication of the diameter of the hole formed is derived. The derivation (9.35) assumes steady state conditions, which is only true for a cavity being made deep in the target and remote from the surface; also because there is reduced constraint to flow at the surface it is therefore to be expected that penetrations predicted by (9.35) would be slightly underestimated. Experiments show that (9.35) makes reasonably good predictions. For the set-up shown in Fig. 9.15, a graph of penetration, P, against stand-off, S, should show P increasing from h at $S = 0$ to $(h + h')$ at $S = h'$; for $S > h'$, P declines due to break-up of the jet and the onset of instabilities and waver in it. Thus the shape of the S-P curve might be expected to be as shown in Fig. 9.17; the shape of a typical experimental curve[9.8] is shown in Fig. 9.18. Cross-sectional views of cavities made in various metals by lined-cavity charges appear in Plate 49.

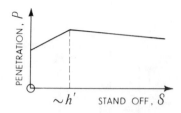

Fig. 9.17.

The influence of stand-off distance is, in fact, more complicated than that suggested which is really only a first approximation theory.

With conical lined-cavity charges, because of the manner in which the thickness of the explosive is distributed, the metal lining is moved the slower the further away it is initially from the axis; this leads to a lengthening jet which, if jet instabilities do not intervene and provided the jet speed is large enough, may result in deeper penetration though a smaller diameter cavity. However if the speed is too low penetration will be reduced.

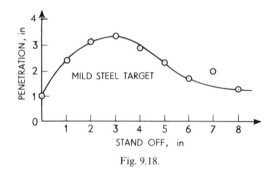

Fig. 9.18.

Extra terms may be added as in for example,

$$\tfrac{1}{2}\rho_P(V - U)^2 = \tfrac{1}{2}\rho_T U^2 + k \tag{9.36}$$

to allow for the influence of the projectile and target hardness and when the jet speed is not relatively large. Also (9.34) may be adapted to allow for the possibility of a non-coherent jet as in,

$$\tfrac{1}{2}\lambda\rho_P(V - U)^2 = \tfrac{1}{2}\rho_T U^2 \tag{9.37}$$

where $\lambda = 1$ for a continuous jet and $\lambda = 2$ for a fragmented one. Lead liners are known to move as a spray, copper as a more-or-less continuous jet, and steel as a particulated jet[9.9]. Other adaptations to (9.34) to allow for departure from steady motion and the effects of the slug or rigid body impact have been made. More detailed considerations of this topic have recently been given by Tate[9.10].

Other observations concerning hollow charge penetrations are that,

(i) for conical charges, maximum penetration occurs when the stand-off is between two and six diameters;

(ii) copper and steel make the best liners and copper is better for penetrating steel, probably due to its greater density;

(iii) the optimum thickness of liners is about $\frac{1}{20}$ of the diameter of the base of the cone;

(iv) penetration is fairly insensitive to liner shape, i.e. hemispheres, paraboloids, pear shapes and trumpet shapes do almost as well as conical configurations.

Plate 50 shows the hole made in a mild steel block by filling a brandy bottle with explosive to some distance above the apex of its re-entrant base and by standing it off by one diameter.

In hollow charge very high speed impact the minimum crater radius possible is $r_c = r_p\sqrt{2}$ where r_p is the radius of the impinging jet; this relation holds when the projectile (jet) is just turned back on itself so that

$$\pi r_c^2 = 2\pi r_p^2$$

It is interesting to note that the pressure, p, at impact, created when similar materials encounter one another, using (9.34) is $p = \rho V^2/8$. For a copper jet moving at a speed of 10 000 ft/sec (3040 m/s), $p = 1\,500\,000$ lb/in^2 (10.35 . 10^9 N/m^2); this pressure is nearly two orders of magnitude greater than the yield stress of the material.

Shaped charges are now used in the following ways:

(i) for cutting cables, plates and beams etc.,

(ii) as anti-tank missiles,

(iii) to perforate oil-well casings, i.e. used to produce radial holes to induce seepage,

(iv) to facilitate blast furnace tapping,

(v) in geophysical prospecting,

(vi) mining and quarrying, and

(vii) in salvage operations.

Hypervelocity impact

In the last section we saw how jets of metal having a speed of up to twice the explosive detonation speed—about 40 000 ft/sec (12 200 m/s)—may be created, and it was demonstrated how at normal impact against a deep target, they create a characteristic cavity which is deep and trumpet-shaped. Since the jet speed created may well exceed elastic wave speeds in the materials used, such jet speeds are said to be hypervelocity.

Hypervelocity impacts are not confined to artificially created lined cavity charges. Meteoric particles for instance may well possess speeds of up to 200 000 ft/sec (60 700 m/s). Projectiles of various shapes which possess speeds in excess of elastic wave speeds give rise, at impact, to characteristic craters and we now discuss these.

The sequence of events leading up to the creation of a hypervelocity crater are:

(i) At the moment of impact, shock waves are propagated into both the target and the projectile; they are so intense that the material which they traverse becomes highly compressed, heated to a high temperature and the target material is accelerated. The pressures generated are so large that by comparison the yield stress of projectile and target materials is negligible. Thus the materials can be treated as fluids and gases. A flash of light sometimes takes place when metals impinge on one another, and this is probably associated with the intense deformation, heating, melting, vaporisation and perhaps ionisation.

(ii) Some target material is displaced by the projectile and appears as an annular curtain of spray; the tiny particles in it *may* be ejected with a speed several times as great as the projectile impact speed. As the compressive wave travels into the target from beneath the projectile, a relief wave also travels into it from the periphery of the projectile. Release of this pressure gives rise to the high speed of the annular particles —compare the splash and fragmentation of a water drop, see p. 325. In water, this ejection speed is twice the projectile speed, but in metals it is reported up to ten times as great.

(iii) The projectile mushrooms on impact and as this tendency continues it becomes in effect a fluid jet forcing itself deeply into the target, the material of which moves away, more or less radially, from the region of impact. This expanding crater follows the shock wave which is attenuated as the crater size grows, being also overtaken by unloading tension waves from the free surface.

(iv) Some target and projectile materials are ejected completely from the crater; a sizeable coronet to the crater is formed and some target material remains to line the inside of the crater.

Hypervelocity cavities

(i) At one extreme is the typical micro-meteorite weighing 10^{-7} gm and impinging on plates at a relative speed of about 25 (± 15) km/sec, as seen in Plate 51. The upper limit of speed for meteorites is said to be about 70 km/sec and micro-meteorite crater dimensions have been recorded in the range 290/180 microns across and 32 microns deep, to 17 microns across to only 7 microns deep. And, at the other extreme, is the Barringer or Meteor crater of Winslow, Arizona, which today is $\frac{4}{5}$ mile in diameter, has a rim 130/160 feet high and is more than 350 feet deep, see Plate 52; the meteor which formed this crater is variously estimated as having been between 80 and 500 ft diameter travelling at 10 and 5 miles/sec respectively.

Jeffreys[9.12] states that the relative velocity of a meteor in a highly eccentric orbit about the sun and striking the moon would be about 40 km/sec. At 1 km/sec the kinetic energy possessed by an asteroid is 5×10^9 ergs/gm and, with a specific heat of 0·3, dissipation of this energy would lead to a rise in temperature of about 400 °C. Thus dissipation of planetary velocities by impact would lead to complete volatilisation: as there would be some penetration before vaporisation, etc., was complete, the effect would be indistinguishable from that of a sub-surface explosion.

(ii) At another extreme, Plate 50 shows a $14\frac{1}{2}$ in penetration through a cylindrical steel block; notice of its similarity to those in Plate 47 cannot be avoided.

(iii) A four-coloured Plasticine projectile, or short jet, was fired from a gun[9.11] at about 2000 ft/sec into a semi-infinite mass of white Plasticine which was then sectioned. It was observed that the coloured bands in the cavity, taken from the surface, appeared in the order in which the projectile impinged on the target; evidently the projectile behaved as a fluid jet because it turned itself inside out[9.11]. Solid copper cylinders can be turned inside out to form tubes by projecting them at sufficiently high speeds. A medium may delaminate at its surface and also material will become deformed below the cavity.

(iv) Obliquity of incident jets leads to cavities which in section are ovoid (blunter in the direction of travel) and their volume is proportional to projectile momentum normal to the surface[9.11].

(v) The volume of a crater may be up to 1000 times as large as the volume of the projectile. The final volume may be 15 % less in volume than the maximum reached before restitution occurs: recall p. 305 and Plate 54.

Influence of fineness ratio

The two features of great interest in hypervelocity impact work are

(i) crater volume, and (ii) crater shape,

and, for axially symmetric situations, penetration and crater diameter mainly define these.

Fineness ratio for cylindrical projectiles is the ratio of cylinder length, l, to diameter, d. Supposing that the density and hardness for projectile and target are of the same order, then for $l/d \simeq 1$ (which can be taken to include spheres), the crater is nearly hemispherical and the greater is l/d, the greater is the penetration depth to diameter ratio P/d. Correspondingly, the more is $(l/d) < 1$, the smaller (shallower) is P/d. Writing,

$$P/d = k(l/d)^n$$

where k and n are constants, then,

(i) the more (l/d) exceeds unity, the more nearly $n \to 1$; this is in agreement with jet penetration outlined above.

(ii) for $\frac{1}{6} < l/d \leq 1$, $n \simeq \frac{1}{4}$ to $\frac{1}{3}$.

For spherical projectiles (or $l/d \simeq 1$) many investigators have assumed that the crater volume, V_c, is proportional to the kinetic energy of the projectile and (speed v and mass m_p), this gives,

$$V_c \propto v^2 \quad \text{and} \quad V_c \propto m_p$$

or, if the crater is assumed to be nearly hemispherical of diameter D,

$$D^3 \propto v^2 \quad \text{i.e.} \quad D \propto v^{2/3} \tag{9.38}$$

Craters due to the hypervelocity impact of stocky projectiles are somewha similar to those of surface explosions of corresponding energy; the depth o such craters is usually found to be $0.4D$ to $0.3D$.

Expression (9.38) is similar to (4.98ii) or (9.3), wherein the work done to form a cavity is equal to $k\overline{Y}$. V_c, k being a constant. Some researchers have associated V_c with the momentum of the projectile rather than the energy.

Reflection leads one to appreciate that no simple all-embracing formula is likely to emerge and those referred to are at best likely to be crude first approximations. Problems and situations are ones in solid and fluid mechanics together with thermodynamics, the appropriate material data and its method of analytical treatment perhaps not being known. For specific problems it is clear that the use of computer codes and computer modelling are likely to be the future lines of development.

We shall not therefore catalogue the various relationhips which have been proposed or try to summarise the reported findings which are many and conflicting, but the interested reader may refer especially to the extensive article by Kornhauser[9.14] and those by Riney and Gehring in ref. 9.2.

Water cannons

The water cannon, developed mainly in the USSR for boring subway tunnels, coal and ice breaking and tree cutting, is a device for imparting a speed of a few thousand ft/sec to a jet of water usually with the object of directing it on to a target, which it crushes and fractures, or cuts, or erodes and penetrates. Figure 9.19 shows the essential details of such a cannon. The piston, P, is held off by high pressure water, W, and compresses gas, G. Quick opening valves, V, release the water pressure and P is driven forward at high speed. Water trapped in the recess, in R, is expelled through the nozzle, N, against a target, T. Pressures of 10^5 lb/in^2 ($0.689 . 10^9$ N/m^2) are easily produced by this technique using a driving pump of 100 hp ($74.5 . 10^3$ W) and expulsions occurring in 10 m sec work at a rate of 10^4 hp($74.5 . 10^3$ W) against target faces. The speed of expulsion of a jet is approximately given, using Bernouilli's theorem, by,

$$\frac{p_1}{\rho} + \frac{V_1^2}{2} = \frac{p_2}{\rho} + \frac{V_2^2}{2}$$

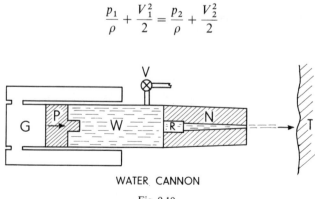

WATER CANNON

Fig. 9.19.

where p_1, V_1 and p_2, V_2 refer to the pressure and speed of the water at the entrance and exit from the nozzle respectively. Since $V_1 \simeq 0$ and atmospheric pressure $p_2 \simeq 0$ by comparison with p_1, we have

$$V_2 = \sqrt{2gp_1/w} \qquad (9.39)$$

where $w = \rho g$ is the weight per unit volume of the water. Hence $V_2 = 12\sqrt{p_1}$ if V_2 is in ft/sec and p_1 is in lb/in^2; for a pressure of 10^5 lb/in^2, a jet speed of 3700 ft/sec would be expected.

Water cannons have been used repetitively to cut rock under water. In a water environment, using equation (9.35), the expelled jet should penetrate a distance equal to its own length—a 10 m sec pulse for a pressure of 10^5 lb/in^2 produces a jet 37 ft in length. Thus for small stand-off distances, results for cutting in air and in water should be little different. As noted on p. 320, there is an optimum stand-off distance; at less than this distance water returning from a crater spoils the jet flow and reduces its penetrating ability, whilst at distances in excess of the optimum, energy is dissipated by turbulent mixing with the surrounding medium.

Cooley and Clipp[9.13] state that it is advantageous to use jet pressures at least ten times the rock strength, i.e. $\rho V^2/Y > 10$. For this, pressures in excess of $3 \cdot 10^5$ lb/in^2 ($2 \cdot 06 \cdot 10^9$ N/m^2) are necessary to cut into granite and they describe an "annular cumulation technique" for attaining this magnitude of pressure, see Fig. 9.20. The piston impinges on a liquid annulus—presumably achieved by injecting the water tangentially and causing it to spin—which flows as a conical jet towards the apex on the centre line of the apparatus.

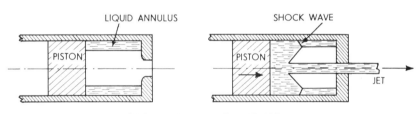

ANNULAR CUMULATION DEVICE

Fig. 9.20.

Using this shaped-charge principle a small very high speed jet is formed which emerges through the centre of the device. The very high pressure needed for this system is internally generated; for jet speeds of 25 000 ft/sec (7600 m/s), stagnation jet pressures are about $5 \cdot 10^6$ lb/in^2 ($34 \cdot 4 \cdot 10^9$ N/m^2). A jet $\frac{1}{16}$ in in diameter and a few inches long easily penetrates 1 inch of aluminium.

Ultra hypervelocity impact

For machining very high strength materials, optical and electrical energy sources are employed[9.15]. The former is typified by the laser (see details on p. 347) and the latter by electrical discharge machines, the electron beam and plasma jet machining.

The 'erosion process' in all these processes has features in common with hypervelocity impact phenomena, though the two are seldom thought of as being related—the formation of a crater, with attendant melting, ionisation and ejection. But, in the last analysis, it is likely that ultra hypervelocity impact can be thought of in terms of a study of a liquid drop splashing into the horizontal surface of a mass of liquid; certainly there are many apparently similar characteristics. The book, "A study of splashes" by A. M. Worthington[9.16], can be recommended for its fascinating collection of high speed photographs showing the details of splash impact. Plate 53 contrasts the penetration of a liquid drop into a horizontal liquid surface with that of a bullet into a plate, attention to the similarity being drawn by Worthington in the following words:

"To take a single illustration of a possible application in an unexpected quarter, I would invite the attention of the reader to the two photographs ... which exhibit the splash of a projectile on striking the steel armour-plate of a battleship. These are ordinary photographs taken after the plate had been used as a target. They represent the side on which the projectile has entered. In one picture the projectile is still seen embedded in the plate.

"No one looking at these photographs can fail to be struck with the close resemblance to some of the splashes that we have studied. There is the same *slight* upheaval of the neighbouring surface, the same crater, with the same curled lip, leading to the inference that, under the immense and suddenly applied pressure, the steel behaved like a liquid.

"Such flow of metals under great pressure is familiar enough to mechanical engineers, but what I desire to suggest is that, from a study of the motions set up in a liquid in an analogous case, it may be possible to deduce information about the distribution of internal stress, which may apply also to a solid, and may thus lead to improvements in the construction of a plate that is intended to resist penetration."

Of special interest is Worthington's sequence of photographs shown in Plate 54. A small globule of water impinging on a water surface creates a hemispherical cavity which has a volume two orders of magnitude greater than the globule. The coronet should be noted and how the globule tendency is to become gradually smeared, thin, and to have a shape which is shallow U.

Surface explosions, camouflet and earth shifting

A projectile impinging at very high speed against a semi-infinite mass forms a crater much larger than the original projectile size, because much energy is concentrated on a very small area; this incident may well be described as a surface explosion. There is this much in common between a hypervelocity surface impact—say, against the earth's surface by a meteorite—and the effect of detonating a charge of high explosive placed on a surface. Both are of small size initially but cause large cavities.

If an explosive charge tamped into direct contact with surrounding earth is detonated deep inside a semi-infinite mass it will form a near spherical or ovoid cavity and this is known as a *camouflet*. Large man-made craters and camouflet are projected for use as reservoirs.

When there is actual contact between the explosive and the medium being deliberately deformed as in the two circumstances described above, the process is referred to as a *contact operation*. If the explosive and the medium are separated and some other medium is interposed, e.g. water as in Fig. 4.32, the circumstance is described as a *stand-off operation* and the explosive and the medium are therefore to some extent *decoupled*.

Explosives are used in earth-moving operations[9.17] to break-up rock and other hard material to a size which can be handled by mechanical earth-moving equipment as in road building and quarrying. Rock blasting is dealt with at length by Langefors and Kihlstrom[9.18].

The availability of nuclear explosives has aroused interest in the possibility of using explosives to move quantities of earth with little or no assistance from mechanical equipment. Basically this is done by burying an explosive a small distance underground and detonating it to form a crater. A large proportion of the ejected material rises nearly vertically, and tends to fall back into the newly formed crater so that the efficiency of the process is low. One can distinguish between the true crater, which includes all the ruptured material, and the apparent crater after fall-back; the apparent crater in many cases is only a fraction of the size of the true crater[9.19].

The effectiveness of an explosive varies greatly with the material in which it is exploded, but if we consider a single known material, explosives of different magnitude exploded at different depths obey quite well-defined laws. The size of the apparent crater is strongly influenced by the depth of the explosive charge. If the charge is exploded on the surface a relatively small crater results and as the depth of the charge is increased the crater size rises to an optimum at a critical depth. Beyond this depth the size of the apparent crater falls as an increasing volume of material is merely loosened to fall back into the crater. On increasing the depth still further a containment depth is reached when the apparent crater size falls to zero. Typical curves showing how crater dimensions and charge depth are related are shown in Fig. 9.21. References 4.49 and 9.25 are useful for detailed results in model experiments.

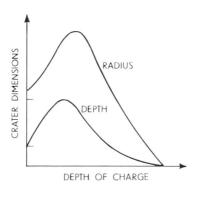

Fig. 9.21.

Charges of differing sizes are correlated by *cube-root scaling*. The critical depth and the containment depth are proportional to the cube root of the weight of the charge. If charges of different weights are exploded at depths proportional to the cube root of the weight of the charge, then all crater dimensions are proportional to the cube root of the weight of the charge. This behaviour is expected from energy considerations and holds well for all but the highest yield chemical explosives and some nuclear explosives. For these very large explosions the extreme temperatures and plastic deformation cause some small departure from cube-root scaling and a theory to explain these departures has been developed by Chadwick, Cox and Hopkins[9.20].

A single crater is useful for investigating the effects of an underground explosion, but practical applications involve the creation of channels. Simultaneously detonated single charges 1 or $1\frac{1}{4}$ crater radii apart create a continuous channel; material is mainly ejected at the sides but little at the ends. This appears to be due to the underground gas cavities merging and then behaving as an exploding cylinder; linear charges can be used to give the same result but the channel dimensions are then proportional to the square root of charge weight[9.21]. Soviet engineers[9.23] used a giant explosion to dam a river and raise its level 50 m; they have recently made artificial lakes in this way. The possibility of cutting a sea-level Panama Canal by the use of nuclear explosives has been responsible for recent interest and research work on the effectiveness of underground explosives. The book, ref. 9.22 should be consulted for information about the constructive uses of nuclear explosives.

When a 100 kton ($110 . 10^6$ kg) nuclear explosion takes place underground, 10^{14} cal ($4.19 . 10^{14}$ J) of energy are released in 1 millionth of a sec giving rise to a local pressure of 10^9 atm at a temperature of $10^7 \,°C$; strong shock waves move outward cracking, crushing and vaporising everything in their path for a considerable distance around.

Decoupling has assumed importance because a nuclear explosion occurring inside a very large cavity gives rise to weak and hardly detectable seismic signals. The implication of this for disarmament purposes[9.24] is clear. Some discussion of the mechanics of decoupling is to be found in ref. 9.24 where it is also stated that the pressure P in lb/in^2 generated by a nuclear decoupled charge is given by,

$$P = 10^9 \frac{W}{a^3} \tag{9.40}$$

where W is the yield† in kilotons and a cavity radius in feet.

REFERENCES

9.1   HUFFINGTON, N. J. Behaviour of materials under dynamic loading, *Am. Soc. mech. Engrs*, 187 (1965).

9.2   KINSLOW, R. (editor). *High-Velocity Impact Phenomena*. Academic Press, pp. 579 (1970).

---

† The 'yield' of a nuclear explosion is often given in terms of kilotons of TNT.

9.3 HUNTER, S. C. Energy absorbed by elastic waves during impact. *J. Mech. Phys. Solids*, **5**, 162 (1957).

9.4 OLUBODE, J. A. and CROSSLAND, B. Effect of size on the yield of steels under static contact loads. *I.J.M.S.*, **11**, 551 (1969).

9.5 ALLEN, W. A., MAYFIELD, E. B. and MORRISON, H. L. Dynamics of a projectile penetrating sand. *J. appl. Physics*, **28**, 370 (1957).

9.6 MANDL, P. and GIVENS, G. *Dynamics of High-Velocity Penetration into Clay*. N.R.C. of Canada, No. 8145 (July 1964).

9.7 BIRKHOFF, G., MACDOUGALL, D. P., PUGH, E. M. and TAYLOR, G. I. Explosives with lined cavities. *J. appl. Phys.*, **19**, 563 (1948).

9.8 COUSINS, J. E. Penetration by high-velocity metallic jets. *B.M.E.E.*, **8**, 45 (1969).

9.9 HOPKINS, H. G. Dynamic anelastic deformation of metals. *Appl. Mech. Rev.* **14**, No. 6 (1961).

9.10 TATE, A. Further results in the theory of long rod penetration. *J. Mech. Phys. Solids*, **17**, 141 (1969).

9.11 JOHNSON, W., TRAVIS, F. W. and LOH, S. Y. High speed cratering in wax and plasticine. *I.J.M.S.*, **10**, 583 (1968).

9.12 JEFFREYS, Sir H. *The Earth*. Cambridge Univ. Press, pp. 420 (1959).

9.13 COOLEY, W. C. and CLIPP, L. L. High pressure water jets for undersea rock excavation. *Am. Soc. mech. Engrs, J. Engng Ind.*, 281 (1970).

9.14 KORNHAUSER, M. *Structural Effects of Impact*. Cleaver-Hume, London, 205 (1964).

9.15 SAITO, N. and KOBAYASHI, K. Electric discharge machining at low electrode wear. *Bull. Japan Soc. of Precis. Engrs.*, **2**, 280 (1968).

9.16 WORTHINGTON, A. M. *A Study of Splashes*, Macmillan, New York, pp. 169 (1963).

9.17 MCLEISH, R. D. Applications of explosives to metal cutting. *I.J.M.S.*, **8**, 397 (1966).

9.18 LANGEFORS, U. and KIHLSTRÖM, B. *The Modern Technique of Rock Blasting*. J. Wiley, New York, pp. 405 (1964).

9.19 LEECH, T. D. J. Diffusion blasting and its potential for the development of Australia's inland surface water resources. *J. Instn Engrs Aust.*, 165 (1969).

9.20 CHADWICK, P., COX, A. D. and HOPKINS, H. G. Mechanics of deep underground explosions. *Phil. Trans. R. Soc.*, **256**, 235 (1964).

9.21 CARLSON, R. H. High explosive ditching from linear charges. *J. geophys. Res.*, **68**, 3693 (1963).

9.22 TELLER, E., TALLEY, W. K., HIGGINS, G. H. and JOHNSON, G. W. *The Constructive Uses of Nuclear Explosives*. McGraw-Hill, pp. 320 (1968).

9.23 WHITE, S. Building a dam with a bang. *New Scientist*, 358 (Nov. 1968).

9.24 *Detection and Recognition of Underground Explosions*. A.W.R.E. Rep., London (1965).

9.25 *Simple analyses for the non-symmetric dynamic expansion of cylindrical cavities* by J. B. Hawkyard, W. Johnson and I. O. Utoh, I.J.M.S., **14**, 1972.

10: Plastic deformation in plates due to impact

Plate penetration: general comment

The study of plate perforation by projectiles is of value;
   (i) for the study of plate penetration by bullets and shells: this subject is called 'terminal ballistics',
   (ii) to provide information for designing protective shields against disintegration in high speed environments, e.g. grinding wheel break-up and in gas turbines at one extreme and the skins of space vehicles subject to meteoric impact at the other,
   (iii) the study of problems associated with the use of powered fasteners, and
   (iv) in the study of high speed blanking operations.

The material against which a projectile impinges may be referred to as a plate if the *diameter of the projectile*, or the perforation made, is of about the same magnitude as the plate thickness and if the lateral extent of the plate *is at least an order of magnitude greater than the thickness*.

We describe below some of the phenomena of plate penetration, noting that it can be *partial* or *complete penetration*. This is done largely in terms of clearly visible and characteristic *terminal* damage; this is not entirely satisfactory because the sequence of modes of deformation and energy dissipation can then only be conjectured. Observational difficulties in these circumstances clearly incline us to depend on a study of terminal states.

Some of the factors on which plate damage behaviour depends are,

   (i) speed and angle of impact
   (ii) ductility and/or brittleness of plate and projectile
   (iii) elasticity of the materials
   (iv) shape of projectile nose
   (v) projectile diameter to plate thickness ratio
   (vi) average flow stress, and
   (vii) material density.

There are two aspects to the impact process, whether it be in respect of plates or semi-infinite media, and these are *near contact* phenomena and *distant* phenomena. The former is concerned with deformation immediately around the region in which contact occurs and the latter with elastic stress waves at more than an order of magnitude greater than the plate thickness from the deformation zone; our concern will be with the gross plastic deformation of the former.

Penetration behaviour depends on the speed of the projectile and its nose form. We have in mind here, metal projectiles moving at speeds of several hundreds of ft/sec and up to, say, conventional bullets speeds of less than 5000 ft/sec penetrating plates at room temperature.

There are three categories of projectile, the

(i) ogival and the conical-ended circular cylinder,
(ii) the square-ended circular cylinder, and
(iii) spheres or 'ball',

and we shall describe the impact behaviour of these in this order.

Note that if a projectile does not impinge normally on a plate, a turning moment will be created due to the action of the impact force on the tip of the projectile which will tend to accentuate the angle of incidence or to assist deflection. It is notoriously difficult to obtain *easily* reproducible experimental results using projectiles at speeds of up to, say 3000 ft/sec and this fact should always be kept in mind.

Perforation of plates: Ogival-ended projectiles

Conical-ended, ogival and to some extent ball projectiles impinging normally against metal plates at speeds of up to about 3000 ft/sec—normal bullet speeds—start penetration with some degree of indentation and by throwing up a coronet around the projectile if the metal is ductile, or initiating and propagating fractures if the metal is brittle so that shattered metal is ejected from the crater outside the zone where hydrostatic compressive stress prevails i.e. immediately under the indenter. Since the strain rates involved are high the tendency is to encounter brittle behaviour. If penetration is only partial, a crater is formed; with hard materials there may be scabbing from the rear face of the plate (refer to pp. 63–68) but this depends much on the defects, inclusions and heat treatment the plate has received. Cracks or fractures are initiated in plates ahead of a projectile and in mild steel targets nets of white lines may appear. These are martensitic and are due to the steel having been worked, heated above its transformation temperature (over 700 °C) and swiftly quenched, see Plate 55 and recall the remarks on heat lines on p. 208; the material in these lines is extremely hard.

As the ogival head of a projectile progressively pierces a plate, the deformation mode changes from one of indentation to one in which metal is pushed radially outwards so that much of the material goes into radial compression. Finally, whether or not spalling cracks or fissures have occurred, the bottom layers are bulged or dished, stretched, fractured and bent downwards in a characteristic fashion; if the plate is sufficiently thin and ductile, a distinctive group of 'petals' is left after the projectile has perforated the plate which points in the direction of projectile travel. Plate 56 shows a bullet which has perforated a plate but not passed through it completely; a spall from the bottom surface is also seen perforated. The shape of a projectile nose particularly may be altered due to the plastic deformation brought about by the high compressive pressures created during penetration, see Plate 57. Very intense elastic compression waves generated in an ogival- or conical-ended projectile may, when unloading is possible after perforating a plate, cause fracturing of the ogival end, see Plate 58; passage back and forth of the longitudinal waves with attendant pulse shape changes, with especially the development of tensile tails, should be recalled from the discussion on pp. 60–63.

Some of the most interesting work on plate penetration is that described in 1912 by Hopkinson[10.1]. Plate 59, taken from his paper, shows a plate of wrought iron after penetration by an armour-piercing shell; the shell had a hardened point achieved by thermal treatment, the rest of the body being soft and ductile; note here the fractured coronet or lip to the shell hole, which in the case of hard armour plate is found not to be present. Presumably the radial fractures in the coronet are due to the hoop tension in the (still) ductile material forced out. Hopkinson describes how the performance of this plate was altered by making its face (to the shell) very hard and its rear tough and ductile; Plate 60 shows the new behaviour of the plate. Both the shell (R 583 and 588) and the hardened face were shattered; cracks are only apparent on the rear face of the plate and the shell did *not* come close to penetrating the plate. Hopkinson reports that a soft steel cap affixed to the hardened shell (R 587) enabled the shell to pass clean through the plate. The cap does not pass through the plate; the shell punches a hole in it and thus passes through a metal ring, the pieces of which, when recovered and assembled as a ring, disclose an outer diameter as great as that of the shell but whose internal diameter was very considerably less. The effectiveness of the cap is presumably to alter significantly the pressure-time effect on the shell tip and the plate, and to reduce the magnitude of the impulsive force but extend the time of its operation.

The *predominantly* radial expansion of perforated steel plate is evident in Plates 61, 62 and 63. Plates 61 and 62 refer to ball perforating low carbon steel plate; as Plate 62 shows. Lüder lines may be found in the plate below its surface—testimony to radial stress at the inside of the hole—whilst the rear plate surface, Plate 61, also implies Lüder's bands by the manner in which scale is blown off; this also reveals the extent of the plastic deformation in the plate.

In hard plate, by sectioning some depth below the surface after penetration, a few white lines in the direction of lines of maximum shear stress, which are logarithmic spirals (i.e. along a trajectory which is always at $\pm 45°$ to a radius) may be detected, see Plate 63, and sometimes they occur in the projectile itself. Cracks arise inside the white lines and facilitate break-up or shattering of both projectiles and plates.

Miller[10.2] has described some of the unusual features he found in studying the *adhesion* which arises when a hardened conical-ended pin is explosively driven at an initial speed of about 1500 ft/sec into mild steel plate. Given a metallographic polishing treatment the adhesion is so great that fasteners fracture in tension before being pulled out successfully. As the initial surface treatment becomes coarser, the withdrawal load decreases because the true area of contact between plate hole and fastener reduces. The withdrawal load is low when fasteners are lubricated with molybdenum disulphide. Residual radial compressive stresses are large and heat and high temperature are generated during penetration. These, together with thermal expansion of both metals, the contact area established and their shear strength, control the withdrawal force. With very smooth pins welding with the plate can be complete. The surface of pins may melt; with copper electro-plated pins droplets of molten copper may be collected below the tip of the pin.

In some cartridge operated tools[10.3], hardened steel shafts are shot into steel plate, concrete slabs or bricks, the retention force being derived from the radial compression exerted on the shafts by surrounding compressed material, see Fig. 10.1(a).

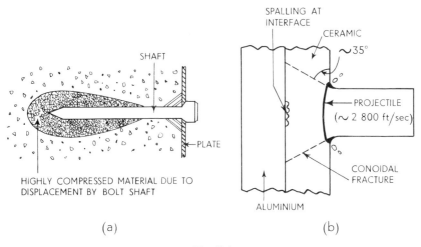

Fig. 10.1.

An interesting phenomenon is that in which an ogival projectile of relatively low tensile strength may be defeated or caused to break up, as intimated in the references to Plate 58 above, by using 'spaced armour'. A given projectile may penetrate a solid plate, of, say, 6 in thickness, but be defeated if instead an equal total thickness of plate is used as a skirting plate one inch thick above a five-inch main plate. If the spacing between the plates, the speed and the length of the projectile are such that after penetrating the skirting piece there is a sufficient time delay before striking the main plate, for tensile stresses to be built up which exceed the critical tensile stress for the projectile material, then a premature failure of the projectile prior to impact with the main plate may occur. If the spacing between the two plates is ill-chosen it may be that the time after penetration of the first plate and before impact with the second plate is insufficient to allow a build-up of tensile stress in the projectile to the critical level; in this case impact with the main plate while still intact may well enhance the likelihood of penetration.

Perforation of plates: square-ended projectiles

When a square-ended, and in some instances, a ball projectile impinges on a plate a number of phenomena different from those found with ogival-ended projectiles arise. The tendency is for a plug to be punched out of the plate, cracks being formed parallel to and ahead of the line of advance of the projectile, see Plate 64. The plug diameter is usually about the same diameter as that of the projectile; a lip is left behind after perforation and with steel the cylindrical crack may well be a thin white surface of the kind already described, see p. 331. Plate 65 shows an example of the white adiabatic shear line cracks, ahead of the projectile[10.4,10.5].

The plug ejected is usually 'dished' in the direction of motion. It tends to be forced out with some high residual speed, v_r, but being anchored around the edges it is therefore held back there, the centre portion moving ahead somewhat.

Throughout ballistic perforation or penetration, the inertia of the plug plays a very significant role as well as do the strength properties of the plate. Experiments[10.6] show the plug and projectile to have nearly the same speed at the instant of release. If v_r denotes the residual plug and projectile speed, then

$$\tfrac{1}{2}m_p v_0^2 - (\tfrac{1}{2}m_p v_r^2 + \tfrac{1}{2}m_s v_r^2) = W + E_0 \tag{10.1}$$

where m_p denotes the mass of the projectile, m_s, that of the slug and v_0 is the initial projectile speed; W denotes the work done in overcoming the shear forces in generating a free plug, and E_0 is the energy lost in other ways such as elastic wave propagation, sound and elastic strain energy in projectile end plug.

The 'ballistic limit' is that projectile speed v^* just sufficient to cause ejection of the slug and then $v_r = 0$, so that

$$\tfrac{1}{2}m_p v^{*2} = W + E_0$$

Assuming $(W + E_0)$ to alter little with speed, equation (10.1) becomes,

$$m_p(v_0^2 - v^{*2}) = v_r^2(m_p + m_s)$$

or

$$v_r^2 = \frac{v_0^2 - v^{*2}}{1 + m_s/m_p} \tag{10.2}$$

Typical plots[10.6] showing that impact speed and projectile residual speed are more or less parabolically related according to the ratio, m_s/m_p i.e., plate thickness/projectile length, are given in Fig. 10.2.

It is unlikely that momentum considerations will lead to a more reliable equation than (10.2) because the momentum delivered to the plate in the form of stress waves is difficult to measure. Paul and Zaid[10.7] state that for thin plate-perforation the speed with which the punched slug emerges is K times v_0 and is a constant depending on v_0 and the plate thickness. Typical results by these authors are given in Table 10.1.

A graph showing how speed of penetration falls off with penetration distance is given in Fig. 10.3 for a brittle plate[10.8]. After penetrating about one third of the plate thickness the resistance has fallen to nearly zero, the crack having been formed through the entire plate.

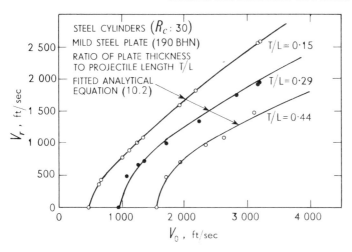

Fig. 10.2   Postperforation velocity of cylindrical fragments. Normal impact with relatively thin plates.

TABLE 10.1

Plate thickness in	v_0 ft/sec	K
0·04	2510	1·33
0·04	900	1·16
0·125	2590	1·23
0.125	900	1.12

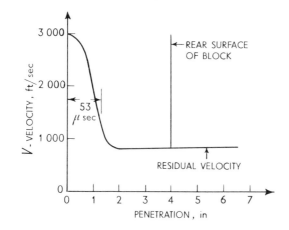

Fig. 10.3   Shaped charge showing jet penetrating a plate.

Recent results

(i) *Ceramic-aluminium plate subject to normal projectile impact*

A protection against small arms fire using armour which is light in weight is obtained today by a combination of about equal thicknesses of ceramic and aluminium. The ceramic, which has a much higher compressive strength than any metal but possesses little ductility, first receives the projectile and, if it is fractured, reveals a conoid, see Fig. 10.1(b). The ogival end of impinging steel projectiles is squashed and undergoes large lateral expansion, which effectively converts it to a square-ended form, assuming that normal impact (the worst case) occurs. The fractured conoid of ceramic is effective in 'defeating' bullets (at up to say 2800 ft/sec) because of the aluminium backing plate which possesses ductility enough to accommodate deflection under impact, yet restrains and holds the conoid in place so that even when fractured its penetration resistance is little impaired. More effective in penetrating armour of the ceramic-aluminium type is the square-ended steel projectile which is likely to cause a plugging type of failure. Thus the capacity of typical ogival-ended and square-ended projectiles are reversed in their ability to defeat duplex plate of the kind just described as compared with normal steel plate. Before the ogival-ended bullet can start to penetrate, much kinetic energy is dissipated in eroding the impacting end and thus reducing its speed before, as a square-ended projectile, it can begin to seriously penetrate the plate. The normal penetration behaviour of ogival-ended projectiles even against lightweight armour is recovered if the projectile is of say boron nitride which is harder than ceramic.

(ii) *Some sheet penetration results†*

Results of the normal impact, at speeds of up to 1000 ft/sec, of ball and conical-ended projectiles with relatively thin plate (0·050 in thick) have recently been described by Calder and Goldsmith[10.19], plugging resulting from ball ($\frac{1}{2}$ in dia) and petalling from the cone. It was noted that the larger the speed of penetration of a projectile, the more concentrated is the zone of intense plastic deformation— a feature to be expected by reference to Parkes work, see p. 268. The perforation region is surrounded by a portion of plate which has undergone plastic deforma-tion—out to a radius of about 3 in; the plastic hinge at this latter radius was found to be propagated at a speed of about 750 ft/sec, a typical plastic wave speed.

High speed blanking

A process related to that of 'free' perforation is blanking which consists in shearing a piece of desired shape from a sheet material using a punch and die assembly, between which there is an operating clearance. Figure 10.4 shows a typical set-up for the axisymmetric blanking of a circular disc. References 6.2 and 10.25 survey the blanking of many different metals in detail but point out such features of special interest to us here as,

---

† See also footnote ref. on p. 140.

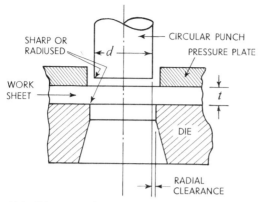

Fig. 10.4   Diagrammatic arrangement for axi-symmetric blanking.

(i) the concentration of the shearing deformation in the clearance zone (this may be several times as wide as the actual clearance), see Plate 66, noting that it reduces as the speed of blanking increases,

(ii) the production of a blank whose sheared edge is made up of three principal zones, see Fig. 10.5,

(iii) that in general the greater the speed of movement of the blanking tool the greater is the energy required to effect physical separation of blank and stock; this effect is the greater the higher the initial work-piece temperature.

Fig. 10.5   Zones at the sheared edge of a blank.

The non-uniform condition of the sheared edge is of major manufacturing concern because it represents poor dimensional accuracy and the presence of ill-disposed peripheral surface cracks; also another costly operation may well be necessary in order to bring the surface to the sort of uniform, smooth condition required for subsequent operations. Mild steel however has tended to show anomalous but beneficial behaviour in that, generally, the higher the speed of blanking the better the surface finish and claims that a smaller amount of energy is required are made. Effort has therefore been devoted to studying this phenomenon.

Reference 10.10 shows a photographic sequence in which blanks were punched out of a copper plate at increasing punch speeds, see Plate 67. The interesting features to observe are,

(i) the increased diameter on the top of the plate at 793 ft/sec,

(ii) the emergence of a distinct coronet on the top of the plate at 930 ft/sec,

(iii) the onset of punch (steel) break-up at 1500 ft/sec,

(iv) the diameter of the punched hole which is considerably greater than that of the punch and the distinctive shape of the hole at 2100 ft/sec,

(v) the very considerable amount of petalling and the hole diameter increase in 'free' perforation at 2350 ft/sec.

Dowling, Harding and Campbell[10.11] recently have measured the force to dynamically punch metals (speed range 5×10^{-5} in/sec to 900 in/sec) and found generally that no, or some, increase in energy with speed is required with annealed (ductile) materials and less for hard-drawn brass and high tensile steel. As with other authors, they attributed alteration in energy requirements to strain rate effects.

A paper of special interest is that by Balendra and Travis[10.12] who dynamically punched steel plate (300 ft/sec) of constant composition but different hardnesses. They usefully distinguish between 'metallurgical separation' of blank and stock and 'blanking'—physical separation—in the conventional sense. The former term is identical with the notion of adiabatic shear lines—white lines of martensite† as previously discussed on p. 331—which these authors found to occur after very small degrees of punch penetration at small clearances; Plate 68 convincingly shows this phenomenon and it is phenomenologically identical with that in Plate 65. This behaviour absorbs smaller amounts of energy and requires a smaller punch force than does conventional 'physical blanking'.

The faster a punching operation is, the higher the strain rate and the larger the flow stress but the narrower the shear zone. Thus the greater the blanking speed the more concentrated is the energy dissipated and hence the larger the resulting temperature rise; hence thermal softening occurs. The interplay of these various factors appears to result in a critical speed or rate of energy input when the resistance to and energy for penetration decreases. This is referred to by some authors as a thermal instability. When a sufficiently high temperature is reached and after a small time austenite is formed when blanking mild steel. Rapid cooling or quenching of the latter by conduction to the surrounding mass of relatively low temperature metal results in martensite formation.

Stock[10.9] and his co-workers have recently provided results on this subject and have also reported aluminium alloys which show adiabatic shear bands associated with a lowering of energy during projectile penetration. Adiabatic shear zones in explosively loaded thick-wall cylinders have also been reported by Thornton and Heiser[10.20].

Ultra-high speed machining

Material can be machined at high cutting speeds by projecting the workpiece from a cannon past a suitable tool and experiments by this method have been

---

† The existence of 'white lines' of martensite which are hard and were found to be a source of fracture by Morden in certain engine components during the Second World War is referred to by Slater[10.13]; they were associated with localised regions of plastic deformation in which high temperature and rapid quenching occurred. In a private communication of June 1967, R. C. Gifkins remarked that around 'shot holes' he had observed "martensitic and even austenitic zones. . . . In the latter, the material has been formed into globules, thus indicating temperatures near to melting." This work was carried out in the NPL, U.K. in the Second World War.

carried out by Vaughn at the Lockheed Co., USA[9.17]. All the cuts were made parallel to the axis of a round test piece. The experiments were prompted by a belief that if cutting speeds increased sufficiently, initial rapid deterioration in tool performance would be followed by an improvement when the cutting speed became so high that there was insufficient time for extensive plastic deformation to develop. Failure mechanisms were found to be largely brittle in character causing a sudden drop in power consumption and tool wear.

To obtain cutting speeds 15 000–180 000 ft/min (4550–54 600 m/min) a tool holder was attached to the end of a 28 in long smooth bore cannon out of which the workpiece was fired, the speed being varied by varying the size of the propelling charge. Blocks of steel in various conditions of heat treatment from fully annealed to fully hardened (UTS 280 000 lb/in^2) were used in combination with 90° vee-tools of positive and negative rake angles and broad-nosed tools with a negative rake angle. In all cases there was a definite cutting action with a surface finish as fine as 15 μin.

Catastrophic shear occurs when the local rate of change of temperature due to external work done, detracts from the strength of a material which generally tends to progressively strain-harden. See remarks on perforating or blanking steel above.

Siekmann has machined mild steel at 20 000 ft/min and according to Recht[10.14] there was evidence of catastrophic thermoplastic shear; Recht also reports that titanium and its alloys are very susceptible to catastrophic shear (at 1/1000th of the strain-rate for mild steel). He gives a criterion for predicting this to happen in a given machining operation. The existence of a plane of intense shear in machining is obviously comparable with that in blanking.

It is likely that for very high speeds of machining, a hydrodynamic type of analysis or model will be appropriate.†

Bar fracture: contact demolition charges[9.17]

Charges of this type are used mainly for military demolition, marine salvage and commercial metal salvage, information on their use can be found in unclassified military and commercial handbooks. For maximum effectiveness two charges are used, one on each side of the workpiece and slightly offset to obtain a shearing action. This is illustrated for an I-beam in Fig. 10.6. With curved sections such as bars, cables and chains good contact cannot be obtained so readily and the process is less efficient. An example of the quantity of TNT recommended for marine salvage purposes per square inch of cross-section to be cut is,

	In air	In water
Structural steel sections	$\frac{3}{8}$ lb	$\frac{3}{4}$ lb
Rods, cables, chains	1 lb	2 lb

---

† Machining at 1770 to 5200 ft/sec, taking cuts 0·005 to 0·088 in. depth and with rake angles +10° to −20° on aluminium, lead and steel, Arndt obtained chip thickness ratios between 1 and 3 and shear plane angles as high as 75°; increases in chip tool interfacial length to depth of cut ratio increased with speed to about 6. (G. Arndt, Ph.D. Thesis, University of Monash, Melbourne, Australia, September 1971.)

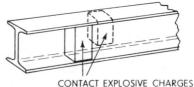

Fig. 10.6.   CONTACT EXPLOSIVE CHARGES

Successful cutting with much smaller quantities of explosives is possible; ref. 9.17 quotes 0·35 lb/sq in of metal section cut but with the help of notches made in bars this figure was reduced to 0·06 lb.

Bars can be fractured using the spalling phenomenon constructively[10.21]; transverse shallow saw cuts made at one end of a bar, to the opposite end of which is administered a sufficiently sharp blow, may be made to give pre-determined spalls due to reflection of the longitudinal compression pulse as a tensile one, helped by the area change effects of the cut.

Lateral restraint of a bar performs the same function as a transverse cut, see p. 50.

Transvelocity and hypervelocity penetration of plate

When a penetration process between more or less equal strength materials occurs at a speed in excess of elastic wave speeds it may be referred to as taking place in the hypervelocity regime. The largest value of the local wave speed is c_d, the elastic dilatational wave speed, which is 10 000–20 000 ft/sec (3040–6070 m/s) for most metals. However, local plastic wave speed, which depends on the degree of strain impressed is typically about $c_d/10$ i.e. 1000–2000 ft/sec. Thus metal projectile speeds at impact, exceeding say 10 000 ft/sec may be expected to give rise to unexpected phenomena; speeds in the region 1000–10 000 ft/sec (304–3040 m/s) can reasonably be referred to as transvelocity because they presage total hypervelocity effects.

The principal feature indicative of transvelocity behaviour is a perforation diameter in excess of that of the projectile; with increase in speed the disparity between these two quantities increases. This is well exemplified in ref. 10.15 and in Fig. 10.7; the latter shows sections of the cavities made in Plasticine plates by firing Plasticine bullets at increasing speed into the same thickness of plate. There is a substantially linear relationship between initial impact speed and plate cavity diameter: this has been observed by others, e.g. see ref. 9.2. Usually in such circumstances there is an increasing tendency for the projectile to undergo immense plastic deformation or to disintegrate. The plastic deformation could be such that a metal projectile is heated to such a degree that it melts and vapourises and for part of it to be smeared inside the cavity it creates. An interesting sequence of photographs is shown in Plate 69 taken from ref. 9.2; the effect of constant speed of attack against reducing thicknesses of plate shows how perforation is achieved. At first, a nearly hemispherical cavity results when hypervelocity impact takes place against the surface of a semi-infinite medium; the same impact against a target of modest thickness causes a similar cavity and, if the material is prone to it, a spall also, because the impact is so strong as

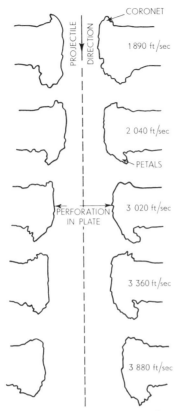

PROJECTILE LENGTH 0·5 in   DIAMETER 0·38 in   Fig. 10.7.

to initiate a very strong compressive pulse. At a sufficiently high speed the cavity developed on the front face connects with the spall on the rear face. It is likely that at the instant the spall detaches itself, because the plate thickness is suddenly reduced, the pressure which can be withstood by the bottom of the cavity suddenly is also reduced; it therefore collapses and allows a hemispherical cavity to become concentrated into a conical one. Such a final situation is well shown in Plate 70.

An understanding of the perforation of finite-thickness plates is essential to the proper design of spacecraft to ensure protection from meteoroid impact. One method of arranging for the impact of small masses on thin aluminium plates at meteoric speeds is to use an exploding foil gun facility; this can fire a large number of shots in a relatively short time with a range of projectile velocities from 1 to 8 km/s. In this gun a foil exploded from a capacitor bank shears a disc-like projectile from, for instance, a 0·25 mm plastic film diaphragm to cause a 6·4 mm dia projectile to be projected down an evacuated 6·4 mm barrel at the end of which it impinges on a target in a high vacuum chamber; such a facility is used to determine the ballistic limits of aluminium plates of varying thickness. A criterion used by many investigators for predicting ballistic limits is to multiply the crater depth caused in a semi-infinite target at a given speed by a numerical factor ranging in value from 1 to 2·5.

The mechanism by which a perforation is made whose diameter is much in excess of that of the original diameter of an impinging cylindrical projectile, when the impact speed is very large, is explained[9.2] as follows, see Fig. 10.8. The area of the interface between the end of the projectile and the target plate rapidly assumes a shallow U-shape of increasing extent—the perforation being created—and from which two shock waves emanate simultaneously, one, S_1, into the projectile and the other, S_2, into the target plate. As in the case of high speed liquid impact, see p. 84, relief waves R_1 and R_2 move radially inwards embracing the highly compressed zone between S_1 and S_2, from the circumference of the interface where the stress is obviously zero. This relief causes both the projectile and plate material to be ejected backwards violently.

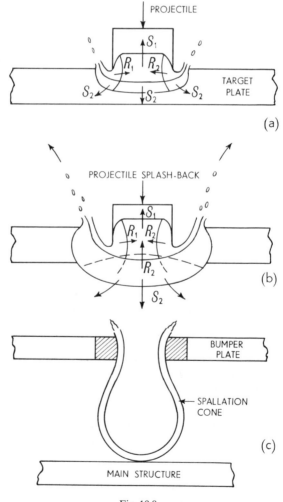

Fig. 10.8.

(This explanation is identical with that which would prevail for impact against a semi-infinite 'solid' body. In the latter case however, S_2 is progressively attenuated since it is a diverging compressive shock.) Back-splash is common with the liquid splash phenomena discussed on p. 326. However, in the case of a plate of finite thickness, S_2 is reflected from the rear face of the target plate as an unloading tensile wave, with the result that the particles of the plate assume a very high forward speed; this is tantamount to a spalling situation. If the intensity of the impact and the consequent strength of the shock waves is high enough, then for some materials a ballooning effect, or a spallation cone occurs, as is revealed by X-ray photographs, see Plate 71. Clearly the material of the balloon will consist of comminuted and high temperature plate and projectile material which is of much reduced density.

Knowledge of these facts may be used in designing protective, complex shields; if the principal skin or plate of a structure is identified with a second plate, if it is of the proper material judiciously placed behind a first or bumper sheet which takes the hypervelocity impact initially, then the system can give sound protection. This subject is discussed at length by Gehring and Riney in ref. 9.2.

Cutting plate using shaped charges

A graphic diagram showing the sequence of events at the perforation of plate[10.76] is given in Fig. 10.9. Reference 10.17 gives detailed results regarding plate cutting using wedge-shaped lined-cavity charges.

Explosive cladding and welding

Explosive cladding is the bonding together of a relatively thick parent plate and a thin plate of another metal—the flyer plate—using high explosives, see Fig. 10.10(a); explosive welding is the fastening together of two more-or-less equal thickness plates also with the help of high explosives, Fig. 10.10(b).

The fortuitous bonding of one metal to another following high speed impact seems to have long been known, but the first publication to mention explosive welding as such appears to have been that by Pearson in a US Naval Report of 1958; since 1960 many papers have appeared on this subject.

Wave formation at a bonding interface is a very characteristic feature of high explosive welding and some understanding of it may be sought in the mechanics of the fluid jet approach to the lined-cavity charge of pp. 313–318.

There are two principal arrangements for securing an explosive weld. In one, the two plates to be joined together are inclined to one another, see Fig. 10.10(b), covered first with a thin layer of rubber and then a layer of high explosive. The rubber acts as a buffer to prevent stress wave induced fractures of the metal sheets. The explosive layers on the outer surfaces of the plates are simultaneously detonated at the apex, with the result that the plates collapse on to one another in a progressive manner as detonation proceeds.

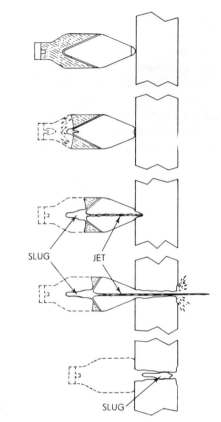

Fig. 10.9.

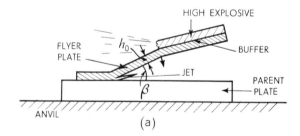

(a)

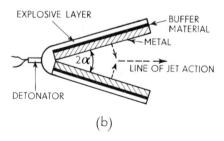

(b)

Fig. 10.10.

A slightly different, parallel arrangement is shown in Fig. 10.11(a). The two plates are set at a small distance apart so that when detonation occurs and travels from one end of the top plate, it is forced downward at high speed and the point of high speed impact travels rapidly along the lower plate, see Fig. 10.11(b). The two plates at impact contain a small angle so that as with the first explosive forming arrangement, the situation is very similar to that prevailing with a wedge-shaped lined-cavity charge, see Fig. 9.15. In effect, the very high speed impact of a pair of metal jets is secured; in consequence, when the acute angle between the jets is in the correct range, there is the production of a rippled or wavy interface. They bring to mind hydrodynamic phenomena and underline the fluid jet treatment previously referred to; they suggest that the pressures at impact are such as make the metals behave *as if* they were fluids, i.e. that the pressures are vastly greater than the yield strength of either material.

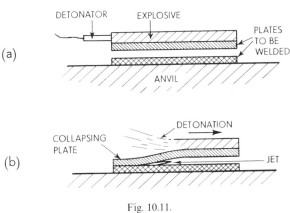

Fig. 10.11.

When the impact point of the two plates is brought to a relative standstill, Fig. 9.14, two typical plates will appear to be colliding at a speed of about 4000 metres/sec and one part of each plate will appear to move to the left and the other to the right, so that two streams are formed. The left-hand one has previously been identified as the slug of the lined-cavity charge and the right-hand one as the jet.

When two *fluid* streams collide at an appropriate angle and divide into two, a hydrodynamic shear or Helmholtz type of instability is realised in the region of the stagnation point or at the boundary where the bifurcation occurs. It will be observed from Fig. 9.14 that the internal surface of the metal which passes through the stagnation point is a dividing plane from which part goes to the left and part to the right; this ensures that clean and unoxidised surfaces are brought together under very high pressure and thus that there should be excellent bonding; the material which is the jet is ejected as spray so that a kind of surface cleaning precedes welding. Waves or ripples also give rise to good interlocking of the surfaces of the plates.

Very many combinations of different metals can now be welded or cladded and areas of 200 sq ft (18·6 m²) and over are reported as capable of being bonded together at one shot.

There are many features of explosive welding which are at present still not understood and the collection of photographs[10.18] in Plate 72 underlines this. This collection may be analysed as follows.

(i) If two typical thin metal plates are inclined at an initial angle of α between 0 and 4°, with most sheet explosives the two metals are usually caused to collide at supersonic speeds, i.e. speeds in excess of the velocity of elastic waves in the two metals concerned; there is *sometimes* a satisfactory bond but no ripples are formed.

(ii) If the plates are set at an angle of more than about 4° and up to about $17\frac{1}{2}°$, on impact the two metals will cause a jet to be emitted, on to which the two plates do not succeed in collapsing; the waves are fewer and larger as the initial angle between the plates increases.

(iii) If the angle of the plates is more than about $17\frac{1}{2}°$ the interface is more-or-less flat but a kind of bonding may take place; the limiting plate angle is about 30°.

With each of these three groups a different type of weld formation is associated. In the first case there is no evident wave formation; there is some degree of bonding. In the second there is a continuous wave formation, and in the third there are intermittent waves with pockets of trapped intermetallic compound.

Other notable features in explosive welding are that

(i) there is a slight increase in wavelength and amplitude in the direction of welding, see Fig. 10.12(a);
(ii) there is sinusoidal symmetry in wave pattern about the plane of contact when welding identical metals;
(iii) there is asymmetry when the metals are dissimilar, the waves possessing crests which are somewhat more pointed than the troughs, the crests pointing towards the less dense metal, see Fig. 10.12(b);
(iv) associated with large amplitude waves the crests appear to be uniformly 'damaged', see Fig. 10.12(c).

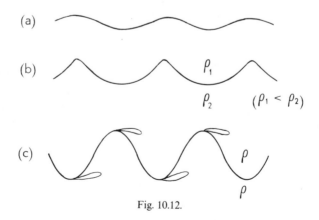

Fig. 10.12.

(Note, incidentally, a resemblance between the uniform wave pattern of explosive welding and that of a typical 'frozen' Karman vortex street.)

However, despite the lack of a mechanism or model for explaining explosive welding and cladding, for facilitating the calculation of wavelength λ and wave speed c, Hunt[10.22], using shear or Helmholtz hydrodynamic instability theory, has derived equations for these two quantities which, for identical materials, may be reduced by making use of small angle formulae, i.e. $\sin \beta \simeq \beta$ and $\cos \beta \simeq 1 - \beta^2/2$ to

$$\lambda = \pi h_0 \beta^2 \tag{10.3i}$$

and

$$c = V_0(1 - e^{-1})/\beta \tag{10.3ii}$$

where h_0 is the flyer plate thickness, see Fig. 10.10(a) and β the impact angle, see Fig. 9.14. Following reference 10.23, an equation due to Tate[9.10] which predicts the speed of penetration of a stagnation point into a target material U, see Fig. 9.16 and p. 319, is

$$\tfrac{1}{2}\rho U^2 + R_t = \tfrac{1}{2}\rho(V_2 - U)^2 + Y_p; \tag{10.3iii}$$

compare equation (9.36) where $V_2 \simeq V_0/\beta$ and see equation (9.25). ρ is the density of the material, Y_p is the pressure above which a flyer plate behaves hydrodynamically and R_t is a stress reflecting the resistance of the parent plate to penetration. From (10.3iii) we have,

$$U = \frac{V_0}{2\beta} - \frac{(R_t - Y_p)}{\rho V_0}\beta, \tag{10.3iv}$$

so that the time for penetration is $\tau = \lambda/4c$. Hence using (10.3i) and (10.3ii), the penetration or amplitude is,

$$U\tau = \frac{\pi h_0}{8(1 - e^{-1})}\left[\beta^2 - \frac{2(R_t - Y_p)}{\rho V_0^2} \cdot \beta^4\right] \tag{10.4}$$

This amplitude is greatest when

$$\beta = \beta_{max} = [\rho V_0^2/4(R_t - Y_p)]^{1/2}$$

and is zero when

$$\beta = [\rho V_0^2/2(R_t - Y_p)]^{1/2} \tag{10.5}$$

References 9.10 and 10.22 give the following values, $(R_t - Y_p) = 25$ k bar, $\tfrac{1}{2}\rho V_0^2 = 0.36 . 10^{10}$ dyne/cm^2 and $h_0 = 0.08$ in. Substituting in equation (10.5) it is found that $\beta_{max} \simeq 15°$ and the corresponding maximum amplitude is $\sim 1.8 . 10^{-3}$ in, both values being typical of many experimental results encountered.

Laser cutting[10.24]

The effect of lasers are in many ways similar to those of hypervelocity impact, e.g. in similarity of crater shapes and melting and vapourisation phenomena.

Laser emission is an intense beam of light or infra-red radiation which is parallel, coherent and of a single wavelength so that it can be focused with a simple lens to concentrate on a small area to give an extremely high energy density which makes cutting possible.

Two types of laser are used for cutting,

(i) there is the CO_2 gas laser in which power of up to about 1 kilowatt is produced in a beam of several mm diameter and which can be focused to a fraction of a sq mm (say 0·04); the beam is of 10·6 μ wavelength in the far infra-red region of the spectrum. CO_2 lasers can be run dc or electrically pulsed to give pulses of 300 μs to several ms duration with peak power of up to 2 kW. Some applications use pulses as short as 0·5 μs with peak powers of many kW generated by 'Q' switching.

(ii) The second kind of laser suited to industrial cutting applications derives from a crystal of yttrium aluminium garnet doped with neodymium, as a beam of 1·06 μ wavelength.

Lasers can be used for cutting both metals and non-metals (e.g. ceramics). The unaided beam cuts by removing as a process of vapourisation or, in the case of metals, by a combination of vapourisation and liquid phase ejection. Cutting is generally confined to thin materials and micro-size components and may use either of the laser types described above.

For macro cutting applications a CO_2 laser with a power output of 200 W or more is used with the beam usually aided by a jet of high speed gas.

For cutting non-metals up to about 50 mm thick the gas, which is usually air, serves to cool the upper surface of the material and also to rapidly eject hot vapour generated within the cut and prevent general damage to vertical faces.

TABLE 10.2   FOCUSED BEAM DIAMETER 0·35 mm

Cutting gas: for metals—oxygen
for non-metals—argon
Typical conditions for cutting with an 850 watt CO_2 laser for
which 70 % of the power output reaches the work-piece

Material	Thickness mm	Speed mm/sec
Mild steel	2·3	30·0
Austenitic stainless steel	3·2	12·7
Nimonic 75	0·7	34·0
Titanium alloy	0·5	55·0
Perspex	32·0	5·0
Softwood	14·0	25·0
Hardwood	5·0	76·0
Plywood	6·5	89·0
Ceramic tile	6·5	10·5

For metal cutting, commercial purity oxygen is used, which oxidises the surface of the metal. This greatly increases absorption of the laser energy, 95 % of which is typically reflected from a clean, cold metal surface. The heat produced by the oxidation reaction helps that from the laser to produce a molten oxide which is blown out of the bottom of the cut by the momentum of the gas stream. Use of the gas jet enables many metals to be cut in thicknesses of up to 6 mm or more with a kilowat laser. Width of cut is generally about 0·5 to 1·0 mm. The unaided beam from a continuous CO_2 laser, because of the high reflectivity of the material, is generally of too low power density to cut metals by vapourisation and is limited to cutting by melting very thin metals at low speeds.

Some typical figures concerning the cutting power of a CO_2 laser are given in Table 10.2.

REFERENCES

10.1   HOPKINSON, B. The Pressure of a Blow. Scientific Papers, Cambridge Univ. Press, 429 (1921).

10.2   MILLER, D. R. The adhesion of explosive powered fasteners to mild steel. J. Aust. Inst. Metals, 10, 295 (1965).

10.3   CHASE, H. G. Cartridge operated tool fixings. Civ. Engng (Aug 1957).

10.4   ZENER, C. and HOLLOMON, J. H. Effect of strain rate upon plastic flow of steel. J. appl. Phys., 15, 22 (1944).

10.5   RECHT, R. F. Catastrophic thermoplastic shear. J. appl. Mech., Paper No. 63-WA37.

10.6   RECHT, R. F. and IPSON, T. W. Ballistic perforation dynamics. J. appl. Mech., Paper No. 63-APM24.

10.7   ZAID, M. and PAUL, B. Normal perforation of a thin plate by truncated projectiles. J. Franklin Inst., 265, 317 (1958).

10.8   EZRA, A. A. Univ. of Denver Res. Centre, Colorado, USA. Annual Rep. (1967).

10.9   STOCK, T. A. C. and WINGROVE, A. L. Energy required for high speed shearing of steel. J. mech. Engng Sci., 13, 110 (1971).

10.10 JOHNSON, W. and TRAVIS, F. W. High speed blanking of copper. Proc. Inst. Mech. Engrs., 180, Paper No. 16 (1966).

10.11 DOWLING, A. R., HARDING, J. and CAMPBELL, J. D. The dynamic punching of metals. J. Inst. Metals, 98, 215 (1970).

10.12 BALENDRA, R. and TRAVIS, F. W. Static and dynamic blanking of steel of varying hardness. Int. J. Mach. Tool Des. Res., 10, 249 (1970).

10.13 SLATER, R. A. C. Velocity and thermal discontinuities encountered during the forging of steels. Manchester Assoc. Engrs., No. 5 (1965–66).

10.14 RECHT, R. F. Catastrophic thermoplastic shear. J. appl. Mech., Paper No. 63–WA67.

10.15 CARRELL, J., JOHNSON, W. and TRAVIS, F. W. High speed impact of Plasticine projectiles with laminated Plasticine targets. I.J.M.S., 10, 677 (1968).

10.16 ——, Fundamentals of Ballistics. U.S. Army, ST9-153 (April 1964).

10.17 ZAID, A. I. O., HAWKYARD, J. B. and JOHNSON, W. Experiments in plate cutting by shaped high explosive charges. J. mech. Engng Sci., 12 (1970).

10.18 BAHRANI, A. S., BLACK, T. J. and CROSSLAND, B. Mechanics of wave forming in explosive welding. Proc. R. Soc., A, 296, 123 (1967).

10.19 CALDER, C. A. and GOLDSMITH, W. Plastic deformation and perforation of thin plates resulting from projectile impact. J. Solids and Structures, 7, 863 (1971).

10.20 THORNTON, P. A. and HEISER, F. A. Observations on adiabatic shear zones in explosively loaded thick-walled cylinders. Met. Trans., 2, 1496 (1971).

10.21 AL-HASSANI, S. T. S. and JOHNSON, W. Stress wave fracturing of a bar. Proc. 1971 Machine Tool Conf., Pergamon Press.

10.22 HUNT, J. N. Wave formation in explosive welding. *Phil. Mag.*, **17**, 609 (1968).

10.23 REID, S. R. and JOHNSON, W. The amplitude of interface waves in explosive welding. *Nature* (1971).

10.24 Laser cutting. *Engineering, Lond.* (1971).

10.25 JOHNSON, W. and SLATER, R. A. C. A survey of the slow and fast blanking of metals at ambient and high temperatures. *Int. Conf. Mfg. Technology*, A.S.T.M.E., 825 (1967).

APPENDIX 1: Useful Conversion Factors

Length
1 in = 25·4 mm
1 mile = 1·609 km

Area
1 in^2 = 645 mm^2

Volume
1 in^3 = 16 387 mm^3
1 ft^3 = 0·0283 m^3

Velocity
1 ft/s = 0·305 m/s
1 mile/h = 0·447 m/s

Mass
1 lb = 0·454 kg

Density
1 lb/ft^3 = 16·0 kg/m^3

Force
1 lbf = 4·45 N

Pressure
1 lbf/in^2 = 6·895 kN/m^2

Energy
1 ft lbf = 1·356 J
1 cal = 4·19 J

Power
1 hp = 745·7 W

Temperature
1 Rankine unit = $\frac{5}{9}$ of kelvin unit

APPENDIX 2: Test Tables in SI Units

TABLE 1.1 ELASTIC LONGITUDINAL AND TORSIONAL WAVE SPEEDS

$$c_L = \sqrt{\frac{E}{\rho_0}} \quad \text{and} \quad c_T = \sqrt{\frac{G}{\rho_0}}$$

	Cast Iron	Carbon Steel	Brass	Copper	Lead	Aluminium	Glass
E N/m^2	$114 \cdot 10^9$	$204 \cdot 10^9$	$93 \cdot 3 \cdot 10^9$	$114 \cdot 10^9$	$17 \cdot 6 \cdot 10^9$	$69 \cdot 10^9$	$55 \cdot 10^9$
$\rho_0 = $ kg/m^3	$0 \cdot 72 \cdot 10^4$	$0 \cdot 775 \cdot 10^4$	$0 \cdot 83 \cdot 10^4$	$0 \cdot 887 \cdot 10^4$	$1 \cdot 13 \cdot 10^4$	$0 \cdot 266 \cdot 10^4$	$0 \cdot 187 \cdot 10^4$
$c_L = \sqrt{E/\rho_0}$ m/s ($g \simeq 981$ m/sec/sec)	3980	5150	3360	3690	1190	5100	5340
$c_T = \sqrt{G/\rho_0}$ m/sec	2470	3230	2040	2290	700	3100	3260

TABLE 2.2

	σ_F N/m^2	Differential Particle Speed m/s
Copper	$2 \cdot 82 \cdot 10^9$	$80 \cdot 4$
Brass	$2 \cdot 13 \cdot 10^9$	$65 \cdot 7$
4130 Steel	$3 \cdot 03 \cdot 10^9$	$71 \cdot 5$
1020 Steel	$1 \cdot 10 \cdot 10^9$	$25 \cdot 6$

TABLE[2.8] 2.3

	σ_C Compressive Strength N/m^2	σ_T Tensile Strength N/m^2	σ_C/σ_T	c_L m/s	Specific Gravity
Granite	193 . 10^6	2·83 . 10^6	68	3120	2·7
Sandstone	124 . 10^6	2·14 . 10^6	58	2930	2·5
Limestone	69 . 10^6	2·76 . 10^6	25	4920	2·6
Rhyolite	—	—	—	1830	2·7

TABLE 4.2

Material	Density kg/m^3	B (N/m^2) ÷ 10^6	C	n	m/s v_0^* sphere	m/s v_0^{**} cylinder	Instability Hoop Strain, ε_θ sphere	Instability Hoop Strain, ε_θ cylinder
Copper (½-hard)	850	42·7	0·114	0·3	70·0	57·3	0·043	0·051
Brass (½-hard)	830	75·5	0·127	0·48	126	109	0·0177	0·130
Stainless Steel	755	153	0·016	0·50	224	201	0·240	0·236

TABLE 4.3   EXPERIMENTAL RESULTS

Loading			Response	
P N/m^2	Impulse N/m^2 ms	T ms	Vibration Frequency Cycles/s	Strain Amplitude $e_\theta \times 10^4$
3·64 . 10^6	72·2 . 10^3	0·040	2190	1·68
3·22 . 10^6	54·4 . 10^3	0·034	2260	1·87

Tabulation appearing on page 228.

Stress in the zones identified in Fig. 5.16 in MN/m^2 are,

[1] 189   [2] 155 + 74·4 = 229·4
[3] 155 + 149 = 304   [4] 189 + 74·4 = 263·4
[5] 189 + 149 = 338   [6] 155 + 223 ≡ 378
[7] 155 + 297 = 452   [8] 189 + 223 = 412
[9] 189 + 297 = 486   [10] 189 + 372 = 561
[11] 155 + 440 = 595   [12] 189 + 372 = 561

TABLE 5.2

$\rho_0 v_0^2/Y$	0·011	0·050	0·128	0·267	0·500	0·900	1·633	3·200
c_p/v_0	4·23	4·27	2·57	1·71	1·19	0·84	0·575	0·40
v_0 m/s	36·5	78	152	180	246	356	445	620
c_p, m/s	152	363	396	307	294	276	255	249
H/L	—	—	0·19	0·34	0·38	0·425	0·409	0·310
$\dfrac{H}{c_p}\cdot\dfrac{v_0}{L}$	—	—	0·074	0·199	0·319	0·503	0·712	0·775
$10^5\dfrac{H}{c_p}$ s	—	—	1·44	4·1	4·7	5·5	5·9	4·7

TABLE 9.1

m/s	$\rho v^2/Y$	Regime
0·762	10^{-5}	quasi-static elastic
7·62	10^{-3}	plastic behaviour starts
76·2	10^{-1}	slow bullet speeds
762	10^1	extensive plastic deformation— ordinary bullet speeds
7620	10^3	hypervelocity impact
—	—	laser, electron beam

TABLE 10.1

Plate Thickness mm	v_0 m/s	K
1·00	766	1·33
1·00	275	1·16
3·18	790	1·23
3·18	275	1·12

Table appearing on page 339.

	In air	In water
Structural steel sections	0·17 kg	0·34 kg
Rods, cables, chains	0·45 kg	0·91 kg

Author Index

Subject Index